Speech Development, Improvement, and Correction

METHODS AND MATERIALS FOR THE CLASSROOM TEACHER AND THE SPEECH THERAPIST

Lucile Cypreansen

SUPERVISOR, SPEECH AND HEARING LABORATORIES
ASSOCIATE PROFESSOR OF SPEECH AND SPEECH CORRECTION

John H. Wiley

DIRECTOR, SPEECH AND HEARING LABORATORIES
ASSOCIATE PROFESSOR OF SPEECH PATHOLOGY

Leroy T. Laase

CHAIRMAN, DEPARTMENT OF SPEECH
PROFESSOR OF SPEECH AND SPEECH PATHOLOGY

THE UNIVERSITY OF NEBRASKA

THE RONALD PRESS COMPANY · NEW YORK

Library of Congress Catalog Card Number: 59-10137
PRINTED IN THE UNITED STATES OF AMERICA

*To our teachers-in-training,
our teachers and speech therapists
in the schools, and to the children
with whom they work.*

PREFACE

A professor of the old school once spoke informally to a group of modern-day speech therapists. "Why don't you folks stick to your job," he said, "and teach these youngsters how to talk? You waste too much time fooling around with sociological, psychological, and physiological rigmarole." It is obvious that the good professor was unaware that the day had passed when developing good speech habits in school children consisted of reading aloud, memorizing, reciting such poems as *The Village Blacksmith*, and acting in a play. Although the speech development of a child is a natural process, his sociological, psychological, and physiological environments are definitely involved. As his past has influenced him, as his present life influences him, and as his future shall influence him, so shall he speak. American schools now recognize the importance of these environments in their effort to give each child the opportunity to achieve adequate speech development. If the child is handicapped by a physical or psychological abnormality, the school's speech therapist must make use of modern techniques of speech correction and improvement.

This book has been written as a text for the beginning courses in speech correction methods for students training to teach in the elementary school and for students training to become public school speech therapists. It acquaints them with the normal speech development of the child, and with the common speech deviations. It presents methods and graded materials which both the teacher and the therapist will need for developing adequate speech, improving careless speech, and correcting speech difficulties. It includes speech testing materials for readers and nonreaders, and provides for speech development through individual and group activities. The organization and content recognizes that the speech therapist will seek training beyond the scope of these pages. Happily, the view expressed by the professor of the old school does not reflect the current attitudes, which exist on both national and state levels, concerning modern methods of helping children with speech handicaps.

The authors have sought to make this book practical and usable. Part I is a discussion of the speech development of children. Its four chapters consider normal speech development, the deviations from normal speech, speech training and retraining, and understanding children with particular speech problems. As a group, the chapters should aid in teacher–child relationships and teacher–parent relationships. Part II presents materials for testing speech and keeping records of the individual child's development. Part III presents materials to be used in speech improvement and correction through individual and group therapy. The methods and materials in Parts II and III are the outgrowth of the authors' research in speech therapy at the University of Nebraska Speech and Hearing Laboratories, in the Summer Speech Clinic and the University's daily Preschool Clinic, in public schools in Nebraska and Oregon, and in the Elementary Demonstration School of Central Washington College.

LUCILE CYPREANSEN
JOHN H. WILEY
LEROY T. LAASE

Lincoln, Nebraska
March, 1959

CONTENTS

PART I. The Speech Development of the Child

PART II. Finding Individual Speech Needs

PART III. Methods and Graded Materials

APPENDIX

PART I

The Speech Development
of the Child

Chapter 1

NORMAL SPEECH
DEVELOPMENT

Place the newborn infant on an island by himself with adequate food, water, and shelter about him and he will die. He is helpless by himself. Many animals could survive under the same conditions, even without the potential intelligence of the human infant. Suppose the human infant, by a miracle, did survive. Suppose he grew to be a child of two, four, or six years of age. He would still be "animal-like" in many ways. He would grunt and yell and make other unintelligible noises because he would have the capacity for producing sounds, but he would have no "speech" as we understand the term.

Now, suppose we place an adult on the island with the infant. The infant will, if he is "normal," learn speech as the adult speaks it, whether it be English, French, German, Italian, or Hindustani. If the adult speaks with a French-English dialect, that will be the child's speech. If the adult has a speech defect and says, "Thee the bwight thtarth in the thky tonight," that will very likely be the child's pattern of speech also. A child learns to use a language as those in his environment use a language. Only the human being has the mental and physical capacity to learn to speak. The animal that survives on the island by himself will be able to grunt and growl; but even if a speaking adult is present, the animal will not learn a useful language. Because man has a language and can speak, he has a means of communication; and be-

3

cause he has a means of communication, he has books, telephones, radios, television, and a long heritage of the arts and sciences of the world.

Evolution of Language and Speech

MEANING OF THE WORD "LANGUAGE." Theoretically, we may think of the word *language* as having many meanings. The definitions of the word may vary according to which aspect of the process is being emphasized. In its broadest definition, language may mean any form of intercommunicative behavior. Wood (30)[*] defines language as "any means, vocal or other, of expressing or communicating thought or feeling." Hayakawa (6) considers language as symbolism; that is, language in any form is only a symbol of the "thing" that language represents, be it an object, action, feeling, or wishful thinking. He says,

Of all forms of symbolism, language is the most highly developed, most subtle, and most complicated ... human beings, by agreement, can make anything stand for anything. Now, human beings have agreed, in the course of centuries of mutual dependency, to let the various noises that they can produce with their lungs, throats, tongues, teeth, and lips systematically stand for specified happenings in their nervous systems. We call that system of agreements *language* (p. 27).

MEANING OF THE WORD "SPEECH." We may consider that a definition of the word *language* includes a definition of the word *speech*. Speech is the audible aspect of language: that which we hear ourselves say, what others hear us say, and what we hear others say. Wood (30) defines *speech* more formally as "communication through conventional vocal and oral symbols." Simon (30), becoming more technical, defines *speech*

... in its noun form, as an established communicative system of *arbitrary* and *conventionalized* acoustic *symbols,* produced mainly by action of the muscles of the respiratory and upper alimentary tracts. In its verb form, the term implies *communicative* behavior through the use of these conventionalized and arbitrary symbols (p. 4).

[*] References will be found in the Bibliography at the end of this chapter.

Speech, then, may be considered a learned behavior, unique to man, and essential to his social, psychological, educational, and philosophical growth and development. Speech also may be thought of as an "overlaid" process in relation to its biological aspects. We find in our physical and anatomical make-up no specific "organs of speech." For the production of the sounds and syllables that form the mechanical basis of speech, man uses certain organs that serve primarily some of the basic biological functions of the body. For instance, man needs his lips to put food and liquid into his body; he uses his teeth and tongue for chewing, his tongue and throat for swallowing, and his larynx (voice box) and trachea (windpipe) for breathing. Interrelated in the use of these organs, of course, are man's muscles and his highly developed central nervous system. These same organs are used in the production of speech, but we must not think of speech as merely a mechanical process.

Speech as a Learned Behavior in Human Growth and Development

Man has theorized for a long time in his attempt to explain how and when speech began in the human race. We shall neither enumerate nor attempt to evaluate the various speculations here. The subject, however, makes fascinating reading for those who are interested in exploring the theories further. Simon (30) presents an extensive and pertinent discussion of the subject. Let it suffice for the present to say that at some time or another, man acquired speech. The acquisition of this "tool" fostered his development of a completely new world, a new social life, a new agricultural life, and a brilliant literary life; a life that changed, no doubt, from a very simple state of being to a very complex one.

It is quite plausible to believe that man acquired speech through evolutionary processes that were directly related to his growth and development over millions of years. This was possible because man had a mechanism that was capable of making noises; he possessed neural and auditory sensory organs for perceiving sounds and noises and developed a brain capable of associating meaning with certain sounds. It was only natural that speech should evolve as man experienced a need to communicate with others.

From the original languages, whatever they may have been and however they may have started, many languages developed. Groups of people were isolated in different sections of the world. As time passed, members of these groups began to move about and met other tribes with other languages. Both migration and isolation had a part in the development of the many different kinds of languages. Sometimes these languages had marks of similarity, and sometimes there appeared to be no similarity at all. Compare the old Greek and Hebrew languages with modern English, or listen to the differences between an oriental language and ours. Not only does it seem miraculous that so many different languages developed, but it also seems a miracle that any child of physical and mental "normalcy" can, almost without apparent effort, learn the language of the people within whose culture he is born.

We can understand better how the child develops speech in our world of today if we give attention to some of the scientific investigations that have attempted to trace the speech and language development of the individual from the age of early infancy to young adulthood.

Speech and Language Development of the Average Child in Our Culture

UNDERSTANDING THE PROCESS OF SPEECH DEVELOPMENT. Language is basic to our culture. A common language, adequately spoken, written, and understood is necessary for the present maintenance and the future development of our modern culture. Language is also our link to the past, which makes possible our present cultural status. Children who do not develop normally in speech and language are handicapped in communication, in learning, and in social living.

The psychologist is interested in the speech development of the child as it is related to measurements of intelligence and studies of adjustment. The sociologist is interested in the area because it is related to adequate social living, the expression of interests, and the defining of needs. The educator appreciates the relationship of speech and language development to adequacy in school subjects: to reading, writing, spelling, vocabulary growth, comprehension, and the many things in learning that language amplifies. Finally, the parent is usually tremendously interested in the speech and language development of his own child. He watches his child's speech development carefully. If it differs in time, fluency, quality, or quantity from sister Mary's or from the boy's next door, the parent may develop real states of anxiety concerning his child's speech.

RELATIONSHIP OF LANGUAGE AND THOUGHT. Thought is possible without language. The child who is born deaf and who has developed no conception of formal language can think in terms of things, actions, feelings, and experiences. It is almost impossible for those of us who have developed a normal use of language to conceive of "thinking" without the use of words. Our thinking is undoubtedly more extensive and more abstract because we have a language to use in our thinking. As McCarthy (16) points out,

Language, although perhaps not essential for all thinking, is so frequently involved in thought, and especially in making abstractions and fine distinctions and shades in meaning, as well as in communicating to others the results of one's thought processes, that a certain basic level of attainment in linguistic skills is practically an essential prerequisite to the child's formal education (p. 493).

If a child is to make progress in his formal education under our modern educational system, he will be aided in doing so to the best of his ability if he has a record of "normal" speech development. When we refer to the "normal" speech development of the *average* child, we must remember that the *average* child exists only in our imaginations. "Johnny" is not an "average" child. He is an individual with his own level of maturation and intellectual and physical growth.

It will help the teacher, the parent, and the speech therapist to understand Johnny in his individual development, however, if they understand the development of the "average" child. To understand the speech and language problems of those children who differ from the average, it is necessary to know how the *average* child develops in speech and language. In understanding the time when, and the manner in which, most children develop certain abilities, we can understand better the progress or the lack of progress of a given child. When a child is delayed in speech development, we need to understand how he is delayed and to what degree he is delayed. Then perhaps we can be more successful in our efforts to help the child achieve a higher degree of speech proficiency. In general, we can often understand the "abnormal" child better if we first understand the "normal" child.

With these thoughts in mind we will consider the so-called "normal" speech development of the average child from the period of infancy through the age of puberty. We are able to trace this development because studies have been made of many children of a given age. Simon (30), McCarthy (16), and Thompson (29) have made detailed summaries of many of the studies that are related to the early speech development of the child.

Development of Speech Sounds During Infancy

Various writers have called the period of early infancy the *prelinguistic period*, indicating that time in which the infant has nothing that can by any stretch of the imagination be called useful speech or language. McCarthy (16) reminds us that Shultze pointed out in 1880 that the word *infancy* means *without speech*, since it was derived from the Latin word *in*, meaning *without*, and the Latin word *fari*, meaning *to speak*.

EARLY INFANCY: THE FIRST TWO MONTHS. The birth cry, the first sound produced by the infant, is a physiological reaction, an automatic act, without language meaning. It starts the child out in its breathing pattern and may be thought of as the beginning of the child's speech and language development.

Early vowel sounds. After the birth cry, the infant lives through a "crying stage." Irwin (9), studying the early speech development of 40 infants, found that four vowel sounds appeared during the first ten days of life. These first sounds came from the glottis (the opening between the vocal folds). From the back positions, the infant's sound production moved toward more frontal positions. The vowels came before the consonants, and the lip sounds were produced last. Leopold (12) found that the "crying stage" was intercepted by a brief "cooing phase" during the second month of life. During this time the infant used low front and center vowels and high back vowels and some back consonants. If the reader will think of these words as *descriptive* terms, indicating the placement of sounds in the infant's mouth and throat, the words become more meaningful.

Early consonant sounds. Lewis (14) groups all back consonants, including (g), (k), and (r), as the earliest consonants; these, he maintains, are produced by the child "in comfort." The front consonants, (p), (b), and (m), are produced later in "discomfort." The "in comfort" period, we may presume, is related to the "cooing stage," and the "discomfort" period to the "crying stage." From these two stages, we proceed to the "babbling stage." It appears the infant is now beginning to enjoy his "noise making," and he produces more sounds with greater frequency.

THE "BABBLING STAGE": FROM TWO TO SIX MONTHS. During the first six months of the child's life, his production of vowel forms far exceeds his production of consonant forms. According to Lewis (14), the "babbling stage" grows out of the vowel forms produced "in comfort." The infant hears his own sound production, begins to enjoy his "play with sounds," and babbles for pleasure. According to Leopold (12), this is a stage of sound exercises. More varied sounds are brought in, but they are still without meaning. Some back vowel forms may be dropped before the end of the first six months; but new central and front vowels appear, and all sounds are articulated more distinctly.

Growth in consonant sounds. The consonant sounds that develop during the first six months are either plosives (sometimes called "stops"), including the (k), (g), (t), (d), (p), and (b) or fricatives (sounds using friction), including the (h), (ʃ) as in *sho*e, (f), and (v). By the end of the six months' period, our average infant is able to produce most of the vowel elements of speech and approximately half of the consonant sounds that appear in our spoken language.

FROM SIX MONTHS TO ONE YEAR. The "babbling stage" does not stop at the end of the six months' period but continues for the next several months. New sound formations are attempted, practiced, reinforced, and retained for future use in words. During the last half of the first year, the infant gives more attention to the speech of the persons in his environment and begins to distinguish more specifically between the sounds he hears.

FACTOR OF IMITATION. The first free babbling period without specific form is followed by a babbling period wherein the infant imitates his own sound production for the personal pleasure it brings him. Before long he begins to discriminate the sounds of others and also imitates these in his babbling. It becomes a fascinating game. Sometimes mother helps the process along by "talking" with the baby in his own babbling terms. "Ba-ba-ba-ba, ma-ma-ma-ma," and "by-by-by-by" says the parent, and the infant tries to imitate what he hears and sees. Everyone is having a good time and the infant is learning to use new front consonants and is increasing his babbling.

Leopold (12) studied his own child's speech from day to day. Of the imitative period, he comments as follows:

It is well known that children generally favor front consonants in their early imitative speaking. This has been variously explained by their accessibility to visual observation, by the greater mobility of lips and tongue tip, by the preceding practice in sucking and tactile exploration, and by their different acoustic qualities. Usually children reproduce bilabial stops early and correctly, and dental stops next, whereas velar stops are later and are frequently replaced by dental stops (p. 6).

This important observation is more readily understood when the terminology is understood. *Bilabial* refers to sounds produced by the use of the two lips; a *stop* indicates that the breath is stopped at a certain place as the sound is produced. *Bilabial stops* include the (p) and (b). The (m) is a bilabial sound but not a *stop,* since here the breath is not stopped but is directed through the nasal passages. On the *dental stops,* the breath is stopped on the upper front-teeth ridge; these sounds include the (t) and (d). The term *velar stop* refers to those sounds that have the breath stopped with the back of the tongue against the velum (soft palate) and include the sounds (k) and (g). The velar stops are sometimes replaced by dental stops; that is, the (t) or (d) may be substituted for the (k) or (g). Thus, the child may say, "I lite dood tate" for "I like good cake." It is important for us to understand these developments if we are trying to help a child who has an articulatory problem.

FROM YEAR ONE TO YEAR TWO. By the time our average infant reaches the end of his first year, his consonant sound productions begin more nearly to equal his vowel sound forms in number. The consonant sounds are used primarily in the initial and medial positions in his syllable groupings. He will say, "Ba-ba, ma-ma, wa-wa, ga-ga," etc., but does not use "ap, eep, ahm," and "em" or "eb," etc. until later. Between year one and year two, our average child has his front teeth, usually four upper and four lower ones. The dental and the postdental sounds are now learned. The (θ) as in *thin* and the ($\eth$) as in *then* are dental sounds. The postdentals include the (t), (d), and (n). The (n) is also known as a *nasal* sound.

Our child from one to two years gains steadily in psychological and physical growth and consequently gets greater control over the muscles of his body, including the muscles of his tongue and lips. Sound combinations become more complicated, and all the time our child is building new concepts that are directly related to his broadening environment and to his physical and psychological growth.

First words. The first word may be an accidental "ma-ma," growing out of the babbling. When mother is there to hear it she repeats the word and rewards the child with smiles of joy, and the first word may become established. In a like manner, "da-da" becomes identified with "daddy." The sounds become concepts, have meanings, and are recalled with purpose. The first word may be an unintelligible "wa-wa," but it develops meaning when the child expresses it as he gets a drink of water, or when he wants a drink of water. Some of the first words may originally be merely factors of imitation. Only when they are retained and used purposefully can we think of them as being mental concepts reaching the stage of meaningful speech. The single word may be used to name an object or to express an action or a feeling. It may be a noun, a verb, or an adjective. The single word may also stand for a complete sentence. "Wa-wa" may mean, "I want a drink of water." Usually the first words are those that use a repetition of syllables.

After the first single words appear, a few months pass before the child begins to use two- or three-word sentences. These still are not complete sentences in any grammatical sense, but the meaning is there. "Mama go" may mean "mother is going away" or "come, mother, let us go." Not that we think any such formal conception of the sentence is taking place in the child's mind, but the idea is there.

As our average child begins to walk, he discovers and explores a great, new world and gains many new thought concepts. During the learning-to-walk stage, he may slow down a little in word production; but a little later he picks up in his speech development very quickly. There is suddenly, it seems, so much to think about, so much to talk about, and a great need to make his wants known.

"Onset" of Speech, from Year Two to Year Three

By the age of two-and-a-half, the average child is able to use all of the vowel sounds and approximately two-thirds of the consonants. The last sounds to be developed by most children are the sounds referred to as the *liquids*: the (l) and (r). Often, these sounds are not used correctly until near or beyond school age. Rapidly, through the learning process, between two and three years of age, the child develops a greater vocabulary and begins to use longer and more complete sentences.

THE LEARNING PROCESS. Learning is defined by McGeoch (17) as "... a change in performance as a function of practice. In most cases, if not in all, this change has a direction which satisfies the current motivating conditions of the individual." We have seen how our average child changes in performance from crying to cooing to babbling, from imitation of his own sounds to the imitation of the sounds of others, and from this to words, and finally to phrases and sentences. Through all, the child has been constantly stimulated and motivated. He enjoys hearing himself, and the speech of others. He likes the "feelings" he gets when he makes sounds and the reactions and attention he gets when he produces words. Before long, he learns that this sound-making is a very useful instrument. He can cry for help, complain when he is angry, and coo and babble when he is comfortable or wants attention. When words come, they can be used to influence and control others, to get what he wants, or to reject what he does not want. Finally, in a subtle and abstract fashion, words are used to solve many of his problems. We should not think of the child as being influenced only by external forces. While he is learning from his external environment, constant changes are going on within his internal environment.

MATURATION. Thompson (29) points out that

... maturation emphasizes the influence of variables that are internal to the organism, while learning is more concerned with environmental conditions external to the organism. . . . Maturation and learning are so inextricably interwoven in the growth process that it is scientifically futile to attempt complete separation. Both processes are vital in the normal psychological development of man (p. 86).

Thus, as the child grows older and as his environment becomes enriched, he becomes more capable of learning. His use of speech as a social tool develops, slowly at first and then very rapidly between the ages of two and three.

MOTOR ABILITY. The theory of motor development rests upon the assumption that the infant responds at first with general, mass movements. As time brings growth in terms of maturation and psychological development, these mass, general movements are refined and specific muscular coordinations develop. The movements of breathing, sucking, swallowing, and later chewing act to produce better coordination of the muscles used in speaking. If normal speech is to develop, there should be no interference with the muscular activity of the various so-called speech organs. This means also that there must be no interference with the central or peripheral nervous systems that innervate the speech mechanism. Adequate speech in most cases calls for normal functioning of the muscles of the larynx, throat, palate, tongue, lips, jaws, and of the muscles related to breathing.

VOCABULARY GROWTH AND ACCURACY OF SOUNDS. Shirley (25) observed twenty-five infants at periodical intervals throughout the first years of life. She found that the average child at two years of age used thirty-seven different words. The range in number of words spoken by the children at two years, however, was from 6 to 126 words. It is possible that this was an underestimation. Shirley watched the children at regular intervals but not over a long continuous period of time. It is quite likely that, if the parents had kept a constant record, they might have found the children using a greater number of words.

In a study of a group of preschool children, Grigsby (5) reported that children three years of age had an average vocabulary of 1,507 words. The child of three, however, is still not accurate in the production of several sounds. These are usually consonant sounds and may include the (l), (r), (s), and (z); these and other consonants may be distorted or absent at the end of words. Wellman (31) reported that on the average, only 63 per cent of the child's sounds are given correctly at the age of three.

Mastery of Speech as a Useful Tool, from Year Three to Year Five

VOCABULARY GROWTH AND SENTENCE STRUCTURE. Grigsby (5) found that children had an average vocabulary of 2,148 words at the age of four. At year five, the average number of words increased to 2,527. The average three-year-old child's speech, however, is not a refined product. He is not concerned with grammar. Differences in tense concern him not at all, and dangling participles and incomplete sentences are among the least of his worries. Templin (28), studying sentence length, reported that children of three-and-a-half years use sentences averaging four words in length. Davis (3) found that the three-and-a-half-year-old child was nearing the adult distribution in relation to parts of speech used. That is, in his more-or-less limited speech he was using (percentage-wise) nearly the same number of nouns, pronouns, adjectives, verbs, etc., as the adult was using in his more advanced speech. We must proceed with caution in studying the parts of speech used by young children because, as McCarthy (16) points out,

... It is difficult, if not impossible, to arrive at a satisfactory answer as to the relative proportions of the various parts of speech in a child's total vocabulary, first because of the difficulty of determining when a child *knows* a word, second because of the difficulty of determining the total vocabulary, third because of the difficulty in classifying the word according to the part of speech it actually functions as in the child's usage, and fourth because of the difficulty of classifying the same word form according to different functions (pp. 530-531).

ACCURACY OF SOUNDS. From Wellman's studies (31), we find that the average child continues to increase in sound accuracy with increase in age. At four years, 77 per cent of the sounds are produced correctly. At five years, correct production increases to 88 per cent. Metraux (18) reported that vowel productions were 90 per cent correct at thirty months and consonant productions 90 per cent correct at fifty-four months. In a cross-sectional study of the average per cent of correct articulation scores for children from three to eight years of age, Templin (28) found that the percentage of correct articulation changed from approximately 57 per cent at three years to approximately 95 per cent at eight years of age. Most of the improvement is shown in the production of consonant sounds and in consonant blends. Spriestersbach and Curtis (27) have shown that young children are not consistent in their inaccurate production of sounds. As children grow older, consistency in the inaccuracy of sound production becomes greater. That is, the younger child sometimes is wrong and sometimes is right in the production of a given sound at different times, but the older child tends to misuse the same sounds consistently when he produces sounds inaccurately.

Although it is important to give consideration to the average developmental phases of speech, the teacher and the parent should not be too much concerned if an individual child has not developed what some persons might consider "perfect" speech by the time the child enters kindergarten. It is doubtful if there is anything that might be designated as "perfect" speech. It is also doubtful that there are individuals who use what one might call "perfect" speech. We should recall that on the average, 12 per cent of our children will "normally" still be using incorrect consonant sounds and consonant blends when they reach kindergarten age. It is important to understand when a child is within a "normal" range in speech and language development and when he might be regarded as "delayed" or "retarded" in sound production, vocabulary usage, sentence construction and length, etc. Of great importance to the speech development of the child are the considerations of his ability, opportunity, and motivation to learn.

Speech Development in the Elementary Grades

As our average child enters school and proceeds through the elementary grades, he articulates speech sounds with greater precision, gains in vocabulary, uses longer sentences that are more grammatically correct, and in general improves his linguistic style. While the speech of the preschool child is likely to revolve around himself, his interests, reactions, and feelings, the speech of the older child is likely to revolve around other people. The thought content of the older child's speech reflects this interest. At school the child has a greater opportunity to talk with more children. His teachers stimulate him to ask more intelligent questions and to give more adequate answers. He learns to read and write and to form new concepts through extended experiences. His abilities in verbal expression expand accordingly.

VOCABULARY GROWTH. Horn (8) has compiled an interesting list of the "one thousand and three words" most frequently used by kindergarten children. Smith (26) studied the reading vocabulary of children from the end of the first grade through the twelfth grade. She estimated that the average number of basic words known by children at the end of the first grade was 16,900. When the derivatives of the basic words were included in the count for "total" vocabulary, the number was 23,700. In grade twelve, the children knew 47,300 basic words and had a count of 80,300 for total vocabulary.

Rinsland (21) studied the speech and language behavior of a large number of children in the first eight grades according to the words used in their conversation and in their written compositions. By this method of checking he found that the children studied used over 25,000 words. The speaking vocabulary of adults may be limited in comparison with their reading vocabulary; but as the child becomes proficient in reading, his speaking vocabulary expands. It is also likely that experience in written composition helps to bring improvement in sentence structure and growth in sentence length.

GROWTH IN ARTICULATION ADEQUACY. Roe and Milisen (22) studied the effects of maturation upon defective articulation, checking approximately 2,000 children from the first grade through the sixth grade. The children of the first grade level, as a group, averaged 13.30 errors in articulation. The children of the fourth grade level averaged 7.62 errors. The single consonants most frequently misused, listed in order from the greatest frequency to the least frequency, were (z), (ʍ) as in *wh*en, (θ) as in *th*in, (dʒ) as in John, (d), (s), (g) as in go, (ð) as in *th*at, (v), (tʃ) as in *ch*air, (r), (ʃ) as in *sh*oe, (f), (p), (l), (ŋ) as in ri*ng*, and (w). Sayler (23) tested children in grades seven through twelve and found very little improvement in articulation from grade to grade in these upper levels. Improvement was noted, however, in the production of the sounds (f), (d), (t), (ð), and (z). Hockett (7) has stated that the fundamental speech habits of the child are firmly established by the age of puberty.

The studies of articulation adequacy throughout the grades focus our attention upon three assumptions:

1. Many children four, five, and six years of age who do not produce sounds correctly might well be given an additional year or two without any special speech help to see what general maturation might do for them in relation to more accurate sound productions. There will be some children, however, who at an early age can be said to be far below the average in speech development and sound production. These children may need special help in stimulating better speech and sound production.

2. If the child has not corrected his articulatory errors by the time he is in the fourth grade, there appears to be a fairly good chance that the errors will not be "corrected" merely through the process of further maturation.

3. If we are to help children learn to articulate sounds with greater accuracy, we should help those children who need

help at some time before the fifth grade, when their speech habits can be changed with greater ease.

AGE OF PUBERTY. We have already stated that by this age (from about fourteen to sixteen years) most children are firmly established in their speech habits. Some children, however, may appear to have a special speech problem only at this particular time. Curtis (11) comments on this phase:

During the period of this rapid growth and probably during a period of adjustment to the new characteristics of the vocal mechanism, the individual may experience considerable difficulty in controlling the pitch of his voice. Boys, because of the greater extent of the change, have many more such problems than do girls. The mechanism is no longer adapted to the high-pitched voice of childhood, and the individual has not become accustomed to, or learned to control, the lower pitch level of his adult voice (p. 183).

Most boys pass through this stage without any particular difficulties. Those who do not may need some special help in adjustment.

Individual Differences Affect Speech and Language Development

DIFFERENCES IN MATURATION. It is to be presumed that each child, through the influences of his inheritance and his environment, has a different rate of maturation. His internal organic processes will determine his rate of growth and development to some extent regardless of what the external environmental factors may be. Although we know that maturation and learning work together to influence the child's development, we also realize that there are differences in maturational growth. These differences may indicate that we should not "hurry" the speech development of a given child at a given time. In some cases, it may be wise to wait until further maturation takes place.

DIFFERENCES IN MENTAL ABILITY. We assume that there is such a thing as "native intelligence," that some children are able to learn at a faster rate and to a higher degree than others. The child's speech and language development is going to be influenced by his mental ability to learn at a given time. There may be such a thing as "learning readiness" in relation to the different phases of speech and language development. We know that children differ in regard to rate, quantity, and quality in speech development. We also know that verbal factors are important in many measurements of intelligence. Nonverbal intelligence tests can give us information as to whether or not the child who is delayed in speech development is developing normally in other factors when compared with children of his chronological age. It is important that we do not pressure a child beyond his ability to learn at a given time. It is also important to realize that learning is related to many factors, including mental ability.

DIFFERENCES IN CULTURAL AND ECONOMIC FACTORS. It is to be expected that children from superior socioeconomic backgrounds will be superior in speech and language development. From the reported results of a number of studies, this appears to be the case. Superiority may be related to the differences in education of the parents, differences in opportunities for learning, differences in mental ability, or other factors. Lewis (14) reported that children from superior socioeconomic backgrounds used their first words at the age of ten or eleven months. This is a month or two earlier than the reports we find in studies of children who come from a wider spread of socioeconomic backgrounds. Davis (4) found that 73 per cent of the children from five to ten years of age in the upper socioeconomic levels rated "perfect articulation," while only 58 per cent of the children of the same ages in the lower levels received that rating. Anastasi and D'Angelo (1) made a comparison of Negro and white preschool children in language development. They found no significant differences between the two groups of children. Moore (19) found that orphanage children were markedly retarded in language development when compared with nonorphanage children. The results of these studies suggest that differences in cultural and socioeconomic backgrounds have a bearing on the speech and language development of the child. Race difference in children of similar cultural backgrounds appears to have no differential influence.

SEX DIFFERENCES. A number of studies have suggested that there may be developmental differences between boys and girls that are related to differences in speech and language development. Schuell (24) investigated a number of factors, including differences in growth and development, in speech and language, in adjustment, and in attitudes of adults toward boys and girls. As these differences exist, Schuell hypothesizes, they may be detrimental to the speech development of the male child.

McCarthy (15) found that at most age levels the speech of boys was much less readily understood than that of girls. Sayler (23) found that boys made more articulatory errors than girls in grades seven through eleven, and Templin (28) reported that girls were superior to boys in sentence length from preschool years through the early elementary grades. Olson and Koetzle (20) found that boys spoke less than girls in a given time in nursery school and kindergarten; they also found that when the boys did speak, they spoke faster. This brief survey of some of the sex differences that may exist should make us aware of the fact that we should not make comparisons between individual boys and girls in relation to their speech development at given ages, and that we should not expect all boys and girls to develop in exact likeness in speech. In some instances, comparisons may have detrimental effects upon future growth and development.

We have seen that speech development in the growing child is a gradual process that takes place over a period of years. We must understand that "normal" speech for the developing child is something less than perfect. Our findings record in part what we have a reason to expect on the average at any given age. When deviations from the expectations become too great, we may reasonably be concerned about the child's speech development. We will next turn to a consideration of the deviations from normal speech that we find in children.

Bibliography

1. ANASTASI, A., and D'ANGELO, R. "A Comparison of Negro and White Preschool Children in Language Development and Goodenough Draw-a-man I. Q.," *Journal of Genetic Psychology,* 81 (1952), 147-165.
2. CHEN, H. P., and IRWIN, O. C. "Infant Speech: Vowel and Consonant Types," *Journal of Speech Disorders,* 11, No. 1 (March, 1946), 27-29.
3. DAVIS, E. A. "Developmental Changes in the Distribution of Parts of Speech," *Child Development,* 9 (1938), 310-317.
4. ——. "The Development of Linguistic Skill in Twins, Singletons with Siblings, and Only Children Age Five to Ten Years," *Institute of Child Welfare Monograph,* Series No. 14. Minneapolis: University of Minnesota Press (1937).
5. GRIGSBY, O. J. "An Experimental Study of the Development of Concepts of Relationship in Preschool Children as Evidenced by Their Expressive Ability." *Journal of Experimental Education,* 1, No. 2 (December, 1932), 144-162.
6. HAYAKAWA, S. I. *Language in Thought and Action.* New York: Harcourt, Brace & Co., 1956.
7. HOCKETT, C. F. "Age Grading and Linguistic Change," *Language,* 26, No. 4 (December, 1950), 449-457.
8. HORN, M. D. "The Thousand and Three Words Most Frequently Used by Kindergarten Children," *Child Education,* 3, No. 3 (November, 1926), 118-122.
9. IRWIN, O. C. "Research on Speech Sounds for the First Six Months of Life," *Psychological Bulletin,* 38, No. 5 (May, 1941), 277-285.
10. ——. "Speech Development in the Young Child; Some Factors Related to the Speech Development of the Infant and Young Child," *Journal of Speech and Hearing Disorders,* 17, No. 3 (September, 1952), 269-279.
11. JOHNSON, W., BROWN, S. F., CURTIS, J. F., EDNEY, C. W., and KEASTER, J. *Speech Handicapped School Children,* rev. ed. New York: Harper & Bros., 1956.
12. LEOPOLD, W. F. "Patterning in Children's Language Learning," *Language Learning,* 5 (1953-1954), 1-14.
13. ——. "Speech Development of a Bilingual Child," *Northwestern University Studies,* I-IV (1937-1949).
14. LEWIS, M. M. *Infant Speech,* 2d ed. New York: Humanities Press, Inc., 1951.
15. McCARTHY, D. "The Language Development of the Preschool Child," *Institute of Child Welfare Monograph,* Series No. 4. Minneapolis: University of Minnesota Press (1930).
16. ——. "Language Development in Children," Chapter 9 in Carmichael, L. (ed.), *Manual of Child Psychology,* 2d ed. New York: John Wiley & Sons, Inc., 1954.
17. McGEOCH, J. A. *The Psychology of Human Learning.* New York: Longmans, Green & Co., 1942.

18. METRAUX, R. W. "Speech Profiles of the Preschool Child 18-54 Months," *Journal of Speech and Hearing Disorders*, 15, No. 1 (March, 1950), 37-53.
19. MOORE, J. K. "Speech Content of Selected Groups of Orphanage and Non-orphanage Preschool Children," *Journal of Experimental Education*, 16, No. 2 (December, 1947), 122-133.
20. OLSON, W. C., and KOETZLE, V. S. "Amount and Rate of Talking of Young Children," *Journal of Experimental Education*, 5, No. 2 (December, 1936), 175-179.
21. RINSLAND, H. D. *A Basic Vocabulary of Elementary School Children*. New York: The Macmillan Co., 1945.
22. ROE, V., and MILISEN, R. "The Effect of Maturation Upon Defective Articulation in Elementary Grades," *Journal of Speech Disorders*, 7, No. 1 (March, 1942), 37-50.
23. SAYLER, H. D. "The Effect of Maturation Upon Defective Articulation in Grades Seven Through Twelve," *Journal of Speech and Hearing Disorders*, 14, No. 3 (September, 1949), 202-207.
24. SCHUELL, H. *Differences Which Matter: A Study of Boys and Girls*. Austin, Texas: The Delta Kappa Gamma Society, 1947.
25. SHIRLEY, M. M. "The First Two Years: A Study of Twenty-five Babies," *Institute of Child Welfare Monograph*, Series No. 7. Minneapolis: University of Minnesota Press (1933).
26. SMITH, M. K. "Measurement of the Size of General English Vocabulary Through the Elementary Grades and High School," *Genetic Psychology Monographs*, 24 (1941), 311-345.
27. SPRIESTERSBACH, D. C., and CURTIS, J. F. "Misarticulation and Discrimination of Speech Sounds," *Quarterly Journal of Speech*, 37, No. 4 (December, 1951), 483-491.
28. TEMPLIN, M. C. "Certain Language Skills in Children," *Institute of Child Welfare Monograph*, Series No. 26. Minneapolis: University of Minnesota Press (1957).
29. THOMPSON, G. E. *Child Psychology*. Boston: Houghton Mifflin Co., 1952.
30. TRAVIS, L. E. (ed.). *Handbook of Speech Pathology*. New York: Appleton-Century-Crofts, Inc., 1957.
31. WELLMAN, B. L., CASE, I. M., MENGERT, I. G., and BRADBURY, D. E. "Speech Sounds of Young Children," *University of Iowa Studies in Child Welfare*, 5, No. 2 (1931).

Chapter 2

DEVIATIONS FROM NORMAL SPEECH

In one way or another, every child deviates from the normal. That is why children are to be thought of as individuals, not as rote mechanical beings with like behavior patterns. Remembering how we establish averages, we realize that we do not expect all children to meet a certain given, unequivocal state of behavior before being considered "normal." Some children will have superior speech, with accurate articulation, good voice quality, more than adequate vocabulary, and acceptable sentence structure; other children may be less outstanding in speech performance, but will be within the range of the normal speakers. Normal speech indicates a *range* of normalcy.

How then do we determine when a child is outside the normal range? Are there specific rules of measurement? If so, who is to apply the measurement? Is it to be the teacher, the parent, the speech therapist, or the next-door neighbor? Determining whether or not a child has a speech problem or defective speech is more or less a matter of forming an opinion or making a judgment. There are no specific rules or measurements to be applied by the layman. There are times when a deviation may be suspected or obvious, even to an untrained individual. It will be wise, however, to seek the advice of a trained speech therapist or a speech pathologist before passing judgment on any child.

We may suspect that a child has a speech problem when his speech behavior is obviously different from that of most children of his age level. When the child has difficulty in expressing his thoughts to others or when the listener has difficulty understanding what the child is saying, we may suspect that a speech problem exists. If attention is called to *how* the child is speaking rather than to *what* he is saying, the possibility of a speech difficulty should be investigated. Speech may deviate from normal in many different ways, and any one or more of several causal factors may be involved in the deviation. The ability to communicate effectively is of the greatest importance to every individual throughout his entire life, and yet the speech-defective children in our public schools far outnumber the children suffering from any other single type of handicap.

Incidence of Speech Disorders

A speech problem may not be the child's only difficulty. A child may have a speech difficulty because he has a hearing loss, a cleft palate, because he is suffering from a brain injury, or for any other of a number of reasons. However, if we should isolate the one factor and state that this number of children in the United States have speech difficulties, we would probably find that the number of speech difficulties would approximate all the other types of handicaps combined. Since it is impossible to count every single child who has a speech problem, the best we can do in estimating incidence is to consider the surveys that have been made in given populations.

NATURE OF INACCURACIES IN REPORTING INCIDENCE. In making a survey to determine the incidence of speech defects, we have to take into consideration a number of important factors:

1. Is the community to be surveyed a representative population?
2. Is the person who is to make the survey qualified? Has he

sufficient training and experience? How does he make his
survey?

3. What is the "rule of measurement" used in judging when
a speech problem exists?

Each of the above questions presents a problem and
makes for many errors in any attempt to determine incidence. Would a New England community be representative
of the general population in the United States? Could a
community in Minnesota, settled by Swedes and Germans,
be a representative group? Suppose a speech therapist from
the Midwestern states were to conduct a survey in Brooklyn.
Would his report differ from that of the speech therapist
trained in the East? Let us assume the therapist is well
qualified and experienced. How does he make his survey?
Does he interview each child in the school system? Or do
the teachers report the children whom they think have
speech problems? If several persons are making the survey,
do they use the same "yardstick"? When does a speech
difference become a defect?

ESTIMATED INCIDENCE. When many qualified persons
make careful surveys of many children over many different
sections of the country and report their findings, we can at
best make only approximate estimations of the number of
speech-defective children in the United States. In 1949, the
President of the United States appointed a Fact Finding
Committee to study and make a report on speech disorders
and speech correction at the 1950 Midcentury White House
Conference on Children and Youth. This Committee, selected from advanced members of the American Speech and
Hearing Association, presented a paper that, among other
things, included an estimate of the incidence of speech
defects among children in the United States (1). This estimate is based upon an assumed population of 40,000,000
children between the ages of five and twenty-one. Table I is
arranged according to incidence in relation to seven major
types of speech difficulties. It is presented here as probably
the best report of incidence that we can secure. The Com-

mittee stresses the point that the figures are the lowest defensible estimates; these figures would be considered "serious under-estimates in certain respects by some authorities. They leave out of account an estimated additional 5 per cent, or 2,000,000 children who have relatively minor speech and voice defects. . . ." (p. 129).

TABLE I

Estimates of incidence of speech defects among children in the United States between the ages of 5 and 21 based on an assumed total population of 40,000,000.°

Type of defect	Ages 5-21 years (%)	Ages 5-21 years (No.)
Functional articulatory	3.0	1,200,000
Stuttering	0.7	280,000
Voice	0.2	80,000
Cleft palate speech	0.1	40,000
Cerebral palsy speech	0.2	80,000
Retarded speech development	0.3	120,000
Impaired hearing (with speech defect)	0.5	200,000
Total	5.0	2,000,000

° Adapted from the report of the American Speech and Hearing Association Committee on the Midcentury White House Conference (1, p. 130), by permission of the *Journal of Speech and Hearing Disorders* and Wendell Johnson, Chairman of the Committee.

We can expect that five out of every one hundred children and youths between the ages of five and twenty-one will have a speech problem so serious that it may be designated as a speech defect. Five more out of each one hundred will have speech problems of a less serious nature. All of the children with serious and less-serious speech problems will not be in school.

Out-of-school children. In 1949, of the approximately 39,000,000 children between the ages of five and twenty-one in the United States, 3,158,000 between the ages of five and seventeen were not in school. Of these 1,287,000 were children five years of age and 1,525,000 were between the ages of fourteen and seventeen (16).

It is likely that these out-of-school children will have more speech problems percentage-wise and in many cases have more serious speech problems than the in-school children. This is to be expected for several reasons. First, many of the five-year-old children are just waiting until a place is made for them in school. These are, on the average, normal children; but we can expect them to have more speech problems because children of this age do have more speech problems. We can, however, expect that many of these five-year-old children who do not have adequate speech will acquire normal speech in the near future. Second, we can assume that some of the older out-of-school children are physically or mentally handicapped to such an extent that the public school is not prepared to take care of them, and the parents usually cannot pay for private schooling. Speech defects among these children are great in number and are often serious in nature. Of the 1,525,000 children between fourteen and seventeen who were not in school in 1949, we can assume that some left school to go to work, some dropped out because of school failure, others because of illness, and still others may have become discouraged and dropped out because of the handicap of a speech difficulty.

We can expect to find many speech problems among the children placed in institutions for the mentally retarded. In the institutions for the deaf and in the special schools and homes for children affected by cerebral palsy or brain injuries, we will also find a high percentage of speech defects.

There will be some children who are kept out of school specifically because they have a speech problem, or in some cases a speech and a language problem. In some of our public schools, children are not admitted to kindergarten or the first grade unless they can meet certain (or uncertain) standards of speech development. Sometimes children are admitted with very inadequate speech and then are retained for two or more years in the kindergarten or first grade because they continue to have speech difficulties.

We have no record of the number of speech-defective children among the more than three million children between the ages of five and seventeen who are not in school in the United States. The incidence of speech defects is estimated for the most part in relation to children who are in the school population. If the children who are not in school are taken into account, the incidence of speech defects would undoubtedly rise to a higher figure.

Effects of a Speech Defect

We would be foolish if we closed our eyes and said, "All of these children with speech defects are not different from any other children, except in their speech development." This may be true in some cases of the young child, but to say that a speech defect will not affect a child psychologically, socially, or educationally is in many cases wishful thinking. It is against human nature to overlook defects that point out someone as being "different." Both children and adults, in our culture, must conform to a certain degree or be looked upon or treated as "outsiders." This is probably so because those who are different are in the minority. It doesn't usually take a child long to discover that others look upon him as standing apart from the general run of people if he is crippled, deaf, a speech defective, or otherwise "different."

The feelings of insecurity or rejection that the "different" child may develop come to a great extent from the treatment he receives from others. We need to educate the general population to an understanding and acceptance of the handicapped. In our enlightened civilization, we are doing this more and more. Yet the attitudes of the people during the centuries in which there was only rejection of the "unfit" and the "weak" still influence our thinking in many ways, unconscious though it may be. We frequently find it necessary, therefore, to educate the "different" child to accept his difference, to adjust to it, and to conform to what we think of as "normal" to the best of his ability. Of course, it is possible in many cases of speech defectiveness to help the child to a status of normalcy, but this often takes time, and during that time related problems can and often do develop.

We should proceed with caution when discussing the "effects" of a speech difficulty. There is often confusion as to whether given factors may be the cause of a speech difficulty or the result of it. When problems do exist, psychologically, socially, or educationally, the individual child is better off if solutions to his problems can be found. To help a child to better adjustment is a worthy accomplishment in itself, regardless of whether the speech difficulty caused the maladjustment or the maladjustment caused the speech difficulty. The full development of the whole child is the basic philosophy and ultimate aim of a democratic educational system. Scarcely a textbook has been written in relation to speech problems of children which does not discuss the effects that speech problems may have upon the child. Whether or not certain maladjustments are directly related to the speech defect remains to be proved in many instances by means of further research. We know from our clinical observations and from observations of school children that children with speech problems quite frequently have other problems as well.

Speech Problems in Relation to Psychological Growth and Development. Psychologists have maintained that there is a close relationship between language development and intellectual development. As McCarthy (15) points out:

> Language is an area of the child's development in which more marked and more striking degrees of individual variation can be observed than in almost any other [area of development] . . . Individual differences in linguistic development closely parallel the differences which have been shown to exist in intellectual development. . . . It is also quite certain that language development has contributed heavily to the variations in intellectual differences as they have thus far been measured. . . . The age of onset of talking has often been regarded as symptomatic of the child's later intellectual development (p. 598).

Children known to be mentally retarded will have a history of delayed speech development in their earlier years. Irwin (10) studied ten low-grade feeble-minded children with an average age of four years and an average intelligence quotient of 29. He found that in their speech they approximated the vowel and consonant production of normal children one year in age. Schlanger (22) found in a survey of institutionalized mentally handicapped children that from 55 to 66 per cent had speech deviations of one kind or another. Although children who are severely mentally retarded will have speech problems, the reverse of this statement is not necessarily true. Children who have speech problems are *not* necessarily mentally retarded.

The child with a serious speech defect is often handicapped when efforts are made to establish his mental ability by means of standardized intelligence tests. This is especially likely to be so when "verbal" forms of intelligence tests are used. The "nonverbal" testing procedures give the speech-defective child a better chance to perform to the best of his ability. A child with a serious speech difficulty may be withdrawn, shy, frightened, or emotionally disturbed in one way or another. Under these circumstances, he is not likely to do his best on any type of examination. It may be necessary to have a qualified psychologist give a series of tests over a period of time—and this may be a matter of years—before one is able to determine with any reliability the mental capacity of a child with a serious speech problem.

When the child reaches the middle and upper grade levels, the achievement tests can be helpful in determining whether or not the child is making satisfactory progress in relation to his age expectations. However, a serious speech difficulty through the lower grades may be the determining factor in his inability to learn to read or to keep up with his class in reading and writing performance. When a child is retarded in speech and in reading and writing, it is quite understandable that the teacher might think such a child mentally retarded as well, but it is quite possible that the deviation in speech and the failure to learn stem from factors wholly unrelated to mental retardation.

SPEECH PROBLEMS IN RELATION TO SOCIAL GROWTH AND DEVELOPMENT. When we come to a general consideration of the social and personal adjustment of the speech-defective child, we find ourselves surging about in a multitude of different opinions. Research reports vary regarding the conclusions drawn in studies of the personal adjustment of the speech-defective child. Those who have worked in speech clinics or in public school sytems as speech therapists will confirm the statement that there are children who suffer from a speech defect who also have personal and social adjustment problems. When these problems are coexistent, they may or may not be related factors. It is quite possible that the maladjustment may be neither the result nor the cause of the speech disturbance. Instead, an additional contributing factor may be causing the maladjustment. Finally, it is also possible that a child may have a speech defect and have no personal or social maladjustments.

In a careful consideration of the subject, several related factors should be taken into account: First, one must consider the problems of the individual child; and second, one must realize that the individual child gets "lost" in a consideration of the "average" findings when a large group of children are studied. A third factor, of great importance, is that the instruments by which we measure "social" and "personal" adjustment are far from perfect. We do not always know for certain *what* we are measuring; and because many of the measurements call for subjective opinions, we do not always know how reliable our measurements are.

McCarthy (15) has observed that ". . . social adjustment is usually very poor in older children who manifest serious language disorders. Such children seem to be either very shy or very aggressive and to have no wholesome friendships with their peers . . ." (p. 602). Wood (26) studied fifty children who had functional articulatory defects. When the California Test of Personality was used as a testing instrument, these children were found to be not significantly different from children with normal speech in personality. When the Thematic Apperception Test was applied, however, evidence of maladjustment was shown. The children with articulatory defects showed greater evidence of withdrawal tendencies, lack of affection, anxiety and insecurity, lack of achievement, aggressiveness, and tendencies of hostility and escape.

Perrin (20) studied the speech-defective child in relation to his social position in the classroom. Children with speech defects, when compared with children with normal speech, were found to be more often isolated from their classmates and more often neglected; and in this study these children were never chosen as "stars" or leaders in the classroom.

Spriestersbach (23) reviewed "every appropriate study" abstracted or published in *Speech Monographs*, the *Journal of Speech and Hearing Disorders*, and those listed in the *Psychological Abstracts* since 1950, which were related to the personality of the individual with an articulatory disorder. He points out in his summary that

... one is forced to conclude that the contribution of research to an understanding of the relationship between articulatory defects and personality is largely negative. The data do not justify a statement about the relationships. . . . It would appear that the choice of a testing instrument in such studies is a crucial question. . . . Most of the measures which have been used are nonempirically derived measures that are unreliable and lacking in validation (p. 334).

Moncur (17) studied forty-eight stuttering children between the ages of five and eight, compared them with a group of nonstutterers of like ages and intelligence, and reported that "every stuttering child exhibited several symptoms of maladjustment." Glasner (9) studied seventy stuttering children between the ages of two and five. Fifty-four per cent of these children were found to have feeding problems, twenty-seven per cent were enuretic, and twenty per cent were reported to have fears and nightmares.

Johnson (13) reports that Darley used the Rogers Test of Personality Adjustment in studying fifty stuttering children and fifty nonstuttering children, matched in age and sex. In distribution of scores, the two groups were found to be not significantly different in "Personal Inferiority," "Social Maladjustment," "Family Maladjustment," "Daydreaming," or in total scores. There was, however, a tendency for the stuttering children to make higher scores in each area and higher total scores than the nonstuttering children; and more stuttering children than nonstuttering children rated "high" in more than one of the five areas. A "high" classification suggested a rather serious degree of maladjustment.

In reviewing studies related to the personal, social, or emotional maladjustment of stutterers, Johnson (12) concluded that it would appear that stutterers

.... differ slightly or not at all, depending on the type of test, from presumably normal nonstutterers, and that whenever stutterers are found to differ from nonstutterers on measures of personality they differ in tending to be a bit more depressed or discouraged, a bit more anxious or uneasy or unresponsive, especially in speech situations, and somewhat more withdrawing socially. The kinds and degrees of difference indicate not a serious personality maladjustment, but rather a normal kind and amount of emotional reaction to the sorts of frustrating, threatening, and unpleasant experience that stuttering involves (p. 239).

A number of techniques are used to indicate the extent of personal and social maladjustment. The Vineland Social Maturity Scale, created by Doll (6) is frequently used to determine the extent to which the child is developing normally in social traits and self help, the extent to which he is able to achieve independence, and the extent to which he remains dependent upon his parents or society. The Rorschach techniques and the Murray Thematic Apperception Test give us a better understanding of the individual and his problems, but the application and interpretation of these require that the examiner have special training and experience. Children with serious social and personal adjustment problems should be referred to a qualified clinical psychologist or psychiatrist. These specialists will administer the most appropriate examinations, interpret the results of the tests, and make recommendations for the particular child.

The child can be observed in his periods of free play and in home and school situations. Social and personal maladjustments may be indicated by certain behavior patterns. Children may show tendencies toward withdrawal or aggression; they may display fears or anxieties, or may be negative or destructive in their relationships with other children or adults. Children who show these tendencies will need help in finding better social and personal adjustment.

If our Johnny who has a speech defect, also bites his nails or sucks his thumb, or if he bullies the other children, or runs away and cries much too frequently, one can suspect that Johnny has an adjustment problem. If he "shoots" his mother, father, sister, and brother in his play activities, or if he "steals" the family car and "kills" six policemen in his imagined "joyride" around the city, one can wonder if Johnny has a social problem. If he says "no" every time he is asked if he wants to play with the other children, "no" when asked if he would like an ice cream cone, if he hides under the table and sulks time after time, if he all too frequently kicks other children and maybe the teacher and his mother as well, one can conclude that he may have a problem in personal adjustment.

In the discovery and acceptance of more approved behavioral patterns, the child may show improvement in speech. The reverse of this statement may also be experienced; the development of more acceptable speech may lead to better personal and social adjustment. The child with a speech difficulty should be carefully studied. If an effort is made to understand the whole child in relation to his adjustment to his environment and in relation to his psychological growth and development, we may be able to avoid the mistake of "treating the symptoms," and consequently are likely to be more successful in guiding the child to the development of more normal speech.

SPEECH PROBLEMS IN RELATION TO EDUCATIONAL GROWTH AND DEVELOPMENT. In an ideal state, we could wish that at the age of five every child would have adequate speech as he enters school and begins his formal education. The United States is nearing the realization of at least one ideal in its move toward universal education. More children are in school than ever before, not only because we have a growing population, but also because a greater proportion of our school-age children are attending school. The graph below shows the school population from 1900 through that which may be expected in 1960, according to the report of the Midcentury White House Conference (16). An increase in school population will undoubtedly bring about an increase in school problems, speech problems as well as others. It has been stated in the White House Conference report that 28,000 additional teachers were needed to care for increasing enrollments in 1951. A total of 271,000 new teachers might effectively manage the increased enrollment of 1960, allowing for 30 pupils to a teacher. The report does not state whether or not this number takes into account the special teachers needed, including the speech therapists.

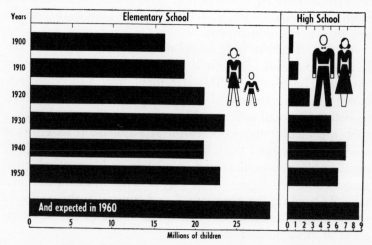

Source: *Report of the Midcentury White House Conference (16)*

Increase in School Population

With adequate parent and teacher education and with increased medical, physical, and psychological care, it is pleasant to think that we might, in the Utopia of the future, have a school population that would need little if any speech improvement work or corrective training. But such thinking, now at least, does not appear to be realistic. We are very likely going to have speech problems in our school population for a long time to come. As our civilization becomes more complicated and as more children suffering from illness and organic malformations are living longer under improved medical care, it is quite possible that we may see an increase in special educational problems, including problems in speech and language development.

Children who do not develop adequate speech and language skills are going to continue to be handicapped in our increasingly complicated world. Thompson (24) aptly describes it,

As our culture evolves, there are fewer and fewer chances for language-handicapped adults to make contributions to it. In a future era of electronic controls and atomic energy one can only surmise that the illiterates will be wards of the state, unable to comprehend or contribute to a social system built on such complex word-concept models (p. 336). . . . Certainly in these days of international misunderstanding, propaganda, and counter-propaganda no one can afford to underestimate the importance of language in our adjustments to a complex social world (p. 370).

If it is unrealistic to expect every child to acquire adequate speech by the age of five, we might well wish that such a state could be reached at least by the time the child attains a *mental* age of six-and-a-half years, since this is when most children are regarded as psychologically "ready" to learn to read. Even this, however, we know is not possible in many instances. We do not know just how much, if at all, the acquisition of the ability to read is influenced negatively by the presence of a speech defect. It has been presumed by many that an inability to use the spoken language adequately may lead to the development of inadequate skills in reading and writing and to difficulties in related school subjects such as spelling and arithmetic.

SPEECH DEFECTS AND SCHOOL SUBJECTS. The number of children who have reading difficulties appears to be increasing in our public school systems, or perhaps we have had reading problems called to our attention more frequently during recent years. Since we are accustomed to thinking of speech development as having a close relationship to the development of reading and writing, we might well ask if the results of research tell us that there is a positive relationship between reading and speech difficulties. Does a relationship also exist between speech problems and spelling errors? If a child has a speech problem, is this likely to affect his learning ability in arithmetic?

Carrell and Pendergast (5) studied the relationship between speech and spelling errors. In their study, thirty-three children with "delayed" speech were matched in age, sex, intelligence, and a teacher's estimate of academic achievement, personality traits, and home background with a like number of children having normal speech. Data on spelling errors were gathered from written papers over a two-month period. The data seemed to justify the conclusion that there were no outstanding or significant differences between the two groups of children either in spelling ability or in the types of errors made in spelling.

In a recent study, Everhart (7) was concerned with the relationship of physical, mental, and environmental variables in relation to elementary school children with and without defective articulation. Among other things, he desired to determine the relationship between articulatory defectiveness and reading and arithmetic ability. The data secured revealed no significant differences in these subjects between elementary boys and girls with and without articulatory handicaps. The investigator comments, however, that there is "evidence that if larger sample sizes had been available, a significant relationship might have been observed between reading and the occurrence of inferior articulation" (p. 335).

Schaper (21) studied the speech and reading testing records of 1,547 entering freshmen students at the University of Nebraska. Sixty of these students were defective in speech. Eighty-eight were retarded in reading vocabulary and comprehension to an extent that they were required to attend the reading clinic. An additional sixty-five students were recommended for reading improvement work, and an additional 342 students were recommended for speech improvement training. The speech and reading records of 100 of the 1,547 students were selected at random to serve as a control group for the purpose of a statistical study. The results of the analysis of the data secured indicated that a significant relationship existed between reading and speech disabilities. It is interesting to note that one half of the eighty-eight students who were required to take the reading laboratory work were defective in speech.

When a relationship between speech and reading disabilities has been shown to exist in young adults, we are inclined to assume that the young child with a speech defect may quite possibly have difficulty in the reading process. Monroe (18) was of the opinion that the factors affecting speech may also affect reading when she wrote:

Inaccurate articulation may directly affect reading by presenting a confusion in the sounds of words to be associated with the printed symbols. A child who has an articulatory defect hears the word as spoken by others in one way and as spoken by himself in another way. Either of the two memories may be aroused in presentation of a printed word. Thus, he may read "pig," "pid," in his own articulation. He may, similarly, read "beg," "bed," since he substitutes the d for g in speech. Now "bed" may arouse a totally different meaning from "beg." The child may therefore develop confusions in reading in both mechanics and comprehension which would not have been present if his articulation were accurate (pp. 92-93).

In 1948, Artley (2) reviewed a number of pertinent studies that were concerned with the relationship of speech and reading difficulties. As reported by Artley, Monroe (18) found that 27 per cent of 415 children having reading difficulties also had speech difficulties. Jackson (11) compared

300 advanced readers with a like number of retarded readers and found that 10 per cent of the advanced group and 23 per cent of the retarded group had speech defects. Using children in grades two and three, Bond (3) studied sixty-four poor readers and a like number of good readers. Speech difficulties did not appear to retard *silent* reading ability. When Bond turned his attention to a study of oral reading, he found that 35 per cent of the children who were good in silent reading but poor in oral reading had speech defects. The children who were retarded in silent reading but were good in oral reading had no speech defects.

Moss (19) matched thirty-six second-grade pupils who had speech defects with a like number of pupils without speech defects and used the Gray Standardized Oral Reading Test to compare the two groups. She found that the normal speakers surpassed the defective speakers in both speed of reading and freedom from reading errors. In the conclusion of her survey, Artley (2) states:

There appears to be a relationship between speech difficulties and deficiencies in reading ability, though there is absence of agreement as to the extent of this relationship . . . (p. 359) . . . It would seem that situations could arise in which deficient reading and speaking appeared together, not in a causal relationship, but as the result of both arising out of a common background. . . . One such factor may be intelligence (p. 355).

UNDERSTANDING FACTOR RELATIONSHIPS. There are other factors that might bring about both a speech and a reading difficulty. A serious loss in hearing might affect the child's speech development and also his reading proficiency. It is possible that his oral reading ability may be retarded more than his silent reading ability. The child learns to speak words to a great extent as he hears them. If he does not hear words distinctly, he may fear using certain words in oral reading. This fear and lack of knowledge in regard to correct pronunciation may cause him to give a retarded oral reading performance. The bilingual child who is constantly exposed to two languages at home and the child who hears "broken" English at home may have both speech and language problems.

It is unscientific to assume that when a child has a speech difficulty and other problems that all of his problems are necessarily related or that they stem from a given causal factor. It may be that his problems are related or it may be that no relationship exists. A child's problems may very well be related to multiple causal factors. It is difficult to isolate one factor and say "this is the causal factor in this case." We can be in error too many times when we make such an assumption. Whatever the studies of groups may tell us and whatever the performance of the "average" child may be, we are still confronted with the problem of understanding the individual child and his individual problems.

A study of the whole child in all of his relationships is necessary if we are to help him develop to the best of his ability, educationally, psychologically, and socially. It is quite possible that improvement in speech may bring about improvement in reading, spelling, and perhaps even in arithmetic. What the exact relationships may be we do not know. Perhaps in helping the child to improve his speech, we give him better adjustment to his life's environment. In his improved environment, he may find that reading and other academic subjects become less of a problem to him. Of course, a reverse of the situation is possible. Improved reading ability may bring about improved speech. The goal of improved speech performance is a worthy one, even if we cannot at times understand all of the mechanics in which we find ourselves involved in the process of speech improvement.

"Causes" of Speech Disorders

For many years it has been customary in much of the literature on defective speech to enumerate lists of things or situations that might act as "causes" of speech difficulties. We have already seen from our discussions up to this point that it is necessary to proceed with caution in trying to discover precipitating factors that may be related to speech difficulties. Using prudence regarding the dangers involved, let us discuss some of the factors that are believed to be associated with speech defects in the sense of having "causal" relationships.

Environmental Factors that May Adversely Influence the Child's Speech Development

We can expect that children who come from homes in which the parents have a high educational, cultural, and socioeconomic status will, on the average, have fewer speech difficulties than children who come from homes in which the parents are less well educated, more lacking in favorable cultural opportunities, and lower on the socioeconomic scale. Important in the child's speech development are his opportunities to be stimulated by correct speech examples, his possibilities of being exposed to many and varied types of worthy cultural experiences, and his feelings of security in his social and economic world. The parents in the home set the pattern of the child's educational, cultural, and socioeconomic field. Upon this pattern, the school, the teacher, and the child's ever-growing and changing environment build a constantly changing child personality.

EFFECTS OF SIBLINGS, BIRTH ORDER, AND TWINS. In careless evaluations, one can frequently be too quick in drawing conclusions when looking for "causal" factors in relation to speech problems or in relation to any other of a number of childhood problems. How often do we hear someone thoughtlessly say, "Well, what can you expect from an 'only' child?" Of perhaps we hear a remark about the oldest child, the youngest, or the middle one. We may hear that the oldest child is a "mother's child," that the youngest child is "spoiled," that the middle child is a "neglected" child. Such conditions may develop; but no one has proved, to our knowledge, that the birth order of siblings is significantly related to the development of speech problems. In individual cases, we may *suspect* that the youngest child has developed a speech problem because he has been "spoiled," "babied," over-protected, or not allowed to speak for himself.

In our clinical experience, we have known of twins who have developed "twin speech," usually a jargon that only the twins concerned appear to understand with any degree of accuracy. We must remember that we have also known of many sets of twins who have had no speech difficulties whatsoever. We must look for all possible contributing factors when studying children with speech defects, and we should make a similar search when dealing with the problems of the child who is the oldest, the youngest, or the middle one.

VARIATIONS IN METHODS OF SPEECH TRAINING. Parents vary in their "methods" of speech training; consciously or unconsciously, they guide their children in their speech development. Children learn speech, we have said, to a great extent by hearing speech. Given poor speech patterns, then, can we not expect the child to learn poor speech? Perhaps, if the child gets most of his speech stimulation from the one who has poor speech. Thus if the mother has a speech defect and is the child's most constant companion during the years in which he is developing speech, we are probably safe in saying that there is a fairly good chance the child will copy his mother's defective speech patterns. We cannot be sure of this in all types of speech difficulties. We do not think that the child necessarily copies a stuttering pattern. Could we expect that a child would copy the cleft-palate speech of his cleft-palate mother? The imitation theory needs to be questioned in some cases because most children are not influenced in their speech development by one member of the family alone.

It is understandable that a child may be retarded in speech development because of the lack of proper speech stimulation and motivation. If members of the family do not talk to and with the child, if others hurry to wait upon the child before he has a chance to express any need vocally, if others speak for the child before he has a chance to open his mouth and speak for himself, it would not be surprising if the child were delayed in speech development. If later the same child is highly motivated to speak for himself, we may find that he is not ready to speak without using sound substitutions and omissions. It may be that this deficiency is related to his lack of speech experience and exercise, due to the understimulation and lack of motivation that the child has experienced.

A delayed speech experience may have dire results if the child is growing up in a family circle in which the parents have established high standards of speech performance. What happens? There comes a time when a parent decides that "Johnny" is not developing speech as adequately as he should. Then the parent may decide to "do something about it," and that "something" may be started right in the home, without the advice of those who may know what should be done about it. Johnny may be told to say this and say that, to say it correctly, and to say it again. If such treatment continues, problems in speech may follow. Perhaps Johnny at this time has no real speech "problem" at all, but the parents may not realize this. Johnny may not be speaking as well or as soon as sister Mary did, and pressures for a higher standard of speech than Johnny is ready for may be imposed upon him by well-meaning parents. Again, real speech problems may follow.

SOCIAL DEPRIVATION AND SOCIAL IMMATURITY. Children who lack normal opportunities for social growth and development may be delayed in speech development. Fisichelli (8) found that infants who were institutionalized were much more delayed in their prelinguistic speech development than children who lived with their own families. Brodbeck (4) compared the frequency and variety of sounds and syllables uttered by a group of orphanage infants with those of a group of infants living with their own families and found the orphanage children were significantly delayed in these aspects of speech development. We can expect that children who are deprived in the early years of a normal social growth and development are going to be more likely to develop speech problems; this may be due perhaps to a delayed start in speech development and to the lack of normal stimulation, attention, and affection. In the speech-clinic situation, we frequently find children with speech defects who are also socially immature and unable to do the things for themselves and for others that we normally expect children of a given age level to do. We need to consider all of the factors that may have led to the observed social immaturity. In some cases mental retardation and/or physical or organic deficiencies may be related factors.

BILINGUALISM AND THE INFLUENCE OF A FOREIGN LANGUAGE. We have previously mentioned the case of the child who comes from a home in which two languages are spoken. Whether such a child will develop a speech problem or not depends upon the circumstances that exist. Leopold (14) reports that there is likely to be a period wherein the bilingual child may be a little confused in language and appear to be somewhat delayed in the development of the language of his country. The intelligent child may later profit in his development of the English language due to his early exposure to another language. If the parents and the child are intelligent and well adjusted, the learning of two languages simultaneously may have advantages. On the other hand, problems may arise if the parents and the child are not well adjusted to the situation. If a child comes from a home in which a parent uses a mutilated form of English due to the influence of an earlier learned foreign language, it is quite possible that the child may suffer in his language development and have articulatory and rhythm difficulties.

IMPROPER DIAGNOSIS AND "LABELING." Johnson (12) was the first to present the theory that children may become speech defective because they are diagnosed and labeled as "defective" by their parents or other over-anxious or overly concerned adults. The young child may use what is referred to as "normal nonfluencies" in his speech. Overly critical adults may label or name this normal speech performance "stuttering." The trouble starts when parents or other individuals begin to interfere with the child's normal speech development by calling attention to inconsequential speech errors, repetitions, or hesitations. Frequent criticism may follow and the child may become disturbed concerning his own speech performance. In time, the child may be caught in a "vicious circle." He may begin to fear the act of speaking because he feels that it may be looked upon with disfavor by his parents and others. Eventually, he may become afraid of "stuttering" and stutter because he is afraid he is going to stutter. An anxiety-tension pattern is set up and sometimes before anything can be done about it the child has "learned" to stutter. Many years of painful consequences may follow as the child establishes himself as a speech defective.

Psychological Factors that May Adversely Influence the Child's Speech Development

There can be no real separation between that which is environmental and that which is psychological. All factors work together in creating the climate in which the child is to grow and learn. The limits supposedly set by the child's mental ability are so frequently influenced by his environmental opportunities or lack of opportunities that we can seldom distinguish where mental ability ends and environmental influences begin. We know that the child's psychological adjustment is greatly influenced through environmental situations. We also know that the parents are most influential in developing the environmental climate.

PARENT-CHILD RELATIONSHIPS. Fortunate is the child who is born into a family circle headed by kind, affectionate, and understanding parents. Barring physical or organic deficiencies, the child who is wanted, loved, and tenderly cared for by well-adjusted parents is likely to grow up into a well-adjusted adult with normal speech. The child who is cared for by a neurotic or maladjusted parent is likely to develop many problems in the process of growing up. He may or may not be able to solve some of these problems in a manner that will lead to good personal adjustment. His developing frustrations and maladjustments will seek expression in his daily life activities. He may become emotionally disturbed and traits of his disturbance may be observed in his behavior. The child's speech appears to be vulnerable to the expression of frustrations, fears, and anxieties. Children are not born tense, anxious, and fearful; they learn these patterns of emotional behavior. Since speech is such an important element in our culture and so thoroughly involved in our psychological development, it is logical to expect that maladjustments may be expressed through the channel of speech.

What kind of parental problems exist that can influence the speech development of the child? We may find a mother who is overly dependent upon her child for emotional satisfaction. As a result the child may become too emotionally dependent upon his mother. This makes it difficult for the child to adjust in his relationships with others. Problems may arise when the child must break away from the parent, as he must when he begins school. Strong emotional attachments may result in delayed speech development or other forms of speech difficulties.

The overly anxious parent often transfers his anxiety-tensions to the child. This is the "worrying" parent who frets and fusses and hovers over the child, trying to protect him from the many little "natural" dangers of the child's world. Every new experience becomes fraught with fear and anxiety. Children are not born with the tendency to worry. We teach the child to worry; the "best" teacher is the parent, and the "best" time is during the child's early years at home. We are not surprised when we find that anxious children with speech defects have anxious parents at home.

Sometimes unintentional harm is done by the parent who is a "perfectionist." Most parents naturally want their children to have every advantage possible. They want their children to have the things they could not have and to be the things they could not be. Some parents carry in their thoughts an image of what they consider to be the "perfect child" and sometimes, without realizing that they may be harming the child, place pressure upon the child to behave as they think the perfect child should behave. These parents are expecting too much, too soon. Children are not perfect and neither are adults. When parents demand a standard of performance that the child is not ready to meet, problems develop. When parents are not satisfied with the present speech development of the child, they may pressure him to "speak better." When they constantly criticize and correct the child's speech, they are laying the groundwork for real speech problems.

THE PSYCHOLOGICAL ADJUSTMENT OF THE CHILD. As the child reacts to his environment and to the persons in his environment, he sets up his own personal pattern of adjustment to the world. Disturbing elements give rise to problems. Problems must be solved, and the child either learns to solve his problems in a manner that leads to good adjustment or learns to solve his problems in ways that lead to poor adjustment. Every child's life is filled with frustrations and disturbing elements. The fortunate child who learns to face his problems intelligently and to work his way out of frustrations without developing emotional disturbances is not likely to have a speech disturbance, assuming that he has normal mental ability and a normal speech mechanism. Conversely, the child who becomes anxious concerning his speech performance when his attempt to meet the parent's demands end in failure becomes discouraged and develops feelings of insecurity. Here we are likely to find a "problem child."

What we "see" of the problem may be only the symptoms. We may "see" a child who is aggressive or one who is withdrawn, one who is shy and quiet, or one who is a boisterous bully, one who cries and whines, or one who kicks and yells; or we may find a child who squints his eyes, chews his nails, sucks his thumb, or maybe one who has a speech difficulty. We must be aware of the symptoms; but even more specifically, we must be willing to look for the contributing causal factors. Finding these, we must help each child find the best possible adjustment in his personal world.

We should pause for another word of caution here. Parents are people, and most of them are well-intentioned people. We must not foolishly jump to conclusions and blame the parents for every child problem that arises. Most parents are highly cooperative individuals who desire to do the things that are best for their children. The cooperative efforts of the parents, teacher, speech therapist, psychologist, or other specialist when indicated can often lead a disturbed child to better adjustment and a speech-defective child to better speech habits.

INTELLECTUAL VARIABLES AND MENTAL RETARDATION. Occasionally we hear the remark, "The child's speech problem is due to mental retardation." Such retardation may be a contributing factor but frequently is not the sole cause of a speech defect. There are mentally retarded individuals who have normal speech; they may be delayed in language development but their speech (such as it is) may be without flaws. We have stated that severe mental retardation may be associated with the inability to learn to speak. Retarded individuals who speak without a defect will be unable to use language on a highly abstract level. High intelligence, on the other hand, does not guarantee that the child will not develop a speech defect. Degree of intelligence is one of the factors to be taken into consideration when we are studying the child who has a speech difficulty. An understanding of the degree of mental ability will help us to understand the child as a whole and will guide us when remedial procedures are necessary.

Psychoneurosis and Psychosis. There are children who are emotionally disturbed to such an extent that they are spoken of as being psychoneurotic or psychotic individuals. These extreme cases of maladjustment are problems for the clinical psychologist or the psychiatrist. Unusual speech patterns are often associated with the child who is suffering from a serious emotional disturbance. The child may be without speech; he may be repetitious in his speech to the extent that he will use a given phrase or remark over and over; he may have no normal communication with other persons. The responsibility of the parent, the teacher, or the speech therapist in these cases is to cooperate with the psychologist or psychiatrist and carry out precisely the prescribed recommendations for therapy.

Physical and Structural Factors that May Adversely Influence the Child's Speech

Congenital or developmental malformations or malfunctionings of the child's physical, anatomical, organic, or neurological being may be the direct or indirect causitive factors in the development of speech problems.

DISEASES AND INFECTIONS.   High febrile diseases can bring about speech problems.   High fevers over a period of time can cause damage to the central nervous system and this can result in a speech defect. Ear infections following measles or scarlet fever or other childhood diseases can cause hearing losses, and a serious hearing loss will interfere with normal speech development. General protection of the child's health is good insurance against the development of problems. Today's child is much more protected against disease than was the child of fifty years ago. Inoculations and vaccinations make for a safer childhood. Poliomyelitis and the various meningitides continue at times to leave their marks on children in the form of crippled limbs, paralyzed muscles, or in some cases of meningitis, serious mental retardation or deafness. Because at times various parts of the speech mechanism are involved in the after-effects of disease, we need to be aware of the possible after-effects of a serious illness.

Childhood illnesses may have more than physical after-effects; the experiences of the child during long periods of illness may affect his personal and emotional growth and it is not unusual to find that a child becomes delayed in speech after a period of serious illness. We find parents who think that diseased tonsils may have "caused" a child's speech difficulty. It is unlikely that diseased tonsils alone will cause a speech defect, but they can be detrimental to the child's general health and should be removed upon recommendation of the physician.

FACIAL AND ORAL VARIATIONS AND MALFORMATIONS. Abnormalities of the bone structure of the face, of the oral cavities, the nose, the palate, jaws, tongue, or lips may result in speech disturbances. A high, narrow palate, an overlarge tongue, or dental "over-bite," "under-bite," or "open-bite" may be the direct causes of differences in articulation. Adenoidal growths may lead to a voice defect. A congenital cleft palate and/or cleft lip often lead to malformations, even after surgery, that frequently cause articulatory and/or voice defects. Congenital disorders are those originating in the prenatal period. Congenital disorders take many forms and may be either hereditary or developmental in nature; they may or may not affect the speech, depending upon the location and degree of injury.

LARYNX ABNORMALITIES. These may be congenital in nature or may develop after birth as the result of disease or accident. A child may be born with a web between his vocal bands. This will affect the pitch range. Growths on the vocal folds in the form of nodules will affect the quality of voice. Cancer of the larynx appears infrequently in adults and seldom in children; but when it does appear, the results are drastic, usually calling for removal of the larynx for the preservation of life. With the larynx removed, the individual is voiceless and can speak only in a whisper, until taught to speak otherwise. Paralysis of some of the muscles of the larynx can also result in voicelessness.

INJURIES TO THE CENTRAL NERVOUS SYSTEM. Damage to the nerves in the various parts of the brain or the spinal cord frequently leads to speech disturbances. The type of speech difficulty that may result from such injuries depends to a great extent upon the place and degree of nerve injury. Children who are designated as cerebral palsied and those who are diagnosed as "aphasic" are the victims of injury to the central nervous system. The injury may take place during the prenatal period or may be the result of an illness or accident that occurred after birth. A blood clot or a cerebral hemorrhage may result in injury to the nerves of the brain. The "aphasic" child is usually speechless. The cerebral-palsied child may or may not have a speech defect.

INJURIES TO NERVES OUTSIDE THE CENTRAL NERVOUS SYSTEM. Damage to a nerve that lies outside the brain or the spinal cord produces an effect somewhat different from that which results from damage to a nerve in the central nervous system. Damage to such outside nerves leads to "flaccid" paralysis. Flaccid here means limp or without resistance. Injuries to nerves that innervate the muscles related to the use of the speech mechanism are likely to result in speech disturbances of one kind or another. Nerves outside the central nervous system, when damaged, are sometimes capable of recovery; and in such cases a speech defect may be only temporary.

ABNORMALITIES IN BREATHING. Breathing abnormalities may be related to physical or organic disturbances. Nerve injuries of the central nervous system can disrupt the normal breathing pattern. Physical conditions may interfere with the development of good breathing habits. In some instances, abnormalities in breathing may be related to abnormalities in speech.

IMPAIRED HEARING. Hearing deficiences may be due to a diseased condition of the ear or may be related to congenital deformities of different parts of the ear. A bony growth over the ear canal or a perforated tympanic membrane (broken ear drum) will reduce acuity of hearing. Damage to the ear nerves may result in partial or total deafness. The effect that a hearing loss has upon the speech development of the child depends to a great extent upon the type of loss, the degree of loss, and the time of the appearance of the loss. A child can have a slight or even a moderate hearing loss and not suffer from any noticeable deficiency in speech. A hearing loss that is serious enough to interfere with the hearing of speech as it is normally spoken will interfere with the development of normal speech. The speech defect may be of an articulatory or of a vocal nature, or both. Without special training, children who are deaf or whose hearing is so seriously impaired that they cannot hear speech without amplification will not develop the ability to use speech. Even with special training the speech of these children is likely to be defective to some degree.

PSYCHOSOMATIC RELATIONSHIPS. As we have noted, physical or organic abnormalities may be the basic causal factors in the development of speech defects, but we frequently find that psychological factors are also involved. The problems may be so complicated that one cannot determine what is due to psychological conditioning and what is due to a somatic condition. It is possible for a person to become so seriously disturbed psychologically that he may actually feel pain or find that certain organs of the body refuse to function normally, even when no real physical or organic abnormalities exist. The clinical psychologist and the psychiatrist can help us to understand these cases and can direct the therapeutic procedures that need to be followed.

Classifications of Speech Disorders as Reported in the Literature

We may suppose there is justification for an attempt to classify disorders of speech, since many writers in the field of speech pathology do present classifications or categories of speech defects. Presumably one justification might be that it is more convenient to study, understand, diagnose, and treat speech difficulties if we have a procedure established by means which we may classify speech disorders. If speech disorders could be "typed" as easily as we classify animal life, vegetable life, or minerals, there might be greater justification for classification. In the broadest sense, we might consider that there are as many types of speech disorders as there are individuals having speech problems. When we attempt to find definite distinctions by which to establish classifications, we are likely to find overlapping from one classification to another.

LIMITATIONS AND DANGERS OF CLASSIFICATION. We should classify only for the purpose of understanding general principles, not for the purpose of labeling or naming individual children. It is better psychologically to say "here is a child who hesitates or repeats" than to say "here is a stutterer." To say that Johnny is a cleft-palate child tells us little about Johnny except that he has or has had an opening in the roof of his mouth. The cleft may be open or mended; it is quite possible that it may be so well mended that no one would know from Johnny's speech or appearance that he has a cleft palate. But if we point out that "Johnny is a stutterer," we place a plague upon Johnny and may mark him for life by this ignoble identification. It is quite certain that we will be doing him no good, and we may do him harm by this type of labeling. Most teachers and parents know these things but nevertheless sometimes thoughtlessly label a child a "defective." Labels sometimes stick too well and frequently are hard to displace. Realizing the limitations and the dangers of classifying, we will discuss some of the most commonly-mentioned categories of speech disorders.

GENERAL CLASSIFICATIONS. One large classification includes a descriptive analysis of what is heard and observed and divides speech disorders according to whether the difficulty is:

1. An articulatory disorder (errors in sound production)
2. A vocal disorder (a disorder in voice production)
3. Both an articulatory and a vocal disorder
4. A linguistic disorder (language defect)

A second large classification divides speech disorders according to the "causal" relationships as (a) those that are considered *functional* in nature, and (b) those that are considered *organic* in nature. Functional disorders are those that have as causal factors no known physical or organic malformations. Psychological or environmental factors may be involved in functional disorders. In these, we presume that the speech mechanism is normal, but misused. Care must be taken that we do not label a speech difficulty a "simple functional disorder" just because we are unsuccessful in determining any related causal factors. Functional disorders may include articulatory disorders or vocal disorders, or both types of disorders.

As the term implies, organic disorders are the result of a malfunctioning of one or more parts of the speech mechanism, due to an existing organic malformation of one kind or another. Organic disorders may also result in either articulatory or voice problems, or both types of problems may be present.

ARTICULATORY DISORDERS. These may be subclassified according to types of errors in sound production, as follows:

1. Sound substitutions (one sound is substituted for another)
2. Sound distortions (the right sound is used, but it is distorted)
3. Sound omissions (sounds are left out)
4. Sound additions (extra sounds are added)

Labeling in articulatory disorders. Sometimes a child is referred to as a "lisper," or it is said that he "lisps" or is "lisping." These terms usually refer to a misuse of the (s) and the (z), but at times may include the misuse of other sibilant sounds such as (ʃ) as in *sh*ut, (tʃ) as in *ch*in, and (dʒ) as in *J*ohn. The most frequently mentioned lisp refers to the substitution of the (θ) for the (s) and the (ð) for the (z); as the result of substitutions the child says, "I thaw the thebra." The term "lalling" is sometimes used in reference to the misuse of the sounds (l) and (r); the child may be saying, "the yady wooks at the wittle wed wose." The term "cluttering" is defined in different ways by different writers; an appropriate definition might be: a serious confusion of consonant sounds.

VOCAL DISORDERS. These are also called "voice" or "phonatory" defects. They may be subclassified according to what is heard, as follows:

1. Disorders of voice quality, including
   (a) Nasal quality (with nasal resonance)
   (b) Denasal quality (without nasal resonance)
   (c) Breathy quality (with too much breath)
   (d) Hoarse-husky quality (sounds are "low-pitched" and "throaty")
   (e) Harsh quality (sounds are "high-pitched" and "shrill")
   (f) Monotonous quality (a monotone)
2. Disorders of pitch, including a voice that is
   (a) Of unpleasant high-pitched level
   (b) Of unpleasant low-pitched level
   (c) Without adequate pitch variations (monopitch)
3. Disorders of intensity, including a voice that is
   (a) Too weak
   (b) Too loud
   (c) Lacking in variation in intensity (monoforce)
4. Disorders in time (or rhythm), including speech that is
   (a) Too fast
   (b) Too slow
   (c) Monotonous in time (monorate)
   (d) Abnormal in sound duration or rhythm patterns

SIMULTANEOUS ARTICULATORY AND VOCAL DISORDERS. Quite frequently a speech disorder cannot be classified in any particular category. A child with a voice problem may be defective in one or more of the attributes of voice or may have both voice problems and articulatory problems. Therefore, we may run into difficulties when trying to classify a particular speech problem in any specific category.

LINGUISTIC DISORDERS. A speech disorder is not to be confused with a language disorder. Both disorders may, of course, appear together. If Johnny has only a language disorder he may be handicapped in vocabulary learning, sentence structure, sentence length, and his language disorder may extend to both reading and writing.

ORGANIC SPEECH DISORDERS. When we classify speech disorders as organic in nature, we may subclassify them according to place or type of organic deviations as follows:

1. Injuries to the nerves of the central nervous system, resulting in
   (a) Cerebral palsy (speech problems associated with cerebral palsy)
   (b) Aphasia (lacking in speech)
   (c) Dysphasia (partial loss of speech)
2. Injuries to nerves outside the central nervous system (flaccid paralysis)
3. Cleft palate and/or cleft lip (speech problems associated with cleft palate and/or cleft lip)
4. Orthodontic and dental anomolies (including overbite, underbite, and faulty dentition)
5. Deafness or hearing loss (speech problems associated with deafness or hearing loss)
6. Other physical or structural malformations, including speech disorders that are due to abnormalities of the lips, tongue, throat, nose, larynx, etc., other than those enumerated above.

OTHER POSSIBLE CLASSIFICATIONS AND SUBCLASSIFICATIONS. It might be logical to break down "rhythm defects" in relation to stuttering as follows:

1. Nonfluent speech ("normal-like" nonfluencies)
2. Hesitant speech ("normal-like" hesitancies)
3. Primary stuttering (early period of stuttering)
4. Secondary stuttering (the advanced period of stuttering)
5. Neurotic stuttering (with onset in adolescence or adult life)

Although these terms are not found in the literature as subclassifications, they are used and are considered as being descriptive of certain types of speech.

Additional descriptive terms are also used, such as:

1. Delayed speech
2. Retarded speech
3. Infantile speech (at times referred to as "baby talk")
4. Foreign accent (or foreign dialect)

It is not always clear whether a real distinction is made between speech that is referred to as "delayed" and speech that is referred to as "retarded." Usually *delayed* is taken to mean that the child is normal in intelligence but delayed in speech development, while *retarded* indicates that the child is subnormal in mental ability and slow in speech development.

Finally, a long list of scientific terminology is used to classify speech disorders, and the terms usually mystify the beginning student in speech therapy. These terms include: dyslalia, dysarthria, dyslogia, dysphasia, dysphemia, dysphonia, etc. Most of the scientific terms will not be explained in this text. Those who are interested in a further study of the scientific terminology in the field are referred to Travis' *Handbook of Speech Pathology* (25), which contains a chapter on terminology and nomenclature. This same source includes a broad classification presented by Milisen (25, p. 267), in which classification of speech disorders is determined by the ability of the individual to *communicate,* and which includes four descriptive forms of communication. The individual with a speech disorder may have:

1. No understanding of or expression through oral language
2. Understanding of but no expression through oral language
3. Deteriorated understanding of and/or expression through oral language
4. Understanding of and expression through oral language, but speech is not acceptable to the listener and/or the speaker

In using this type of classification, the listener evaluates what he observes, and describes the nature of the speech disorder. The divisions are broad enough to include all types of speech difficulties. It is understood that after classification in one of the four categories, it will be necessary to follow through with a further investigation of each speech disorder. The investigator may wish to get a complete case history, study possible causal factors, analyze voice and articulatory disorders, and make an estimate of the possibilities for attaining adequate speech. In addition, there may be referrals to other agencies or specialists; and finally plans for therapy will be made and carried out over a period of time.

Bibliography

1. American Speech and Hearing Association Committee on the Mid-century White House Conference. "Speech Disorders and Speech Correction," (fact finding report), *Journal of Speech and Hearing Disorders*, 17, No. 2 (June, 1952), 129-137.
2. ARTLEY, A. S. "A Study of Certain Factors Presumed to be Associated with Reading and Speech Difficulties," *Journal of Speech and Hearing Disorders*, 13, No. 4 (December, 1948), 351-360.
3. BOND, G. L. "The Auditory and Speech Characteristics of Poor Readers," *Teachers College Contributions to Education*, No. 657. New York: Bureau of Publications, Teachers College, Columbia University, 1935.
4. BRODBECK, A. J., and IRWIN, O. D. "The Speech Behavior of Infants Without Families," *Child Development*, 17 (September, 1946), 145-156.
5. CARRELL, J., and PENDERGAST, K. "An Experimental Study of the Possible Relation Between Errors of Speech and Spelling," *Journal of Speech and Hearing Disorders*, 19, No. 3 (September, 1954), 327-334.
6. DOLL, E. A. *The Vineland Social Maturity Scale*. Minneapolis: Educational Testing Bureau, 1946.
7. EVERHART, R. W. "The Relationship Between Articulation and Other Developmental Factors in Children," *Journal of Speech and Hearing Disorders*, 18, No. 4 (December, 1953), 332-338.
8. FISICHELLI, R. M. *A Study of Prelinguistic Speech Development of Institutionalized Infants*. Fordham University, Ph.D. dissertation, 1950.
9. GLASNER, P. J. "Personality Characteristics and Emotional Problems in Stutterers Under the Age of Five," *Journal of Speech and Hearing Disorders*, 14, No. 2 (June, 1949), 135-138.
10. IRWIN, O. C. "The Developmental Status of Speech Sounds of Ten Feeble-Minded Children," *Child Development*, 13 (1942), 29-39.
11. JACKSON, J. "A Survey of Psychological, Social and Environmental Differences Between Advanced and Retarded Readers," *Journal of Genetic Psychology*, 65, No. 1 (September, 1944), 113-131.
12. JOHNSON, W., BROWN, S. F., CURTIS, J. F., EDNEY, C. W., and KEASTER, J. *Speech Handicapped School Children*, rev. ed. New York: Harper & Brothers, 1956.
13. JOHNSON, W. (ed.). *Stuttering in Children and Adults*. Minneapolis: University of Minnesota Press, 1955.
14. LEOPOLD, W. F. "Patterning in Children's Language Learning," *Language Learning*, 5 (1953-1954), 1-14.
15. MCCARTHY, D. "Language Development in Children," Chapter 9, in Carmichael, L. (ed.), *Manual of Child Psychology*, 2d ed. New York: John Wiley & Sons, Inc., 1954.

16. Midcentury White House Conference on Children and Youth. *Children and Youth at the Midcentury: A Chart Book.* Washington, D.C.: National Publishing Co., 1951.

17. MONCUR, J. P. "Environmental Factors Differentiating Stuttering Children from Non-Stuttering Children," *Speech Monographs,* 18, No. 4 (November, 1951), 312-325.

18. MONROE, M. *Children Who Cannot Read.* Chicago: University of Chicago Press, 1932.

19. MOSS, M. "The Effect of Speech Defects on Second-Grade Reading Achievement," *Quarterly Journal of Speech,* 24, No. 4 (December, 1938), 642-654.

20. PERRIN, E. H. "The Social Position of th Speech Defective Child," *Journal of Speech and Hearing Disorders,* 19, No. 2 (June, 1954), 250-252.

21. SCHAPER, L. C. *The Relationship of Reading and Speech Disabilities.* University of Nebraska: M.A. thesis, Department of Educational Psychology, 1943.

22. SCHLANGER, B. B. "Speech Measurements of Institutionalized Mentally Handicapped Children," *American Journal of Mental Deficiency,* 58, No. 1 (July 1953), 114-122.

23. SPRIESTERSBACH, D. C. "Research in Articulation Disorders and Personality," *Journal of Speech and Hearing Disorders,* 21, No. 3 (September, 1956), 329-335.

24. THOMPSON, G. G. *Child Psychology.* Boston: Houghton Mifflin Co., 1953.

25. TRAVIS, E. L. (ed.). *Handbook of Speech Pathology.* New York: Appleton-Century-Crofts, Inc., 1957.

26. WOOD, K. S. "Parental Maladjustment and Functional Articulatory Defects in Children," *Journal of Speech Disorders,* 11, No. 4 (December, 1946), 255-275.

Chapter 3

SPEECH TRAINING
AND RETRAINING

We have stated that speech is a natural process in our culture and that it is fundamentally a learned reaction. If every child could be born into a home wherein an ideal environment exists, and if each child could have a normal speech mechanism and good physical and mental health, we would have few, if any, speech problems to cope with when children reach school age. Since this ideal state is not likely ever to exist, we must plan for adequate speech education, improvement, and correction for all school children.

An adequate speech environment in the school should offer all children an opportunity to participate in speech activities without fear or anxiety. It should allow for the development of good speaking habits and good listening habits and provide opportunities for growth and improvement in speech. The child with poor speaking habits and the child with a specific speech problem should have an opportunity to correct their difficulties.

In some of our more advanced schools of today, speech training does not seek to help only those children who have speech defects. Sometimes we find speech training and speech improvement taking place in the regular classroom with all children taking part in the procedures. Speech activities in the school need to be an integral part of the everyday activities, and each child should be given a chance to develop to the best of his ability, in speech as well as in

61

his other school subjects. In the past several years, there has been both national and state interest in helping the school child who has a speech handicap. Many states have developed special education programs that operate in such a manner as to subsidize the school program to the extent that special teachers may be employed to work with children who have speech problems.

If we take as our goal the provision of speech activities for all children according to their individual needs, it will be necessary for us to know and understand the different speech needs of school children. We speak of speech defects, disorders, problems, difficulties, differences, and of speech-handicapped school children. We find school children with careless speech habits, with adequate speech habits, and quite frequently we discover children who are superior in speech. Before we try to decide what school children need in the way of speech training, we should define some of the terms that are frequently used in the fields of speech education, improvement, and correction.

DEFINITION OF TERMS. The term *speech defect* has been previously defined in relation to its existence. A child has a speech defect when (a) he differs in the communicative process to the extent that his manner of speaking detracts from *what* he is saying and calls attention to *how* he is speaking and/or (b) when he is not well adjusted to the speaking situation. The terms *speech disorder, speech problem, speech difficulty* and *speech handicap* are used interchangeably by some writers in the field of speech correction. It is likely that these terms came into use in an effort to reduce the undesirable connotations of the term *speech defect,* since the word "defect" has perhaps more of a stigma attached to it than do the other terms. Wood (12) defines a *speech defect* as "any deviation of speech which is outside the range of acceptable variation in a given environment," and a *speech disorder* as "a deviation of speech together with the underlying conditions causing such a deviation; often the same as *speech defect*" (p. 65).

In the process of helping children and adults to speak to the best of their ability, a number of terms have been devised that are descriptive of the procedures taken. Some of these terms are scarcely to be distinguished in meaning one from the other, and then again some of the terms are meant to carry differences in meaning. We think of *speech development* as being a general term used to describe the speech progress of the child from infancy through adulthood. Wood (12) defines *speech education* as "the broad field dealing with the training of the person to speak and listen more effectively," *speech improvement* as "the betterment of poor or average speech; sometimes distinguished from *speech correction*," and *speech correction* as "the professional field which deals with the elimination and alleviation of speech defects or with the development and improvement of speaking intelligibility; sometimes distinguished from *speech improvement*" (p. 65).

The specially trained teacher who does the speech correction work is sometimes referred to as the *speech correctionist* and sometimes called the *speech therapist*. Wood (12) defines *therapy* as "the science which deals with the treatment or application of remedies for the cure, alleviation, or prevention of disorders" (p. 66). There appears to be a trend in school systems and speech clinics toward adopting the term *speech therapist* rather than the term *speech correctionist*. We suspect that the adoption is coming about not so much because Wood's definition of *therapy* better describes what this type of special teacher does, but because the idea of a "correctionist" also bears a certain stigma, whereas the word "therapist" carries with it certain professional connotations. Besides, *speech therapist* is much more euphonic than *speech correctionist*.

With our terms defined to a certain extent, we will proceed to outline a speech program for every child. Such an ideal program would include:

1. Normal speech development as far as is possible for every preschool child

2. Speech education for all school children, elementary through secondary levels
3. Speech improvement training for all school children having poor or average speech
4. Speech correction (or therapy) for all children having speech defects (problems or difficulties)

Our program would of necessity involve the cooperation of the classroom teacher, the speech therapist and, in some cases, the parents and perhaps certain professional workers. Types of speech activities would include both individual and group procedures as needed.

INDIVIDUAL THERAPY. In individual therapy, the speech therapist works with one client at a time. Individual speech correction is becoming less frequently used as methods in group instruction become better known and are put into practice in speech clinics and public schools. There are times, however, when certain serious or unique speech problems call for individual treatment. This is the case especially when organic malformations are involved or when a child is emotionally or socially disturbed to the extent that he will not participate adequately in a group situation. The period of individual therapy may be a preparatory period in which the child is given training that will make it possible for him to join a group when he appears to be ready to do so.

Individual therapy may also be indicated at times with certain older children and adults. The speech therapist must make the decision as to the type of therapy to follow in each case. The kind of speech problem and the degree of the abnormality of speech will help the speech therapist to determine which type of therapy is to be recommended. At times we make the mistake of using individual therapy when a child might profit more from group therapy. The reverse of this statement may also be made. In either group or individual therapy there can be the danger of falling into a routine of drill that is boring and unsuccessful in results obtained. Therapy should never simmer down merely to a repeated list of words and phrases spoken after the therapist.

Each therapy session should be well planned, with a variety of materials and methods suitable to the individual child's needs and level of ability. Many group methods and techniques can be adapted to individual therapy and vice versa.

INDIVIDUAL THERAPY IN CONTRAST TO GROUP THERAPY. In the minds of some members of the professions of speech pathology and speech therapy, there appears to be controversy over the question of the type of therapy to be used. This controversy stems from the assumption that there is a distinct difference between the techniques used in individual therapy and those used in group therapy, and from the assumption that the results of one type of therapy differ from the results of the other type. Those who believe that speech therapy should be to a great extent an individual process base their belief upon the assumption that individuals differ in kinds of speech difficulties, in sounds misused, and in manner of producing sounds. It is also pointed out that the causes of speech difficulties are different and that the needs of the individuals differ. In addition, it is noted that individuals have different rates of ability in learning, and that they also have different levels of emotional adjustment. Certain withdrawn persons may find it difficult to participate in group activities. Instead of being motivated to greater speech activity, they may become still further inhibited because of the pressures in a group situation. For these various reasons, time and effort may be wasted when some individuals are placed in the group situation. However, it should not be forgotten that speech is a social tool, and that the group situation lends itself naturally to speech therapy.

ADVANTAGES OF GROUP THERAPY. The advocates of group therapy maintain that participation in group activities tends to stimulate and motivate speech participation. In group activities, it is claimed, speaking situations become more realistic. Furthermore, those who participate in group activities benefit from a sociological and psychological viewpoint. The individual does not feel alone with his speech problem; he sees that others have speech difficulties also. Another argument presented in favor of group therapy is the declaration that it is a time-saving device. This, however, is considered a minor factor in relation to the major benefits of group therapy.

In relation to the social and psychological benefits, the attitudes of permissiveness and acceptance that prevail in the group situation are conducive to the stimulation of communication, to the release of emotional tension, and to a change from hostile and antisocial behavior to more acceptable patterns of social behavior. The individual learns to conform, to use self-control, and to cooperate with others. Backus (2) points out that speech is to be thought of as "an aspect of behavior" and group therapy is of value because of its "potential for facilitating psychotherapeutic change" (pp. 1027-28). Backus and Beasley (3), using a type of "intensive group therapy," maintain that each different kind of speech disorder does not require a different type of therapy. Their "theoretical structure" for speech therapy is based upon the interpersonal relationships existing within the group. They believe that "group instruction should form the core of speech therapy," that children should not be separated for group instruction according to their respective kinds of speech symptoms, that the teaching situation within the group should allow for corrective "emotional" experiences, and that the "teaching situation should be structured in terms of interpersonal relationships which involve conversational speech" (p. 5). In the many activities that take place in well-planned group therapy, the individual is allowed to participate as a member of a group and not as "Johnny who has a speech difficulty." Instead, Johnny is just one of the group; everyone of which is working for speech improvement. Although Johnny's difficulty may be different from that of Jane's, they are both working toward a common goal, that of more acceptable speech. If this goal can be reached by means of group therapy that allows children an opportunity to formulate more acceptable speech through "real-life situations," it would appear that the

Backus-Beasley type of group therapy is a real boon to the field of speech therapy.

RESEARCH IN GROUP THERAPY. Although the methods and techniques of group therapy have been used in the public schools and college and university clinics for several years, very little has been reported in the way of research findings in relation to speech therapy in the group situation. The reason for this is very likely related to the difficulty of isolating related factors and of controlling various influential elements. Wilson (11) attempted to evaluate a speech-improvement program for kindergarten children in the Lafayette, Indiana city schools. A twelve-week speech-improvement program was devised. An experimental group receiving periodical group instruction in speech was compared with a control group receiving no such training. The children were tested for articulatory errors at the beginning and close of the twelve-week period. When a comparison was made between the two groups, the final check on articulation disclosed that the children who had received training used fewer articulation errors on sounds that were included in the training syllabus and also used fewer articulation errors on sounds not included in the syllabus.

Sommer (9) studied the effects of group speech training upon nursery school and kindergarten children. An experimental group that received speech training over a period of time showed an improvement of 57 per cent in correction of articulatory defects. The control group, which received no speech training, improved only 28 per cent in the same period of time. It is to be understood that some improvement took place through the process of general maturation, but the greater improvement of the group receiving speech training was believed to be due to the special training given in speech.

COMBINED GROUP AND INDIVIDUAL THERAPY. The majority of our trained speech therapists are likely to use a combination of the two approaches to therapy, realizing that there are times when the need for individual therapy is definitely indicated and other times when group therapy appears to be the answer to a child's problems. The important decision for the therapist to make is to determine in consideration of the needs of the child when individual therapy should be given, when group therapy is advisable, and when a combination of both should be used, one to supplement the other. Sometimes group therapy should come first; at other times individual therapy may be beneficial before group therapy is attempted. Quite frequently young children overcome their speech problems and gain confidence and ease in speaking situations through the more or less natural and nondirective activities undertaken in group therapy. Most of our speech problems first appear in the lower grades; therefore, it is important that the methods and techniques of group therapy be applied in the early years of school attendance. Since it is also acknowledged that these techniques have therapeutic value in other phases than speech, in relation to the child's growth and development, it is beneficial to expose all children, regardless of their speech adequacy, to the activities experienced through the use of group therapy. To achieve maximum returns, speech development and improvement programs should be a regular part of the classroom schedule from kindergarten through the fourth grade at least.

Speech Improvement in the Classroom

In school systems where a speech therapist is available or in those that have teachers in the elementary grades who have had training in speech therapy, perhaps only a course or two, it is becoming customary to plan and carry out speech-improvement activities in the regular classroom. The teacher or the visiting speech therapist often follows many of the same methods and techniques used in the group therapy sessions that are planned for special groups of children who have specific speech difficulties. Perspectively, the difference lies in giving all the children in the classroom an opportunity to improve in speech performance. The children learn how sounds are formed. They relate the study of the phonic elements to the spoken word as well as to the written word. Speaking becomes an interesting and pleasant activity, whether used in choral-reading activities, creative drama, speech games, oral reading, conversation, or class recitation. Children can be taught to speak with ease and fluency, without self-consciousness, fear, or anxiety. They can learn to produce sounds and words accurately and clearly, to listen to others, to appraise good voice quality, and to strive for a pleasant voice quality themselves. Through the use of group speech activities in the classroom, the shy, quiet child may learn to be more aggressive; the bold, aggressive child may learn to be more thoughtful of others. Hostilities, fears, anxieties, and conflicts may find expression; and emotional problems may be worked out through the speech activities in the classroom.

In an unobtrusive manner, the speech therapist and the teacher can help the child who has a special speech difficulty to understand his problem. The other children in the classroom can be led to understand the problems of the children having speech difficulties. After a period of time when the class has had a chance to get acquainted with the principles involved in good speech production, it is quite possible to talk objectively to the class as a whole about specific problems in speech. Adequate understanding will bring about helpful attitudes that will benefit all members of the class, including those children who may have speech defects.

The ideal situation in the classroom speech-improvement program would be to set aside regular periods during the week for this function; such periods are set aside for art, music, reading, arithmetic, etc. A forty- or fifty-minute period twice a week may be preferred by some teachers and a twenty- or thirty-minute daily period may be the preference of others. The speech activities undertaken would be limited only by the training and experience of the teacher or therapist. Sometimes the speech therapist may wish to start the program, planning and directing the activities for a few weeks and then letting the teacher continue the sessions.

Approaches to Group Therapy

The idea of the group approach is not, of course, a new concept. Public school teachers have been using the group approach in their teaching for a long time. Long before the speech therapist began to experiment with group therapy in speech correction, the psychologists were using the group situation in psychotherapy, psychodrama, role-playing, and play therapy. The sociologist used the group approach in sociodrama; and the speech teacher used it in creative drama, creative play, and choral reading. Since speech therapy has psychological and sociological as well as speech aspects, it is not surprising that the speech therapist and the speech pathologist should borrow from the related sciences some of the methods and techniques used in their group interactions. As a matter of fact, speech pathology in the beginning might be said to have grown out of the field of psychology. As the need for the use of scientific procedures in dealing with speech handicaps was recognized, this segment of psychology came to be known as speech pathology and developed as a young science.

We have been speaking of the speech therapist and speech pathologist as if they were two different entities, which they are to a certain extent. The speech pathologist is academically advanced over the speech therapist in the study and treatment of all aspects of functional and organic speech defects and disorders. The speech pathologist usually makes the diagnoses, does the scientific research, and directs the teacher-training; and the speech therapist carries on the speech correction procedures.

As the science of speech pathology continues to grow and develop new concepts, it will continue to borrow from the fields of psychology and sociology, as well as from the fields of medicine and the physical sciences, as it discovers its own problems and submits its theories to the processes of scientific investigation. Further, it will at times even delve into the field of psychiatry as it searches for greater understanding and for the solutions to problems. No science stands apart by itself, and if the speech pathologist and the speech therapist are to do commendable work in their fields they must have the full cooperation and understanding of the older sciences. It is important that the speech therapist not attempt to do the work of the psychologist, the sociologist, and the psychiatrist, nor attempt to do the diagnostic work of the physician or the surgeon. But he must cooperate with all of these specialists. There are, however, aspects of psychology and sociology with which the speech therapist can and does work. There is no harm in this and the results can be good as long as the speech therapist understands his limitations.

We have been speaking of group therapy in the speech-correction process as if it were a single, designated type of therapy. This is not necessarily the case. To understand the nature of the particular types of group therapy that may be used in speech correction and improvement it is necessary to understand, at least to a limited extent, the various types of therapy as they have developed in the fields of psychiatry, clinical psychology, and sociology. Let us again define a number of terms and procedures.

PSYCHIATRY. This branch of medicine deals with mental disorders. No one should practice psychiatric therapy except the psychiatrist who has had several years of training in medicine as well as in psychiatry. The speech therapist does not attempt to play the part of the psychiatrist. If the speech therapist suspects that a severe emotional disorder or mental disturbance exists, he refers the client to a psychiatrist for examination and possible treatment. Sometimes the parents of the child also need psychiatric examination and treatment.

PSYCHOANALYSIS. Psychoanalytical treatment is the therapy carried on by the psychoanalyst. His examination and treatment rests upon the theory that abnormal mental reactions are due to repression of desires consciously rejected but subconsciously persistent. The speech therapist does not attempt psychoanalytical examination or treatment. He may refer disturbed persons to the psychoanalyst for examination and treatment and may in his therapy follow the recommendations given to him by the psychoanalyst. Psychoanalysis is the dynamic system of psychology developed by Freud. The techniques used in psychoanalysis are highly specialized and their use requires several years of special training.

PSYCHOTHERAPY. This term broadly describes a wide variety of psychological methods used to treat many different types of emotional disorders. Some of the techniques and methods used in psychotherapy can be applied by the speech therapist. However, the speech therapist must be cautioned not to go beyond the limits of his training and experience in his attempt to apply psychotherapeutic principles. It is the psychologist who applies psychotherapeutical measures when one is dealing with deep, underlying emotional conflicts. The different projective techniques used in psychotherapy can be applied and interpreted only by a trained psychotherapist. The speech therapist should shy away from using materials and methods that he does not understand. Some of the methods and techniques used in psychotherapy, however, are put into use by the speech therapist in his work with speech defective individuals who are not suffering from serious emotional problems. Some of the methods used in psychotherapy are particularly applicable to group therapy. Who is to deny that there can be psychotherapeutical value in play therapy, creative play and creative dramatics, and even in the speech games and various group or individual activities used by the speech therapist? The more the speech therapist understands the methods and techniques of psychotherapy, the more he is likely to understand his limitations and to abide by these limitations in any attempt to interpret, or to read interpretations into, actions and behaviors that he is not qualified to analyze.

PSYCHODRAMA. The psychiatrist and the psychologist use psychodrama with individuals who are seriously disturbed emotionally. The client acts out his fears, hatreds, anxieties, and fantasies, and by so doing may gain emotional release. The speech therapist uses the technique in a modified form when he asks children to choose a situation from their experience and act it out, creating conversation spontaneously as they proceed. This procedure creates a "speech situation" and may help to give the speech therapist and the children an insight in relation to the attitudes and feelings of the participants.

ROLE PLAYING. Through the use of role playing we give the child an opportunity, temporarily at least, to be someone besides himself. The shy, withdrawn child may revel in being the Pirate Don Durk of Dowdee. The aggressive child who demands attention and creates a disturbance may gain understanding by playing the part of the old man who gives his money to the poor and spends his time helping the unfortunate. Role playing is employed in psychodrama, creative play and creative dramatics, play therapy, and in formal dramatization. The therapeutic possibilities of role playing have been recognized by psychologists and are often put to good use by the speech therapist.

SOCIODRAMA. While psychodrama is concerned more with the personal problems of the individual, sociodrama has more to do with problems that may be shared by the members of the group. Activities taking place in "our gang," "our town," "our school," or "our family" may provide material for group interaction. The members of the group may at times wish to suggest themes for dramatization, at other times, the therapist may wish to present several situations and allow the group to make a choice among these. The source of material is almost endless. The theme or incident to be dramatized may be worked out in relation to action, characters, and dialogue, but should always allow for spontaneous speech or action on the part of any participant. Perfection in dramatization is not significant. After the presentation, general discussion takes place and feelings and attitudes are expressed. The speech therapist follows the technique of the sociologist or the psychologist and does not take a critical attitude if the feelings expressed are not particularly in agreement with personal ideals. Suggestions for change are presented to the group, not to individuals.

PLAY THERAPY. This term is to be interpreted first in the manner in which it is used by the psychologist, as described by Axline (1). In play therapy, the emotionally disturbed child expresses his fears and anxieties through a nondirective play technique. The therapist provides the child with various tools, toys, and activity materials and allows the child to proceed in his play activities without direction. The child is allowed to express himself freely and is not censured for his statements or activities; on the contrary, he is encouraged to say and do anything that he wishes. His statements are frequently "reflected" by the psychologist. If Johnny says, "I hate my brother; I'd like to smash him," the psychologist shows no concern and may reply in a matter-of-fact tone, without criticism, "You hate your brother." Johnny may proceed to smash the ball of clay the therapist has given him. He may be thinking of the clay as representing his brother and may be releasing some of his feelings of antagonism toward his brother by smashing the clay. Some of the techniques of play therapy are borrowed by the speech therapist in the use of permissiveness and approval in the group activities.

There are necessarily a few exceptions to the rule of permissiveness in group therapy. The child is not to be granted permissiveness to the extent that he continuously destroys property or does bodily injury to himself or to others in the group. When Johnny is disturbed and aggressive to the point where he knocks a smaller child down and jumps upon his stomach, it is likely that Johnny needs to be referred to a psychologist for examination and possible treatment.

Through the techniques of play therapy, as used by the psychologist, the child may be led to an understanding of his problems and may be able in time to work out his own solutions to his problems. The speech therapist, through the use of a free-play period, is able to observe the emotional expressions of the children in the group. Some children may be withdrawn and refuse to join with the others in their play; others may be aggressive and antisocial in their relationships with other children. If a child is allowed self-expression without the constant interference of an adult, he may be able to work out a solution to some of his problems through play activities with other children. The child who refuses to talk at home may be willing to express himself freely in the activities of the group if he is not pressured for speech or constantly directed in his play activities.

GROUP THERAPY. Here we speak of the type of group therapy which Slavson (7 and 8) sponsored. He arranged for the psychotherapeutical treatment of underprivileged and maladjusted children who were contacted through social service agencies in New York City. The children were organized into club groups according to age level. They met periodically in their specially equipped club rooms where they could take part in activities of their choice. An atmosphere of permissiveness was maintained at all times, and the children were restricted only to the extent that they could not attack the group leader, bring physical harm to the other children, or destroy equipment. By participating in activities that interested them and by learning to cooperate with the members of their group, they were given a chance to work out their personal problems and antisocial tendencies. The group leaders were carefully chosen and were given a period of special training before taking over the direction of a group. Many of the group leaders were previously social workers. The speech therapist can effectively use some of the procedures of Slavson, especially his techniques of permissiveness, acceptance, and approval, when working with groups of children who have personality problems as well as speech problems.

CREATIVE DRAMATICS AND DRAMATIC PLAY. Ward (10) defines *creative dramatics* as playmaking or creative dramatics: "*Playmaking,* the term used interchangeably with *creative dramatics,* is an inclusive expression designating all forms of improvised drama: dramatic play, story dramatization, impromptu work in pantomime, shadow and puppet plays, and all other extemporaneous drama. It is the activity in which informal drama is created by the players themselves. Such drama may be original as to idea, plot, and character, or it may be based on a story written by someone else" (p. 3). *Dramatic play* is described as "the make-believe of young children. There is no plot in *dramatic play* nor is there any thought of audience. It is a spontaneous activity full of adventure and discovery" (pp. 9-10). "It is the play-living in which a child 'tries on life' by putting himself in the place of any grownup who catches his interest, to say nothing of all the animals and inanimate objects he is quite as likely to become when he is four" (p. 2).* The therapeutic possibilities of these activities include opportunities for the child to gain recognition and find security through experiences of success; the child is given acceptance, approval, and a chance for successful self-expression. In creative dramatics, the children may select and study a story to be dramatized informally, without scenery, properties, or costumes. Small units of the story are acted out by volunteer members of the group; the scenes are repeated again and again, with different children taking the parts of the different characters, improvising the dialogue as they perform the action. No child is interrupted while playing, and both the children and the leader participate in the constructive criticism which follows the conclusion of each scene.

The teacher must understand the methods and techniques used in creative play. It takes a resourceful teacher with training and imagination to lead the group in this type of activity. The clever speech therapist can include in the

---

* From *Playmaking with Children,* by Winifred Ward. Copyright 1947, D. Appleton-Century Co., Inc. Second edition 1957. Reprinted by permission of Appleton-Century-Crofts, Inc.

constructive criticism periods suggestions to the group as a whole on the procedures necessary to develop adequate speech. It will not be pointed out to Johnny that he did not use his "s" sounds correctly in acting out the part of Simple Simon; instead, the teacher will explain to the group how the "s" sound is formed and will suggest that everyone try to produce a good "s" sound in isolation, in words, and perhaps in a few practice phrases. The leader may ask the group to listen and to try to discriminate between the "th" sound and the "s" sound. Johnny, who cannot say his "s" sounds, will listen to the others; try it himself; will *see, hear,* and *feel* what is going on; and very likely be influenced to a better production of the sound. This type of procedure can, of course, be used in all forms of group therapy. In creative dramatics the child has a chance to forget himself; he can be someone else, and a successful someone else. Being successful as someone else may give him the courage to try to find success for himself. The natural, easy conversational situations that are usual in creative dramatics and creative play are conducive to the release of tension, and the comradeships that develop in the groups are conducive to better social relationships. Group activities, creative dramatics, and creative play are very popular with children, once they have experienced these activities under the direction of a well-trained and enthusiastic teacher. They have great possibilities, both therapeutically and educationally. There is scarcely a school subject that cannot be "lived through" by means of the application of the techniques of creative dramatics and creative play. The processes are rich in opportunities when used as media for correlating school subject matter with development and improvement in speech.

CHORAL READING. Sometimes known as choric speaking, this activity is somewhat more formalized than some of the other suggested group activities. When used for the purpose of speech improvement, the emphasis is not placed upon formality or upon the perfection of the performance. Lacking some of the opportunities for socialization that some of the other group activities offer, the use of choral reading is nevertheless of value. The speech therapist or the classroom teacher can use it to bring variety to their program of speech improvement. The material chosen for choral reading should be on the age and interest level of the children. An opportunity for establishing good articulation and for improving voice quality is found in choral reading. For successful leadership in choral-reading activities the teacher should possess a good speaking voice, should know the methods involved, and should have a knowledge of the literature adaptable to choral reading.

OTHER GROUP ACTIVITIES. Formal play acting offers opportunities for the improvement of voice and articulation, but the speech therapist seldom uses formal play acting because the activity demands that too much time be devoted to the memorizing of lines, the costuming, staging, management of properties, and formal learning of action. Puppet shows, staged informally with extemporized dialogue, are used with success by the speech therapist and the classroom teacher who are interested in speech improvement and speech correction. The use of the flannel-board technique in dramatizing stories is also popular. Sometimes it is best if the teacher or a small group of children prepare the flannel board and the flannel-backed cut-out characters and scenery ahead of the time of the speech lesson; otherwise, too much time may be spent on "busy" work and not enough time on the speech-improvement program.

Speech therapists throughout the country have devised a great many other activities for the purpose of helping the children with whom they work. They also use a great many of the old, familiar childhood activities, encompassing in them, usually most unobtrusively, their methods and techniques of speech improvement and correction. Thus, we may watch a group of children finger-painting, dancing, playing games, singing, or coloring; but if a speech therapist or a teacher trained in speech improvement methods is acting as the leader of the group, there is certain to be speech development, improvement, and correction work going on at the same time. The main objective is not forgotten; the children may be having a wonderful time, but the leader knows that she is guiding the children to better speech habits.

The Speech Therapist

The speech therapist should be a trained special teacher with at least a four-year college education, including a recommended course of study and at least 200 clock hours of supervised clinical practice in speech correction. The therapist should also be a member-in-good-standing of the American Speech and Hearing Association, and at the end of his first year as a therapist should have attained the basic certification in this organization.

THE AMERICAN SPEECH AND HEARING ASSOCIATION. The *Journal of Speech Disorders*, the first official publication of the American Speech and Hearing Association, was first published in March, 1936. The Association in its twelfth year boasted a membership of 185 as of February, 1937. At that time, it was stated that the Journal was "devoted to scientific research concerning, and to improvement of, humanity's speech, voice, and hearing processes." In 1942, the Association adopted a program for certifying speech correctionists; and in 1948, the name of the periodical was changed to *The Journal of Speech and Hearing Disorders*. In 1950, the standards for certification were revised and standards for certification in hearing were included. Carrell (4) in a 1957 report on the progress and goals of the Association stated:

The Association is in every respect a going concern. Scholarly research is opening up new avenues of understanding, and clinical skills are being perfected. Membership in the Association has reached an all-time high of nearly 4,000 individuals. . . . One of the great strengths of this Association is basically psychological. There is no group whose members appear to have a stronger sense of *identification*. . . . Speech and hearing habilitation and rehabilitation is a profession with a long past, but a relatively short history; yet this fact must not . . . prevent us from realizing that this is a unique and distinctive profession (p. 5).

Code of ethics. At the 1951 Annual Convention of the Association, the Committee on Ethical Practice prepared a Code of Ethics (5) that was approved by the Executive Council and the membership of the Association. It was agreed that "the American Speech and Hearing Association is composed of persons having varying interests and professional duties, but certain broad ethical principles apply to the entire membership." Every practicing speech therapist is morally obligated to abide by the rules of this adopted Code of Ethics. The Code divides the ethical responsibilities of persons in clinical professions into (a) those duties arising out of the relation between the professional worker and the person who seeks his assistance, (b) duties owed to other professional workers, and (c) obligations to society (p. 255).

PROFESSIONAL RELATIONSHIPS. In the relationships of the speech therapist to his patient, the welfare of the patient is to be considered the most important factor. To serve his patients adequately, the speech therapist must meet the educational requirements. In addition, "the therapist must use every resource available, including referral to other specialists as needed, to effect as great improvement as possible in the shortest time consistent with good professional practice. Every precaution must be taken against causing any sort of injury to the patient" (p. 255). The duties to other professional workers include the dissemination of the results of research and developments in speech and hearing therapy, the avoidance of personal controversy, the establishment of professional discussion and harmony with others, the promotion of the status of the Association, and the promotion of all therapy for handicapped individuals. Duties owed to society include all the obligations of good citizenship and in addition the responsibility of helping in the education of the public in regard to speech and hearing problems. The Code of Ethics also lists a number of unethical practices to be avoided.

UNETHICAL PRACTICES. It is considered unethical (a) to guarantee the results of any speech or hearing procedures; (b) to employ sensational advertising; (c) to diagnose or treat speech or hearing defects by correspondence; (d) to violate the patient's confidence; (e) to discredit professional colleagues; (f) to exploit patients by treating those whose defects cannot be expected to improve, by continuing therapy unnecessarily, or by charging unreasonable fees; (g) to deal with patients requiring medical treatment without the recommendation of the physician; (h) to treat patients when the therapist is an undergraduate student or an unqualified member of the Association, unless such treatment is given under adequate supervision as a part of a training program; and (i) to accept compensation from a dealer as the result of recommending hearing aids or other devices. In general, the speech therapist is expected to maintain the high standards of the profession and to follow the standards of ethical practice as completely and as seriously as the medical doctor is expected to follow the pledge of his Hippocratic oath.

CERTIFICATION IN THE AMERICAN SPEECH AND HEARING ASSOCIATION. In addition to having at least a bachelor's degree in the general area of the Association's interests, the therapist must qualify for one of the four certificates of clinical competence. These include the basic and advanced certifications in speech and the basic and advanced certifications in hearing. The Basic Certification in Speech requires that the therapist complete six semester hours in any one or more of the following courses: anatomy and physiology of the ear and vocal mechanism, phonetics, semantics, speech and voice science, psychology of speech, experimental phonetics, or similar subjects; twelve hours in speech correction and speech pathology, with at least two courses in speech correction and/or speech pathology, including stuttering, voice disorders, articulation disorders, cleft palate, aphasia, cerebral palsy, or similar areas; three hours in audiology, including hearing problems and the testing of hearing; and nine credit hours in related areas, including child development and mental hygiene. In total, the therapist must complete at least 200 hours of supervised clinical practice. Before the basic certificate is granted, the candidate must have completed one year of *preregistered* experience of actual teaching in the field.

THE SPEECH THERAPIST AS A PERSON. The successful speech therapist needs to have certain basic characteristics and personality traits. He is an intelligent and honest person, one who likes people, especially children and, like the doctor, the nurse, and the teacher, one who feels a need to serve others. The therapist is methodical and efficient, yet creative and original; objective and well adjusted; and still sympathetic and understanding. He possesses an intellectual curiosity that prompts him to pursue research findings and to continue his personal educational growth and development, either through graduate study or by means of following the contemporary publications in the field.

Our successful speech therapist cooperates with others, is liked and respected by the pupils, the parents, the classroom teachers, and the professional workers in the community. The therapist likes working with normal children, with those who have handicaps, and with those who may be problem children. Like all good teachers, the speech therapist should be neat, clean, appropriately dressed, well-mannered, socially acceptable, and a friendly, patient, and capable person.

The duties of the effective public school speech therapist have been outlined by Powers (6). Summarized, these duties include the organization of the speech correction program in the school; planning the therapy schedule and carrying out effective therapy; making of adequate referrals and keeping of adequate, individual records; cooperation with and acceptance by the school staff; work with the teachers in speech improvement activities; parent interviews; effective professional relationships with the specialists; and adherence to the rules in the Code of Ethics as established by the American Speech and Hearing Association.

The Classroom Teacher's Role in Speech Development, Improvement, and Correction

The attitudes of the classroom teacher are of the greatest importance in establishing and maintaining good speaking habits in school children. We have mentioned how important it is that the speech therapist should cooperate with the classroom teacher; we must not overlook the fact that the classroom teacher must also be willing to cooperate with the speech therapist. We mention the speech therapist's obligation first because the speech therapist is, it might be said, the "intruder." The classroom teacher has been the ruler in her little kingdom for a long time. The speech therapist is a newcomer, and because of this we say to the speech therapist, "It is your job to get along with the classroom teachers, win their confidence, let them know how you can help, ask their assistance, listen to their suggestions, and in a very unobtrusive way, get them to see and accept what you have to offer." The classroom teacher of today is getting used to the specialists who come periodically to offer their wares and give the teacher and the children the benefit of their special training. The classroom teacher has accepted the special art teacher, the music teacher, the psychologist, the nurse, and other specialists. She is also beginning to accept the speech therapist; but in school systems where there has never been a speech therapist before, the therapist may have to do a little missionary work before complete acceptance is established. Fortunate is the therapist who finds that there are classroom teachers in the school system who have had an introductory course in speech correction, or teachers who have had previous experience in working with a speech therapist. For the most part, teachers of today are anxious to help their pupils find the way to better speech, and it is only rarely that the teacher must be won over.

Often the teacher has a part in the selection of those children who must have special speech help outside of class. She learns from the speech therapist what she can do to help these pupils in the classroom. The classroom teacher also makes the decision as to the best time for these pupils to be taken from the class for special speech help. Finally, the teacher makes arrangements for the speech therapist's visits to the classroom. During these periodical visits, the speech therapist demonstrates group work in speech development and improvement. When she feels ready for it, the classroom teacher takes over the speech improvement work in the classroom, carrying on the group speech activities during regular speech periods. In addition, the classroom teacher becomes "speech conscious" and encourages the carry-over of better speech habits to all subjects throughout the school day. The classroom teacher is frequently able to help the speech therapist gain a better understanding of the child with a speech difficulty in relation to his general behavior and scholastic achievement. In understanding the basic fundamentals of normal speech development, the classroom teacher can also be of tremendous assistance in the prevention of the development of speech difficulties.

Under the guidance of a well-informed classroom teacher, speech activities in the classroom become enjoyable. The child who finds acceptance, encouragement, and approval in his speech performances learns to like to express himself through speech. The child who has a speech difficulty can learn to accept his problem, face it objectively, and cooperate in the speech work of the class. The teacher can help the other children to understand the problems of the special children. When it has been made clear that everyone can improve in speech and that no one has perfect speech, and when the class works together for better speech through the use of various speech activities, then the teacher can feel that she is doing a commendable piece of work in helping the children in her class develop and maintain adequate speech habits.

The teacher is scarcely limited in her opportunities for speech development and speech improvement in the classroom. Many classroom subject matters fit naturally into speech group activity categories. We have, however, cautioned the speech therapist to abide by the limitations of his training and experience, and we must urge the classroom teacher to do the same. Speech problems can be caused by or can become exaggerated in seriousness by the eagerness of the untrained or unadept teacher to "do something" about Johnny's speech problem. Continual correction, asking Johnny to stop and say it again, and trying to help when one does not know the procedures that should be followed are practices fraught with danger and should be avoided. It is better to do nothing than to do the wrong things. If the classroom teacher does not know *what* to do, let her try nothing except kindness, consideration, understanding, tolerance, acceptance, encouragement, and good speech examples. Then let her seek the help of someone who knows what should be done. In many cases, the speech therapist, if there is one in the school, may be able to help. If there is no speech therapist in the school, perhaps there may be a college or university speech clinic nearby; each state has at least one such clinic, and many states have several speech clinics in operation. Most states also have divisions of special education in their departments of education. A letter of inquiry to the State Department of Public Instruction, usually located in the State House in the capital city, will bring suggestions as to where the teacher can look for assistance when it is needed.

Most teachers are avid readers and fast learners. If the classroom teacher finds it impossible to take courses in speech development and improvement, much can be learned from reading recommended books and periodicals. The bibliographies that follow each chapter in this book present a wealth of material that will be helpful to the teacher in meeting individual speech problems in her classroom and in developing a program of speech development and improvement. However, the classroom teacher must not forget that even a wide reading knowledge will not qualify her to do the work of the speech therapist. There will always be special cases or speech problems with which the classroom teacher will not have the training or experience to cope.

How the speech therapist will deal with these specific cases
will depend upon the needs of the child concerned and upon
the qualifications and training of the therapist. Our next
chapter will be concerned with these specific problems in
relation to the different *types* of speech problems.

Bibliography

1. AXLINE, V. M. *Play Therapy*. Boston: Houghton Mifflin Co., 1947.
2. BACKUS, O. L. Chapter 33, in Travis, L. E. (ed.), *Handbook of Speech Pathology*. New York: Appleton-Century-Crofts, Inc., 1957.
3. BACKUS, O. L., and BEASLEY, J. *Speech Therapy with Children*. Boston: Houghton Mifflin Co., 1951.
4. CARRELL, J. "Progress and Goals of the Association," *Journal of Speech and Hearing Disorders*, 22, No. 1 (March, 1957), 3-9.
5. Committee on Ethical Practice for the American Speech and Hearing Association. "Code of Ethics," *Journal of Speech and Hearing Disorders*, 17, No. 2 (June, 1952), 255-256.
6. POWERS, M. H. "What Makes an Effective Public School Speech Therapist?", *Journal of Speech and Hearing Disorders*, 21, No. 4 (February, 1956), 461-467.
7. SLAVSON, S. R. *An Introduction to Group Therapy*. New York: International Universities Press, Inc., 1952.
8. ———. *Child Psychotherapy*. New York: Columbia University Press, 1952.
9. SOMMER, A. T. "The Effects of Group Training Upon the Correction of Articulatory Defects in Preschool Children," *Child Development*, 3, No. 2 (June, 1932), 91-107.
10. WARD, W. *Playmaking with Children*, 2d ed. New York: Appleton-Century-Crofts, Inc., 1957.
11. WILSON, B. A. "The Development and Evaluation of a Speech Improvement Program for Kindergarten Children," *Journal of Speech and Hearing Disorders*, 19, No. 1 (March, 1954), 4-13.
12. WOOD, K. S. Chapter 2, in Travis, L. E. (ed.), *Handbook of Speech Pathology*. New York: Appleton-Century-Crofts, Inc., 1957.

Chapter 4

UNDERSTANDING SPEECH PROBLEMS*

"Something is wrong with Johnny's speech. I don't know what it is, but he just doesn't talk right." Quite frequently, when teachers and parents refer a child to the speech therapist or to a college or university speech clinic, they cannot accurately describe the speech problem that exists. This is not surprising because even the speech therapist and the speech pathologist sometimes have difficulty making an exact diagnosis. Usually they can tell the parent or the teacher what they *hear* that is wrong, but they cannot always tell at once *why* Johnny has a speech defect. Parents will sometimes say, "Johnny talks too fast," or "He thinks faster than he can talk." Or a parent may declare that Johnny "lisps," when he cannot produce the "s" and the "z" sounds; or the report may be that "Johnny uses 'baby talk'." A common parent-diagnosis is that "Johnny is tongue tied." This is seldom a true diagnosis because most children are not "tongue tied." Sometimes what is called a "speech problem" by parents or teachers is not even primarily a speech problem.

Recognizing the Problem as a Speech Problem

More often than teachers, parents are inclined to believe that all of Johnny's problems stem from the fact that he has

* Selected references for each major topic of this chapter will be found in Appendix B.

a speech defect. In actuality, Johnny's speech difficulty may be the least of his troubles. The defect in his speech may be a minor detail resulting from, related to, or even unrelated to other more basic abnormalities. Sometimes a speech problem exists only in the mind of the parent, or the grand-parent, or the lady who lives down the street. We have stated our definition of a speech defect. Usually, even Johnny's playmates know when he "talks funny," but if there is any question in the minds of the parents or the teacher as to whether or not Johnny has a speech difficulty, let the decision as to whether or not the speech defect is "real" rest upon the diagnosis of the speech therapist or the speech pathologist.

KNOWING WHEN THE DISORDER IS NOT A SPEECH DEFECT. A tired young mother of four children under school age brought her youngest boy, two years old, to the speech clinic because he "stuttered." The speech clinician found that the child had an unusually large vocabulary and that he used phrases and sentences three, four, and even five words in length. The father was in the service and the mother was alone with the children all day, without friends or relatives to relieve her occasionally. This "Johnny" didn't have a speech difficulty; what he needed was to be left alone. Three older children were constantly stimulating him with speech. At times he could not compete with the others; then he stumbled around and repeated words and phrases, but it did not really matter. He had a chance to develop normal speech if attention was not called to his manner of speaking. Therapy in this case was given the mother, indirectly, when a high-school girl came to relieve her of the care of the children three afternoons and evenings a week. The mother found relaxation and rest, family tensions were reduced, and little Johnny fully "recovered."

Sometimes it is unwise to cite cases, even to illustrate a point. The parent or teacher may be inclined to think, "Aha, that is my Johnny!" Quite likely the case is not at all the same with their particular Johnny. At times, parents and teachers may confuse reading or language problems with speech problems. A child may lack adequate language or reading development because of a hearing loss or because of mental retardation or other reasons. We have heard parents say, "There is nothing the matter with Johnny, except that he can't talk right," or "Johnny would be all right if he could only talk." This may be wishful thinking on the part of the parent. It is difficult for a parent to face the fact that he may have a child who is severely retarded mentally, or one who may never talk normally because of extended brain injury. It is easier to accept the supposition that "something is wrong with his speech." The speech therapist is frequently faced with the task of helping parents accept a situation as it exists. The school nurse, the psychologist, the doctor, and the minister are helpful allies when these occasions arise.

IDENTIFYING FACTORS RELATED TO THE SPEECH PROBLEM. Complete diagnostic procedures are of the utmost importance when attempting to identify the factors related to the speech problem of a particular child. Neither the teacher nor the parent, can make the proper diagnosis. The speech therapist and the speech pathologist will proceed as far as they are trained to proceed, and then make a decision as to what referrals may be necessary for a more complete diagnosis. The child's parents may be referred to a physician or a pediatrician for a medical examination of the child. If brain damage is suspected, a neurologist may make an examination. Psychological examination is frequently indicated because it is helpful to know the mental ability of the child for whom therapy is being planned. If emotional maladjustments are apparent or suspected, referral to the psychologist or the psychiatrist may be in order. A complete case history of the child as obtained from the parents is usually mandatory and frequently helpful in the understanding of the speech problem as it has developed over the years. It is also necessary to get a picture of the speech problem as it exists at the present time. This is a diagnostic procedure wherein notations are made of articulatory errors, vocal disorders, and speech performance in various situations.

We have called attention to the dangers that may be encountered in the practice of labeling or typing a speech difficulty. We find it convenient, however, to differentiate among a number of general "types" of speech disorders. Persons suffering from a speech disorder have distinct differences, and generalizations do not always apply to all of the individuals who might be handicapped by a particular "type" of speech disorder. However, those within a category may have in common to some extent similar causes, like symptoms, and occasionally like behavior. Therefore, we take the liberty of speaking of certain kinds of speech difficulties and of making some generalizations within the areas. There is reason to believe, for instance, that persons suffering from cerebral palsy may have some things in common with other persons afflicted with cerebral palsy. In like manner, persons who stutter, who have hearing losses, cleft palates, or those who are mentally retarded may have some similar problems. Quite frequently they may require, in a general way, therapy of a similar nature.

At all times the therapist must realize that it is the problem of the individual that must be studied; and it is the individual who must be treated, according to his individual needs. The greatest justification for the separation of speech disorders into "categories" may be the realization that these categories are for convenience and are not descriptive of anyone. Many factors exist along with the speech difficulty, and perhaps it is the other factors that we categorize to a great extent. However that may be, we shall proceed to discuss some of the various kinds of speech disorders as they are frequently distinguished in the fields of speech therapy, speech pathology, and at times in medicine and psychology as well. Our specific purpose in this chapter is to give general suggestions in relation to the therapeutic measures that may be indicated. We shall begin with a discussion of "articulatory problems," realizing all the while the great inclusiveness of the term as far as related factors are concerned.

The Child with an Articulatory Problem

A child has an articulatory problem when he does not produce the individual sounds of the language accurately or when he cannot make standard productions of the sound combinations that appear in his language. Teachers and parents are aware of the fact that some children make errors in sound production. In the beginning grades, this is quite a common occurrence. We are not too concerned if the otherwise normal child does not produce all speech sounds correctly at the age of five or six. It is more important at this time that the child should be well adjusted and happy in his speech performance.

When do articulatory errors become a speech problem? It is not "abnormal" for the young child to misarticulate some of the sounds that are last learned by most children. These may include the (l), (r), (s), and (z). If these sounds are consistently misarticulated by children at the age of six, we still are not too much concerned about the child's speech. However, if the child at five or six misarticulates so many sounds that we have difficulty in understanding what he has to say, we are probably justified in assuming that the child has an articulatory disorder. If at the age of seven, certain sounds or combinations of sounds are consistently misarticulated, it is likely that the child will need special help if he is to learn to produce the sounds correctly. As the child becomes older, his incorrect speech habits are likely to become more firmly established and his articulatory errors are less likely to be readily corrected.

THE IMPORTANCE OF A PROPER DIAGNOSIS. Before attempting to help a child overcome an articulatory difficulty or any other speech problem, it is necessary to discover the nature and extent of the problem. To begin haphazardly to correct any or all of the sounds a child may misuse is a dangerous procedure, which may lead to further confusion and greater frustration.

Who should make the diagnosis? As we have stated repeatedly, only a qualified speech pathologist or therapist should conduct the diagnostic procedures. They have been especially trained in the methods and techniques that are to be followed in the determination of the existing articulatory difficulties. They know how and where to look for contributing and related factors and when and where it will be necessary to refer a child for further examination. Finally, they are the ones who must outline and carry out the plans for speech therapy.

THE DIAGNOSTIC PROCEDURE. The experienced speech therapist knows that it is first necessary to gain the child's confidence and cooperation before any attempt is made to examine his speech or his speech mechanism. In interviewing young children, it is helpful to arrange for the examination to take place in a pleasant room equipped with a well-chosen number of toys or play objects. When rapport has been established, the therapist should proceed in an orderly manner to make an adequate examination of the child's speech and of the child in relation to his speech performance. The examination will encompass:

1. an evaluation of the present speech status;
2. an investigation of the organic and functional normalcy or abnormalities of the speech mechanism, including an examination of the lips, teeth, tongue, jaws, palate, throat, larynx, and the breathing mechanism;
3. a hearing test;
4. a history of the child's speech development;
5. a history of the child's physical development;
6. referrals for further examinations as indicated by: a psychologist, in regard to mental ability; a psychologist or psychiatrist, in relation to emotional adjustment; a physician, surgeon, dentist, orthodontist, or other specialist, in regard to organic conditions;

7. a report on the probability of a successful response to therapy; and

8. suggestions for a plan of therapeutic procedures.

An Evaluation of the Present Speech Status. The therapist will wish to discover what sounds or combinations of sounds are misused, when they are misused, and how they are misused. He will want to determine whether there are substitutions, distortions, omissions, or additions of sounds in the child's speech. He will wish to find out what malfunctions or organic abnormalities may be influencing the production of the articulatory errors. He will also want to know if the child can produce certain isolated sounds or sounds in combinations under stimulation, or when shown how these sounds might be produced. He will wish to find out if there is consistency in the misarticulation of sounds. In his efforts to discover the present speech status, he will wish to follow recommended methods of speech testing.

Methods of presenting a speech test. In checking the speech performance of the young child, the therapist may use a prepared picture test or an object test. The therapist will also wish to engage the child in conversation for a check on continuous speech adequacy. Older children may be asked to read prepared word lists or a set of phrases or short sentences. The pictures, objects, word lists, phrases, or sentences should elicit responses that will include sounds as they are used in the language in the initial, medial, and final positions in words and as they are used in combinations. The speech responses of the child should be recorded in terms of accuracy of sound production or as sound substitutions, distortions, omissions, or additions. It is convenient to have an assistant or second therapist record the responses of the child on a prepared articulation report blank, using the symbols of the International Phonetic Alphabet for recording purposes.

Determining Relationships. The speech pathologist and the speech therapist must know many more things about the methods of determining the functional or organic adequacy of the speech mechanism. There are many physical, organic, neurological, functional, psychological, and social relationships to be considered. This book, however, is not a text for the speech pathologist or the advanced speech therapist. It is written for the beginning speech therapist and for the use of the classroom teacher. We like to think the beginning speech therapist will be encouraged through the reading of these pages to continue his studies in the field; the classroom teacher will, we hope, get a general understanding of the speech problems of children and enlightenment as to how to proceed in the development of a speech improvement program in the classroom. Because of the limitations of the text, we shall not go into detail on the matter of diagnostic procedures.

When the therapist has completed his examination of the child's speech in regard to articulatory adequacy, when he has noted the functioning and the organic conditions of the speech mechanism, has taken a medical, physical and speech history, and has received the requested reports from referral agencies, he is ready to make his estimation of the probability or the improbability of success in therapy. Finally, he is ready to plan the steps that are to be taken in the therapeutic procedures. The therapist is always careful, as has been stipulated in his Code of Ethics, never to make unwarranted promises of "complete cures." He only states what possibilities he thinks the child has of acquiring normal or near-normal speech habits. He places no dates on possible time of correction but only plans a procedure of therapy which, in the light of his investigations, he believes, will help the child to better speech performance. At times, before the actual speech therapy begins, the child may undergo physical, surgical, psychological, or other treatment as may be indicated from the reports received from the referral agencies. The speech therapist sometimes delays the therapy program upon the recommendations of these other agencies.

Remedial Procedures

In discussing the remedial procedures that are to be undertaken in the process of helping the young child to overcome an articulatory difficulty, we wish to discuss two common statements that we believe may be somewhat misleading to a number of our beginning speech therapists and to the teacher. It has been stated in other sources that "speech correction is, to a considerable extent, an individual process," and that "the child must be convinced he has a problem which he must solve." These philosophical concepts, we believe, are incompatible to a large extent with the precepts of modern child psychology. Just as normal language development is a process that takes place in social group situations involving interpersonal relationships, we believe that speech improvement and speech correction should take place whenever possible in the group situation. As Thompson (15) points out, language is "a fundamental psychological function in the overall development and social adjustment of children. . . . It would appear desirable to promote children's language and social development simultaneously by skillful adult guidance in a social situation."

McCarthy (8) believes that there is "an emotional and functional explanation of most of the language disorder syndromes" and that "these emotional disturbances are for the most part environmentally determined." She cites an abundance of research in the areas of social adjustment and language disorders to prove her point. If the function of speech is to facilitate the meeting of ideas and purposes as related to facts and reality, as Murray (9) maintains, then as he emphasizes, "a corporate part of this process is an increased warmth in the human relations. Security and confidence take the place of fear and anxiety; good fellowship and affection take the place of anger and hostility; respect, mutual support, and cooperation take the place of envy, jealousy, withdrawal, and disruption."

Speech therapy and speech improvement activities in the group situation, directed and guided by the qualified speech therapist, and the well-informed teacher, offer possibilities of integrating the child's social and speech development. Integrated they must be, because they can scarcely develop separately. Certainly a child's social development, and in many ways his speech development, cannot be stimulated effectively in the type of individual therapy that calls for the speech therapist to carry on therapy exclusively with one child at a time. Therefore, we agree with Backus and Beasley (2) that group therapy "should form the core of speech therapy." This does not mean that we would eliminate individual therapy. There will always be times when the therapist will find individuals who need to be treated apart from the group. However, in our clinical experiences with preschool groups, with public school speech correction and improvement, with school children enrolled in the summer speech clinic, with adults who have lost their speech through a cerebral hemorrhage or a thrombosis (blood clot), or with laryngectomies (persons who have suffered the removal of the larynx because of cancer), with articulation disorders, voice disorders, and stuttering, we have found success, cooperation, and enthusiastic response in the use of the group situation.

Returning to our second point of discussion, "The child must be convinced he has a problem that he must solve," we believe that the speech therapist takes an unnecessary risk when attempting precisely to follow this philosophy. The young child who misuses sounds in his speech is often unaware of the errors that he makes. This is a phenomenon often not understood by parents and teachers. The child who says, "The wabbit wuns awound the wose bush" very likely thinks he is saying, "The rabbit runs around the rose bush." It is frustrating and confusing to say to the child, "You are not using the 'r' sound correctly; you say, 'the wabbit wuns'; you must learn to say, 'the rabbit runs.' We will teach you how to use speech correctly." This attack is similar to the mother's approach sometimes when she says to the child, "Don't say 'I want anuder tootie.' Say, 'I want another cookie.'" When the child replies, "I did say I want anuder tootie," the mother cannot understand why Johnny cannot "talk right." She has told him he "talks wrong," she has corrected him and has asked him to repeat, yet he continues to speak incorrectly and sometimes even withdraws and refuses to speak. When a parent or a speech therapist thus attacks the speech of the young child, he attacks the child. It is quite natural for the child to respond in some instances with the feeling, "Mother doesn't like my speech; mother doesn't like me. People don't like my speech; people don't like me." It is not surprising that children become frustrated and confused and sometimes withdraw and become sullen and self-conscious in speech situations.

It appears to us much wiser to use the Rogers (13) or the Axline (1) nondirective techniques in presenting speech therapy to the young child. In the group therapy situations, one can win the cooperation and the confidence of the child and make him feel happy and secure. He can know that you are satisfied with him and with his speech as he and his speech are at present. In all, you think he is a pretty fine little fellow and you let him know it. Then in the group situation, through clever means of presenting new sounds and building new speech habits through game and play activities, you change the child's speech habits and guide him to more adequate speech. You have succeeded in doing this without disrupting the child's social position or his personal opinion of himself.

When working with older children and adults, there may very well be times when the therapist will wish to approach the speech problem directly and attempt to convince the individual he has a problem he must solve. A sixteen-year-old high-school graduate entered the University one fall with an I.Q. of 165 and an articulatory disorder so severe that it was almost impossible at times to understand what he was saying. In our work with him in the speech clinic we were convinced he did not realize that his speech was almost unintelligible. When his speech therapist would try to get him to produce sounds correctly, he would reply, "But dat's edsatly what I ted!" When he heard himself speak by means of the use of the tape recorder, his reaction was, "I'd wada be dead den taught yit dat!" Evidently, even at the age of sixteen with an I.Q. of 165, he thought his speech was not as defective as it was. This young man was given direct, individual therapy. He was faced directly with his problem and told that he had a problem to solve. He found that it wasn't a choice of "being dead or talking like that." Because there were no organic difficulties and no great emotional maladjustments, the young man had a good chance of overcoming his speech disorder. It is interesting to note that when the therapist was taking his "case history" it was discovered that as a child he had been able to avoid daily reading from the Bible at meal time because he had a speech difficulty. The student remarked, "Dis was one dood ting about my thpeesh!" The statement was revealing. Perhaps the independence he gained by going away to college was a help in overcoming his speech difficulty. Here was a student with many sound substitutions and distortions. The therapist was able to work with more than one sound at a time and able to work rapidly and successfully, partly because the student was very intelligent and cooperative. Sometimes the therapist has to work with only one sound at a time and sometimes he has to make a choice as to which sounds will be corrected first.

ORDER IN WHICH SOUNDS ARE TO BE CORRECTED. Different speech pathologists appear to have formed different opinions in relation to the order in which sounds should be corrected. In the literature we find various recommendations presented: (a) sounds should be corrected in the order in which sounds are learned by the child from infancy; (b) the first sounds to be corrected should be those that are the most visible; (c) they should be the ones that are the easiest for the individual to produce; (d) correct first the sounds that the individual produces most readily with stimulation; (e) the most defective or the most conspicuously handicapping sound should be corrected first; and (f) correct first the sound that occurs most frequently in speech.

From these recommendations, it appears that the therapist will be able to justify any approach he may wish to take! With a little thought, however, we see that some of these suggestions make sense. Let us consider suggestion (a). In the case of the very young child who has not developed speech, it may be wise to follow the pattern of the infant's production of sound, first stimulating the child in the process of "babbling." With children and adults who have developed a considerable amount of speech, however, this suggestion does not make sense. Suggestion (b) appears reasonable when we are working with groups of children, and when we do not have complicating organic problems to consider. Suggestion (c) would be considered good psychology because approaching the "easiest" sounds first would give the child an opportunity to feel success; suggestion (d) goes along with this because it appears sensible to teach those sounds first that the child can easily produce upon stimulation. We would hesitate to recommend suggestion (e), as this procedure might lead to frustrating and depressing experiences. However, in some instances, in working with adults, this procedure might be beneficial. If success is experienced within a reasonable time, the adult may be inspired and stimulated by his success in the correction of the most defective sound. In dealing with children, the difficulty of establishing the correct production of the "most defective sound" must be taken into consideration. In like manner, the approach taken in (f), correcting first the sound that occurs most frequently in speech, must be given careful consideration. If this sound is especially difficult for an individual child to produce, it may not be a particularly wise "first choice."

From all the suggestions given in relation to which sounds should be taught first, we can perhaps formulate a constructive plan of procedure. Examining the articulatory test report or reports (in using group therapy), we can discover the sounds that are defective. From this list we can select the sounds that are the most visible (most easily seen in production: (p), (b), (m), (w), (ʍ) as in *wh*at, (f), (θ) as in *th*in, (ð) as in *th*is, (t), (d), (ʃ) as in *sh*ow, (tʃ) as in *ch*op, and (dʒ) as in *j*ump). From this list of the most visible sounds, we might make a second list, made up of those sounds that the child or the children can most frequently produce under direct stimulation. This final list, it would appear, might be the first sounds to start with in our correction program. Individual differences in ability to produce sounds and individual differences in organic abnormalities will influence our selections in choosing the particular sounds with which to start.

How Many Sounds Should Be Corrected at One Time? Some schools of thought maintain that only one sound should be corrected at a time, and that this one sound should be firmly established in the individual's speech before the correction of a second sound is attempted. Others believe that it is possible and profitable to concentrate on more than one sound at a time. It has also been recommended that the voiceless and voiced pairs (s-z, t-d, p-b, k-g, etc.) should be corrected together. A proper decision as to number of sounds to teach at a given time can be made only by giving careful consideration to the needs and abilities of the individual. There will be times when it will be wise to concentrate on the production of one sound; at other times, it will be possible and advisable to correct two or more sounds simultaneously. It has been our practice in working with young children in groups to concentrate unobtrusively upon the stimulation, discrimination, and practice (through the use of group activities) first, upon the sounds most frequently misused by the group, beginning with those sounds most visible and most easily produced. These usually include the (f), (v), (s), (z), (θ), and (ð). We have found that the (k), (g), (tʃ) as in *ch*in, (dʒ) as in *j*ump, (l), and (r) are usually the most difficult to correct; therefore, we usually concentrate on these last. However, it is not unusual to find that children frequently correct themselves in the production of sounds through participation in the group activities, even when no special attention is being given to the production of a particular sound. We are certainly working on more than one sound at a given time, and the children appear to be thriving in speech development and improvement when these methods are used. At times we will use the (s) and (z) in stimulating group activities for weeks, and sometimes some of the children continue to use a substitution for these sounds. Then one bright morning a child who has previously said, "I want to play Thimple Thimon" will say "I want to play Simple Simon."

Approaches to the Correction of Articulatory Errors

In helping children to produce sounds accurately it is to be remembered that we all learn speech by what we hear, see, and feel. Thus, we approach the teaching of correct sound production through the auditory, visual, and kinesthetic methods. The ear can be taught to hear the difference between sounds; the tongue can learn to feel the difference; and the eye can see the difference. Simple sound discrimination games may be used to emphasize the differences in sounds as they are heard. The children may clap their hands as they hear the "s-s-s-" of the "snake sound" and tap their toes on the "th-th-th-" of the "mad goose" sound. Differences between syllables, words, and phrases may be emphasized in a like manner.

IMPORTANCE OF INDIVIDUAL DIFFERENCES. It is important to keep in mind that all problems in articulation are not "simple functional articulatory problems." Sound substitutions, distortions, and omissions may be the result of a great many different causal factors; these may be psychological, organic, or imitative in origin. It is not adequate just to attempt to teach the individual sounds and combinations of sounds to the child. All factors in relation to the total development of the child must be taken into account. The development of normal speech is not to be thought of as separate from the normal development of the whole child. Furthermore, normal speech development is not a thing apart from school subject matter or the total life situation of the child.

It should also be remembered that an emotional disturbance, a hearing loss or brain injury, a disorder of the speech mechanism, low mental ability, or other factors may be related causal factors in delayed speech development and may result in articulatory defects. If organic abnormalities exist, steps should be taken to correct the defects, if correction is possible. There are times when even the specialists may not be able to give the needed assistance. Abnormalities may not be corrected because of the financial costs involved. It may be that the speech therapist or the teacher is faced with the responsibility of finding financial assistance for a child. Use can be made of social welfare agencies or of local or state organizations such as the Crippled Children's Society and the local lodge of the Masons or the Elks. The speech therapist has a moral obligation to see a case through successful therapy, if this is at all possible. If the need for financial assistance is a part of the picture, the therapist finds out where financial assistance can be found.

THE CHILD AND THE PARENT. It is sometimes advocated that we should "make mother a speech therapist," or father, sister, brother, grandparent, or aunt. This can be an unfortunate procedure. It is often difficult for a child to take speech criticism or correction from a member of the family. Criticism from a member of the family too often comes in the form of speech pressure or "nagging." Emotional reactions may result that may be something far more serious than the articulatory difficulty. When it becomes necessary for a parent to help a child correct his speech difficulties at home, it should be done only under the careful supervision of a qualified speech therapist.

HOW THE PARENT CAN HELP. We often suggest that parents may help the child at home through quite indirect methods. Almost always we ask that no direct correction of speech sounds be made. When a child misuses sounds in his speech we suggest that the parents use the words correctly in their conversation with the child. The parents can stimulate the child with accurate speech productions but should not constantly correct his speech differences. They can read to the child, tell him stories, and let him take part in the story-telling. They can let him complete the words of familiar rhymes but should not ask him to repeat when sounds are used incorrectly. Parents should learn to accept the child's speech as adequate *for the time being*. Above all, the child should not feel that the parents are anxious about his speech. If the child already knows that there is something wrong with his speech, let him understand that in time he will be able to speak more accurately. Help him to build the right attitudes toward his speech difference. It is better to have a speech difference that may be improved in time than it is to be deaf, blind, or crippled. If other children tease the child because he has a speech disorder, teach him to take a "so what" attitude and make him feel he will improve. Let him know that you love him as he is, and not only that you love him but that you *like* him too. Let him know that everyone has some differences of one kind or another; no one is "perfect" in speech or in anything else. To achieve a better understanding of a particular child's speech problem or the speech problems of children in general, the parent and the teacher might profit from reading books that are especially concerned with the speech problems of children. A list of recommended books is presented in Appendix B.

The Child with a Voice Problem

Voice disorders in young children are probably not as common and certainly not as easily recognized as articulatory problems. When voice problems do appear, they are likely to be present in the voice of the older child. It is much more difficult to define "the normal voice" than it is to define "normal articulation." The speech therapist, whose ears are "tuned" to the recognition of vocal deviations, will readily perceive when a voice problem is present. The members of a family may at times be oblivious of the fact that a voice problem exists. They can become used to a particular type of voice to the extent that it appears "natural" and "normal." The classroom teacher may have difficulty in recognizing a voice problem. At other times, the teacher may think a voice problem is present when one is not. We may be inclined to be too personal in our own likes or dislikes in judging what constitutes a pleasant or an unpleasant voice. If we think of the voice as being that which is *not present* when we whisper or if we divorce it from the articulation or formation of sounds, we may be able to understand better what we are trying to judge when we listen to voices. In very simple terms, the voice is sound produced by the vibrations of the vocal bands and influenced by the size, shape, and use of the vocal mechanism. The voice may also be influenced by abnormalities of the speech mechanism. Individual voices differ from person to person; it is these individual differences in voice that enable us to identify a speaker, even though we cannot see the person who is speaking. A pleasing voice is a real asset to any individual; it can be the final touch that brings charm to the woman and power and influence to the man. A pleasant voice is worth cultivating, and the voice habits established in childhood can last a lifetime.

When Does a Deviation Become a Voice Problem? Since it is frequently difficult for the parent or the teacher to decide when a voice disorder is present, they should not hesitate to call for the opinion of the speech therapist if there is any question in their minds as to whether or not a child has a voice disorder. Overreferring children who do not have real voice problems is preferable to the neglect of one or more who have definite voice disorders. If the child's voice is unpleasant or annoying to his listeners, if there is an unusual quality of voice or a deviation from that which appears to be normal, we may suspect that the child has a voice problem. We give many names to voices that, to us, seem unpleasant. We hear remarks such as "He talks through his nose," "I can't stand her voice," "He growls and grunts," "She yells," and "He talks like a sissy." Other descriptive terms that we hear used to designate an unpleasant or different voice include: harsh, hard, hoarse, husky, whispered, coarse, shrill, rasping, infantile, strident, whining, etc. These descriptions do not tell us much about the problem that exists. The child with a voice problem must be carefully studied if we are to discover when a voice disorder is present, why the disorder is present, and what can be done to improve or correct the speaking voice of the child.

THE IMPORTANCE OF A PROPER DIAGNOSIS. Although in some instances the layman may be able to realize that a voice disorder exists, we have emphasized that it is almost impossible for an untrained person to determine the deviations that are present and the factors that are related. It is important that a proper diagnosis should be made by a qualified speech pathologist or speech therapist. They can establish the present status of the problem and can arrange for the necessary additional examinations. Psychological, physical, or organic abnormalities are frequently associated with voice disorders. A complete medical examination may be in order, including an examination by the otolaryngologist. A psychological examination is often recommended, because voice disorders may be related to emotional disturbances. The therapist will take a complete case history and will delay therapy until reports have been received from other agencies. Real harm can be done in some cases if therapy is approached before the problem is thoroughly understood. Remedial procedures must be planned by the speech therapist with due regard to the recommendations of the otolaryngologist and the psychologist.

PRESENT STATUS AND RELATED FACTORS. Voice problems may vary greatly in degree of deviation from what is considered to be within "normal range." A serious voice disorder may contribute greatly to the unintelligibility of speech. Voice defects frequently are concerned with more than one attribute of the voice and may be present in any one or more of the following: loudness, pitch, quality, or flexibility, and some authorities include time. Children may have unpleasant voices without any psychological, physical, or organic problems. It is thought by some persons that the speech of people of the Midwestern states is harsh and "twangy." We have heard it said that the people in the East have "softer" voices and that the children of England have the most beautiful voices of all. Some voices may be pleasant at one time and distinctly unpleasant at other times. We know very well that our voices are not beautiful when we become angry and talk too loud. Individuals may have voice problems and articulation difficulties as well, and in some cases a multitude of other problems.

Sometimes children have inadequate speaking voices because they have copied the speaking voice of one of the adults with whom they live. A teacher with a poor voice may be the model whom the child unconsciously imitates. Some voice problems exist only temporarily. The adolescent voice change of boys usually occurs between the ages of fourteen and sixteen. At this time a boy may be speaking in his newly acquired low-pitched voice, when suddenly his voice may without warning change into a childish squeak. Most boys go through this stage of development without any apparent difficulties. Occasionally a boy fails to make the transfer from the child's voice to the adult voice in the normal period. Girls occasionally have similar difficulties. Some children may need help in learning to control the voice. It will be wise to consult with the speech therapist in such cases. The therapist, in turn, may wish to get help from the school psychologist or the physician.

A child who has adenoids may be a mouth breather and have difficulty producing the three nasal sounds (m), (n), and (ŋ). After the adenoids have been removed, the child may still have a voice problem. Sometimes his voice will retain a nonnasal quality and sometimes it will take on a definite nasal quality. If the child has become dependent upon the mass of adenoidal lymph tissue, he may, after the operation, have to be taught to raise the soft palate higher in order to get a closure that will eliminate the nasal quality.

Children with hearing losses often develop voice problems, especially if the loss is of a serious nature. They may speak too loudly, too softly, or may develop an unusual quality of tone. Children who are deaf from birth usually learn to talk, but their voices retain a "deaf quality." The effect of deafness upon the voice is related to the type and degree of deafness and also to the time of the origin of the loss. The use of hearing aids, amplification, and special vocal training can frequently help the hard-of-hearing child retain or develop a pleasant speaking voice.

The child with a cleft palate is likely to have a nasal quality in his voice. Nasality occurs either when the cleft permits air to escape into the nasal cavities, when a mended palate results in an inactive palate, or when the child has a shortened palate. The child with a cleft palate is to be referred to the proper agencies for examination and recommendations before therapy is applied; the dentist, the physician, the surgeon, or the orthodontist may be called upon for assistance.

An attack of poliomyelitis may bring after-effects that influence voice production. There may be a complete loss of voice when the muscles of the larynx are involved. Envolvement of the soft palate may cause nasality. Sometimes recovery takes place after a period of time, or the recovery may be only partial and speech therapy may be indicated.

Many other organic, physical, or neurological abnormalities may be related to vocal disorders; these may be of a congenital, developmental, or accidental nature. Most of the complicated and severe vocal problems, however, never come to the attention of the classroom teacher or the public school speech therapist. With this brief introduction of some of the related factors and abnormalities that may appear in the child, we will discuss the remedial procedures that may be followed in relation to the different types of voice disorders.

Remedial Procedures in Relation to Particular Voice Defects

In a previous chapter we discussed the voice problems that may exist in relation to the various attributes of voice.

Defects in voice were designated as defects in loudness, pitch, quality, and flexibility. Some authorities include the element of time and also consider breathing an important factor in good voice production. Adequate breathing habits are important to good voice production. Good breathing for speech does not differ to any great extent, however, from good breathing for living, except that in speech, inspiration is quick and expiration is slow and controlled. We speak during the expiration of breath. Most children have adequate breathing habits, but we occasionally find a child who has poor breathing habits. This condition may be related to physical, organic, neurological, or psychological factors. If the child appears to need help in establishing adequate breathing habits, the physical therapist may be of assistance in directing the child toward improved habits of breathing.

DEFECTS IN PITCH. An individual may use a voice pitch that is too high, too low, patterned, or lacking in variety. As an aid in correcting pitch difficulties, the teacher may wish to discover the child's pitch range, to know what pitch range he is using most habitually, and to find out what his so-called natural pitch might be. Fairbanks (4) devised a means of estimating the individual's natural pitch level. Johnson (6) presents an adaptation of Fairbanks' method that will be helpful in working with those problems in voice that appear to be related to pitch defects.

A piano may be useful in teaching the child to speak within the range of his natural pitch. Tape or wire recordings permit the children to hear differences in pitch. Choral reading and creative play offer media through which new habits may be established. Certain selections in choral reading may encourage the lowering or the raising of the pitch of the spoken voice. Some selections of poetry appear to be more naturally spoken in a low pitch, others appear to demand a higher pitch, and still other selections encourage variation in pitch.

An infantile type of voice may be closely related to the habitual use of too high a pitch. A hoarse or husky voice may be closely related to the habitual use of too low a pitch. Occasionally we find persons who use what we call "meaningless variations" in pitch. This can be recognized when children read poetry in a sing-song melody, without reference to the meaning to be conveyed. There are also those who speak in a monopitch. Children with these deficiencies can be led to the use of more normal variations in pitch through participation in group activities including choral reading, creative play, and other well-planned group speech activities. They can often learn to imitate the more natural pitch variations of the teacher and the other children in the classroom.

DEFECTS IN LOUDNESS. The corrective techniques that apply specifically to pitch problems can be adapted to an extent to correct problems in loudness. The child who speaks too loudly can be encouraged to speak more softly while working in choral reading on such a selection as "Flow Gently Sweet Afton." The child who habitually speaks too softly may respond with more force if he is asked to play the part of a cheer leader. The response of the volume indicator on the tape or wire recorder can be an aid in controlling the loudness of the voice.

TIME FACTORS. Problems of "time" can be closely related to physical or psychological problems, and referral to the physician or to the psychologist may be of importance here. The child who speaks too fast may be suffering from emotional disturbances. The child who speaks much more slowly than the average person may be suffering from glandular disturbances. Precautions should be observed when dealing with problems of time; but if no physical, organic, or psychological abnormalities are present, the teacher and the speech therapist may proceed to teach more adequate timing through speech activities adaptable to group work. Working for meaning, understanding, and good interpretation will help children understand the time values in communication. Words, phrases, and sentences are used to

communicate ideas to others. Because of their thought
content, some phrases are spoken in fast time; others for the
same reason are spoken in slow time. In creative play,
different characters demand different timing in the deliver-
ance of their speeches. Old Pipes in "Old Pipes and the
Dryad" would probably speak in a slow, plodding voice.
The children in the same story would likely use quick, fast
speech in their play.

A choral reading group may speak "Windy Nights," by
Robert Louis Stevenson, in slow tempo; but when the group
works with Mildred Merryman's "Pirate Don Durk of Dowdee," the tempo should pick up and thus the speaking time
will change. Such techniques in securing variations in time
are natural and are to be preferred to any artificial way of
controlling time changes in speech.

DEFECTS IN QUALITY. When defects of voice quality are
present, first consideration must again be given to possible
causal factors. Are there organic, physical, or psychological
factors related to the voice problem? The specialists should
be able to give us the answers. If no such causal factors
exist, speech retraining is usually in order. Singing, chanting,
choral speaking, creative play, recording, and speech games
may all have a part in the retraining process.

The teacher who has a good speaking voice herself can
do much to help the child develop a pleasing voice. Ear
training is important, and the use of a tape or wire recorder
is helpful. In using auditory training, we let the child hear
the difference between the good voice and the poor voice.
The child hears the difference and sees and feels what he
does to produce the difference. In other words, the ear is
trained to distinguish between the old and the new, the
unpreferred and the preferred voice.

Children working in groups can be taught to listen for
differences in voice production. For instance, the children
may voluntarily try to make all sounds nonnasal. Then they
can try making all sounds nasal ("talk through the nose").
They can thus be taught to hear and feel the differences. By

using a mirror, they can see how the soft palate is lowered on (ŋ) and how it rises on a well-produced (ɑ) sound.

New habits should be established and carried over into daily speaking situations. Give the child opportunity to practice his new learning in group situations through the use of the various speech activities. Remember that it is possible to encourage a change in voice by the type of selection used in choral reading or by the type of character played in creative play. One would probably not be inclined to read Byron's "Roll on thou deep and dark blue ocean, roll . . ." in a thin, high-pitched voice, nor would one be likely to read light lyric poetry with a heavy, base voice. Encourage the child. Let him hear his new voice on a tape recorder. Give him successful speaking experiences. Improvement in voice often follows improvement in the production of sounds, especially in relation to the vowel sounds. If the sounds and syllables are accurately formed, if speech is normal in phrasing and in rhythm, if no pathological or psychological disorders exist, speech is likely to be normal in relation to its vocal aspects.

How the Parent Can Help. From the beginning of the child's speech development, a parent can help most by giving the child a pleasant voice example to follow throughout the years. The parent can cooperate with the teacher and the speech therapist by seeing that physical or medical recommendations are followed through to completion, and can build a home environment for the child that will allow for a tension-free atmosphere. The parent can help the older child to accept his problem and face it realistically and objectively. There should always be *un*emotional interest in the child's speech progress in addition to acceptance, love, and encouragement. But the parent should be careful not to make too great an ado over a minor speech problem.

The Child Who Stutters

Many speech pathologists agree with Johnson (6) that the average stutterer is not basically different—psychologically, physically, or organically—from the nonstutterer, except in his usage of speech and his reactions to his own speech. Stuttering is presumed to be a learned reaction that is perpetuated by the establishment of anxiety-tensions related to the speaking situation. Why some individuals develop stuttering while others do not may be explained by environmental conditions that establish the anxiety-tensions. These environmental conditions are speech-centered and have their origin in the early period of the child's life. A large majority of children during their early years of speech development go through a period of so-called "normal nonfluency." It is considered normal for young children to hesitate and repeat occasionally. Even the adult does not use uninterrupted fluency in his normal speech. According to this theory, the stuttering is instigated when normal repetitions and hesitations are first called to the child's attention. The child's speech is criticized; he is told to "slow down," "take it easy," or is asked to "repeat without stuttering." As he perceives that the parent is not pleased with his speech performance, he may hesitate and "stutter" all the more. Finally, the parent becomes anxious about the child's manner of speaking and this anxiety may be transferred to the child. In his efforts to please his parents, the child becomes tense and self-conscious in speaking situations. A vicious circle may be established, and the child "stutters because he fears he is going to stutter." If the anxiety-tensions and the learned speech behavior pattern persist, the child builds up attitudes toward his stuttering and adopts a particular pattern of speech. He may block, repeat, or hesitate on consonants, vowels, syllables, words, or phrases. He may do any one or more of these things. He may display muscular spasms or facial contortions. No two persons stutter exactly alike. Each develops his own manner of mild, moderate, or severe stuttering according to his individual experiences, frustrations, and anxieties.

The different ways of reacting in speech are the symptoms of stuttering; they are the things we see and hear taking place as the stutterer speaks. In a previous chapter, we mentioned the term "neurotic stuttering," which presumably is something different from the kind of developmental stuttering we have just described. It is quite possible that there are other forms of stuttering related to specific types of abnormalities such as brain damage, neurological disturbances, or psychopathic conditions. For the most part, the layman regards the symptoms and calls all obviously nonfluent speech stuttering.

The nonfluent child who is labeled a stutterer by his parents, teachers, or other uninformed adults becomes a real stutterer when he begins to accept himself as a stutterer. Such a child is not born a stutterer. He is urged on his unhappy way by parents, teachers, and others who wrongly think they are helping him to overcome a speech deficiency.

When does nonfluent speech become a speech problem? When the child becomes concerned about his speech, when he builds up anxiety-tensions that interfere with the communicative processes, and begins to avoid and fear speaking situations, then we can say that the child has a speech problem. As we have said, parents sometimes are convinced that there is a speech problem before one exists. This will be advantageous only if the parents seek the advice of a speech therapist. Guidance may set the parents on the right track and avoid the development of a real speech problem.

IMPORTANCE OF A PROPER DIAGNOSIS. Johnson (5) maintains that the majority of children who stutter have been originally diagnosed by uninformed parents or other adults. This very labeling of a child as a stutterer is the original mistake. If the parent or teacher who is concerned about a child's normal nonfluencies would consult a qualified speech pathologist or therapist, it is believed that many cases of "secondary" stuttering could be avoided. A complete study of the child, physically, psychologically, and organically may uncover related factors. An interview with the parents and the teacher and a study of the child's developmental history and his present environmental conditions may help in understanding the child's problem. In his diagnosis, the speech therapist will wish to secure a picture of the child's present status of speech performance. It will be helpful to know *how* the child stutters, *when* the child stutters more and when he stutters less, and how the child and the parents and others react to his stuttering. When the speech therapist has as complete an understanding of the child as it is possible to get, he will plan for therapy according to the individual child's apparent needs.

REMEDIAL PROCEDURES FOR THE YOUNG CHILD WITH NON-FLUENT SPEECH. Remedial procedures should be nondirective and consist for the most part of suggestions to be given to and followed by the parents. In some instances it may be beneficial to include the young child in a play therapy group. When this is recommended, no direct attack is to be made on the child's speech. The purpose of the speech therapy session is to give the child freedom to express himself in any manner he may happen to be speaking, to help him enjoy speech activities with other children, and to help him become self-assured in speaking situations. At no time will his nonfluent speech be called to his attention.

How the parent can help. Regular physical examinations are important. The child should be kept in as good physical condition as possible, which of course is advisable for all children. The parent is asked to overlook any nonfluency in speech. Attention is not to be called to the child's manner of speaking. He is not to be asked to "slow down," "take it easy," "not stutter," or to "think before he talks." The attitudes of the parents and the atmosphere of the home are important. The child should be given security and love, and his life should be kept as free from fretful worries and anxieties as possible. A happy home that is free from tension is conducive to the development of normal speech. The parents and the other members of the family may need to "slow down, take it easy, relax, watch their speech, and think before they talk." The child should be given an opportunity to speak for himself; others should listen and wait until he has finished speaking. The child may be praised for good work but should not be praised for good speech. In other words, we do not praise the child for not "stuttering"; when we do so we tell the child we do not like him when he "stutters" and thus pave the way for further anxieties. Parents should not show anxiety over a child's speech patterns. They should not show, even by a frown on the face, that they are dissatisfied with his speech. They should encourage the child to do things for himself but should not pressure him beyond his ability, in speech or in anything else.

Parents must guard against being "perfectionists." One sure way to frustrate the child is to demand of him standards that are too high. Children are growing, learning, changing, and making mistakes. It is necessary to let them grow, learn, and change at their own speed. The parent should be cautioned not to talk about the child's speech when he is present and not to let others do so. He should beware of comparing one child's speech development with that of another child. Girls develop in speech faster than boys; and even if Mary has been speaking fluently and with many words since the age of two or three, there is no reason why Johnny should be expected to follow her specific speech pattern. Remember that it is considered normal for young children to hesitate and repeat occasionally. If repetitions and hesitations are not called to the child's attention and if he is not made unhappy or anxious about his speech patterns, there is reason to believe that nonfluent speech will be only a temporary phase, and that normally fluent speech will be established as the child gains in security and experience. The parent should consult a speech therapist, pathologist, or psychologist if he feels that the child's problems are beyond his understanding or control.

HELPING THE OLDER CHILD WHO STUTTERS. Let us consider the child who already has been labeled a stutterer, the child who also has labeled himself a stutterer. What can we do to help the confirmed stutterer? We can let him take part in speaking activities and encourage him to talk. We can accept his speech as it is, and let him know that it is all right for him to talk in any manner that he happens to use at the present time. He may be told that other people repeat some of the time, and that it doesn't matter if he repeats occasionally. The teacher may find it difficult to convince the stuttering child that this is so. A university student who stuttered once remarked, "I wish that my fifth-grade teacher had used stuttering speech a few times herself, just to prove to me that stuttering didn't really matter!"

The teacher may talk to the other children of the class, perhaps at first when the child concerned is not present and again later when the child is present. She can ask the class to help the child by not teasing him about his speech and by giving him time to express his thoughts. The teacher might remind the class members that they would not make fun of a crippled child or a blind child and tell them that this child also needs their consideration and help. With the coopera-tion of the class, the teacher may be able to help the par-ticular child develop better speech habits. The teacher can explain that no one speaks perfectly and that everyone can improve his speaking habits. Special group activities in speech can be planned, and the whole class can be given an opportunity to improve in speech.

The teacher and speech correctionist should work with the school psychologist and with the parents of the child. Suggested reading materials may be given to the parents. They should know that stuttering is not a disease; that it is not inherited; and that physically and mentally, on the aver-age, children who stutter are not different from children who do not stutter. The parents should understand that they are responsible to a great extent for the present and future speech development of their child. Each child must be considered in the light of his own experiences, attitudes, evaluations, and reactions. The speech therapist's part in the remedial program for the older child who stutters will be to help him build the right attitudes toward his speech differ-ences; to help him accept his pattern of speech as it now is, for the present; and to let him know how it came about and what he can do to regain normal speech.

In class, the teacher should provide the child with natural, easy, enjoyable speech outlets and give him a chance at successful speech experiences. Let him forget himself and his speech in the role-taking of creative play. He very likely will have no difficulty in choral speaking. Speaking easily in chorus with other children should help him gain confidence and satisfaction. Praise him for good work (*not* for "good speech"); for good participation; for remembering a point someone else has forgotten; and for his loyalty, courage, and sincerity. Let the stuttering child recite in class when he volunteers and encourage him to volunteer. When he recites, the teacher should not interrupt him or try to help him; she should show him she meant it when she said his "stuttering doesn't matter." He may take more time than the other children; but if the teacher shows anxiety and tries to hurry him, she will only exaggerate his problem and he will need even more time. Keep the classroom tension-free and do not pressure the stuttering child beyond his ability. Encourage him in his hobbies, special aptitudes, and interests.

In order to help the stuttering child grow into a non-stuttering man or woman, the teacher must know what methods to follow. The speech therapist can help her outline a plan of therapy in the classroom. It may be necessary to call for the help of the speech pathologist, the psychologist or psychiatrist, the social worker and, at times, the medical profession. The teacher and the speech therapist should not become discouraged and dismiss a case that appears complicated and beyond comprehension. To save a child from becoming a stuttering adult is worth the time and effort it may involve. Frequently, through the interest and understanding of the speech therapist, the teacher, and the parents, the stuttering child can develop an understanding, build right attitudes, and eventually talk himself out of his stuttering patterns of speech. It has been done and the results are worth the efforts of all concerned.

The Child with a Hearing Problem

The child with a hearing loss may have difficulties in speech. In extreme cases, when the child does not have any usable hearing, he may not develop speech unless he is given special training. Fortunately, the number of children who have complete hearing losses is comparatively small, but even the deaf child can be taught speech if he has normal intelligence and no complicating problems. Education for children with severe hearing losses usually takes place in a day or residential school for the deaf.

There are many children with partial hearing losses. They may have equal losses for all sounds, in relation to frequency or pitch, or they may be able to hear some sounds very poorly and others quite well. In the latter case, the child's hearing loss may pass undetected for years. Frequently this type of hearing loss is in the high-frequency or high-pitched sound range. Children with this type of loss may hear vowels well but may not be able to hear many of the consonants. To such children speech may sound muffled or indistinct. Hearing losses may appear in any degree, from a very minor loss to a very serious loss.

RECOGNIZING THE CHILD WITH A HEARING LOSS. In the classroom, there are certain signs by which the teacher may recognize the hard-of-hearing child. A child who answers only when he can see the teacher's face, but who does not answer otherwise, may be lipreading rather than hearing. The child who appears to be straining to hear, or who consistently turns one ear toward the speaker, may be suffering from a hearing loss. The unresponsive child, the one who does not follow spoken instructions, should have his hearing tested. The hard-of-hearing child may sometimes be a behavior problem, or he may fail to be interested because he cannot follow classroom activities. He may sit and dream, appear to be stupid, may be shy and withdrawn, or he may be an aggressive trouble-maker.

Importance of a proper diagnosis. When the teacher suspects a child has a hearing loss, she should refer him to the appropriate person in the school system; this may be the school nurse, the audiometrist, or the speech therapist. If there is no school hearing-testing program, the child should be referred to the family physician, an otologist (ear specialist), or to the nearest speech and hearing clinic. On general principles, all school children should be given hearing tests periodically. The testing should be done by someone trained in audiometric testing.

The child's hearing should be tested by the use of a standard audiometer, which has been recently checked for accuracy. The results of this audiometric test will be recorded as an audiogram, which charts the child's hearing loss in decibels (a unit of measurement in intensity). The audiogram tells us something about the kind and degree of loss the child has but does not tell us when or how it happened to develop and whether it is a permanent loss. Our facts about the hearing loss are not complete without the report and recommendations of the ear specialist. The speech therapist will wish to know if anything can be done to improve the child's hearing or to prevent additional loss. The therapist is qualified to give the audiometric test but is not qualified to make the examination and the recommendations of the otologist.

The time to consider medical or surgical treatment, if such treatment is indicated, is at the earliest possible moment. Hearing losses discovered early in life can often be corrected, or further hearing loss may be prevented. Infected ears should never be ignored or treated by means of home remedies. Early infections are usually curable, but treatment must be under the direction of the medical profession. The new drugs have made the formerly rather common mastoid operation almost obsolete. The most common ear infection of childhood is that known as otitis media (middle-ear infection). It is a frequent after-effect of influenza, measles, scarlet fever, and other diseases. Some children acquire middle-ear infection with a severe cold. Such infections should not be neglected because they can cause permanent hearing loss. The loss incurred through otitis media is of the conduction type, and the result is a more or less even loss of hearing over the frequencies.

A conduction loss may also be caused by certain organic malformations, which may be congenital or developmental in nature. The ear canal may be closed by a boney growth. The conduction loss caused by otosclerosis usually develops in later life. In this type of deafness, the last of the three little moving bones of the middle ear becomes fastened against the cochlea of the inner ear, wherein the ear nerves are located. A conduction loss may be a slight loss or may be serious enough to give consideration to the use of a hearing aid. In general, the person with a conduction loss responds well to the use of a hearing aid.

The type of loss that results in an uneven loss is known as a perceptive loss; sometimes this is referred to as a nerve loss. In this type of loss, there is damage to the nerves of the cochlea of the inner ear. The otologist can do little if anything to increase the hearing of the person suffering from a perceptive loss. If the auditory nerve that runs from the cochlea to the brain is damaged, complete deafness is the result. Injury to the nerves in the hearing centers of the brain can also cause deafness. In most cases, perceptive losses are only partial losses because some of the nerves of the cochlea will be undamaged. The different types of hearing losses cause the development of different types of problems. This the speech therapist must recognize and understand in order that adequate therapy may be planned.

REMEDIAL PROCEDURES: THE HEARING AID. If everything has been done, from a medical or surgical viewpoint, to improve the child's hearing and if the loss is of such a nature to warrant it, consideration should be given to the possibilities of a hearing aid. Recommendations for the use of an aid should come only from persons qualified to make such a recommendation: the ear specialist, otologist, audiologist, or audiometrist, or from a college or university hearing clinic. As has been stated, the child with a conduction loss will usually respond well to the use of a hearing aid. The child with a nerve involvement may not respond as well, but an aid may be helpful even in this type of loss.

In many cases, with the use of a hearing aid, a hard-of-hearing child can continue his education in the regular school classroom. In some instances, it may be necessary to give the child a period of auditory training so that he may learn to use his hearing aid efficiently. If the child's type and degree of hearing loss indicates the need for an aid, it is important that he be taught to use one as soon as possible. It is usually easier for the young child to adjust to the use of a hearing aid than it is for the adolescent or the adult to adjust to one. The earlier the child accepts the hearing aid, the more likely he is to retain normal or near-normal speech.

SPEECH AND AUDITORY TRAINING. The child should be taught how to care for his aid, how to check and change the batteries and the cord of the aid, and how to adjust the volume and in some instances the frequency. Both the teacher and the speech therapist should be acquainted with these simple mechanics of the aid in order that they may give quick assistance to the child if something goes wrong with his aid. The training program that the speech therapist plans for the child will include both speech training and "hearing" training. A child who has had a hearing loss for a number of years may have forgotten some of the speech sounds and some of the noises of the world. He may have to be taught to listen and to interpret what he hears. In his speech training, he may be hearing some of the speech sounds for the first time. Speech as he hears it through his aid or through the use of other amplification may be entirely different from speech as he hears it otherwise. He may have to learn to listen to and interpret this new speech with his "new ear." He may have to learn to use sounds he has been omitting; he may have to learn new productions for sounds that he has been distorting, and he may have to correct sound substitutions. Since children with hearing losses frequently have voice problems as well as articulatory problems, he may also have to work to develop and maintain a pleasant speaking voice. In addition, the speech therapist and the teacher may have to cope with delayed language development and mispronunciation of words. In helping the hardof-hearing child to improve or correct his speech, the therapist will use many of the same techniques and methods used with children who have articulatory and/or voice problems. The goal is to attain and maintain as normal a pattern of speech as possible. Unless there are children in the school with similar hearing losses, the work with the hard-of-hearing child may necessarily be individual to some extent. However, group therapy is often important since many hard-of-hearing children have a tendency to withdraw from group activities and to develop a preference for isolated work and play situations. They need opportunities for social development.

TRAINING IN SPEECH READING (LIPREADING). Sometimes a hearing aid will not give a child complete hearing satisfaction, and he may have to depend upon speech reading as a supplementary aid to the understanding of speech. The speech therapist is usually qualified to help the child in learning to lipread. Quite frequently, the therapist will combine the training in speech with training in speech reading. The child learns to "hear with his eyes." The term *speech reading* has recently come to be used in place of the term *lipreading*, because more than mere *lip*reading is involved. The child is taught to watch all the changes of expression that take place, including general movements and gestures as well as the actions of the lips.

There may be children who have hearing losses that are not considered severe enough for the use of a hearing aid or children with losses who cannot benefit from the use of an aid. These children may need speech training and speech reading, depending upon the type and degree of loss and upon adequacy of speech. If the speech therapist decides that some children with minor hearing losses do not need special training, this does not mean that the child is not to be included in the speech program. Such children will take part in the speech activities planned for speech improvement. They should also receive periodic hearing tests and their speech should be reevaluated periodically.

In the classroom. The teacher places the child who is hard of hearing in the classroom so that he may easily see the teacher's face; the light should fall upon the teacher's face, not upon the child's. The teacher should not talk loudly to the child but should stand near him and speak normally. The child should be watched to see if he understands and follows directions. If the child uses a hearing aid, he should be given an opportunity to show the aid to the class and tell how it operates. The teacher can help the child to be proud of his hearing aid, to make it a mark of distinction, rather than something he wears unwillingly. The hard-of-hearing child profits from good teaching in a friendly, busy classroom just as other children do. He should be encouraged to take part in the activities of the classroom and should be helped to accept the obligations involved in group participation.

How the parents can help. The parents should not shout to the hard-of-hearing child but should speak normally, raising neither the intensity nor the pitch of the voice. Speech should be distinct and pleasant, and the speaker should remain within the child's vision. Sometimes the audiologist cannot tell exactly how much hearing the very young child has. It is important that parents talk to the child who they think is deaf, even when he is a very young child. Never leave the child out of the conversation of the family. Direct speech to him and check to see that he understands. The parents of the hard-of-hearing or deaf child have much home training to do over the years, and this training must begin as soon as a hearing loss is first suspected. Not only must there be training in speech and speech reading, but there must also be training in child development just as the hearing child receives such training.

The child with a hearing loss must be helped to grow up as normally as possible; parents may not be able to restore his hearing, as they might wish to do, but they can help even the deaf child to grow into a happy, self-sufficient member of society.

The Child with Cerebral Palsy

The condition of cerebral palsy is related to damage to the central nervous system (the nerves of the brain and the spinal cord). The injury may occur during the prenatal period, at the time of birth, or after birth as the result of an injury or very high fever. The condition interferes with the normal control of the motor system of the body. The three main types of cerebral palsy most often differentiated are spaticity, athetosis, and ataxia. The effects of cerebral palsy differ according to the location and extent of the injury. Phelps (11) describes states of "true spasticity" and of "pure athetosis," and it is possible that there may be mixed types in some cases. If the damage is too extensive the child does not live.

The spastic type of cerebral palsy results in a clinical picture that includes a variable amount of motor deficit and a hypertension of muscles. Athetosis is manifested by abnormal movements of the muscles, and ataxia results in a lack of control and coordination with a loss in speed and direction of motion. The child with the athetoid type of cerebral palsy frequently has hearing involvements, and the child with the ataxia type frequently has visual defects.

The exact number of cerebral palsied children in the United States is not known. In December, 1946, forty-three state registers of crippled children showed a total of 36,000 children under twenty-one years of age whose disability was diagnosed as cerebral palsy (12). All children afflicted with cerebral palsy do not have speech defects. Wolfe (17) found that 70 per cent of fifty cerebral palsied subjects studied had inadequate articulation. Palmer (10) reported the extent of communicative problems as having an incidence of from 65 to 75 per cent. While some cerebral palsied children have no speech defects, others have slight or moderate speech difficulties, and still others have serious speech involvements. The condition may result in mental deficiency, but this is not necessarily the case. A child may have a severe or moderate cerebral palsied condition with speech involvements and yet retain normal intelligence. A child suffering from a severe cerebral palsied condition is not seen by the speech therapist and the teacher in the public schools. Frequently, however, when the involvements are not too great, the child may attend the public schools.

IMPORTANCE OF A PROPER DIAGNOSIS. The problems of the child afflicted with cerebral palsy require teamwork planning that will frequently enlist the services of the physician, the physical therapist, the occupational therapist, and the educational specialists. It is important that the speech therapist and the teacher consult and cooperate with the various specialists, since a wrong approach to speech therapy or educational methods may prove unsuccessful or even injurious to the child. The different types of cerebral palsy require at times distinctly different types of therapy, and because the teacher and the speech therapist are not qualified to carry out the necessary diagnostic procedures they often need help in planning the various types of therapy needed.

THE SPEECH PROGRAM. The cerebral palsied child should be encouraged at an early age to develop rhythmical sounds. Rhythm can be developed through the use of rhymes, poetry, musical instruments, recordings, and rhythmical body movements. In some cases, it may be advantageous to use an artificial respirator in developing more rhythmical speech and breathing patterns. This type of training must necessarily be given by a speech therapist trained in the use of this special technique. It is a new technique being used only at a few speech clinics at present, but it promises help for certain types of cerebral palsied children. There will be children who will need an extensive amount of individual speech help over a long period of times, others may need individual speech therapy for a shorter period, and still others may be able to profit best from group therapy alone. Whenever possible, the child should be included in some group activities, even if this must be supplemented by individual therapy. The cerebral palsied child needs to share with others and to work with others toward a common goal. These children are frequently isolated and lonely and in need of social development.

The speech program must of course start with the child's present abilities and build upon these. The child should be encouraged to work for better speech, but perfect speech should not be demanded of him. The child may give up trying to improve his speech if the task is made too hard for him. The ultimate goal is improvement in speech, not perfection. When poor speech patterns are related to abnormal rhythm patterns in speech and breathing, the physical therapist may be able to help in establishing more adequate breathing and speech rhythm patterns.

The spastic child will need to be taught to use his muscular control to better advantage. The jerky movements of the spastic child are likely to be tense. Since all of his muscles are not involved in the spastic condition, he must be taught to compensate for the abnormal behavior of those muscles that cannot be adequately controlled. In this training of muscles, the physical therapist, the occupational therapist, and the speech therapist all have important roles; and their work is frequently coordinated.

The child with the athetoid type of cerebral palsy may be delayed for a long time in speech development. His many uncontrolled movements may make his speech appear slow and labored. The ataxic child may also be delayed in speech development. He may make no recognizable efforts to use speech for the first several years of his life. He may have difficulties in walking and may frequently lose his sense of balance. His movements are likely to be poorly coordinated and his speech may suffer proportionally. In planning speech therapy material for the ataxic child, large simple pictures and words should be used if the child has a visual problem.

The speech development of the child is, of course, only one important part of his total pattern of development. The teacher and the speech therapist might do well to work for speech improvement along with improvement in writing, spelling, reading, and other school subject matter. Some children will have articulatory difficulties, some will have only voice problems, and others may have both articulatory and voice problems. Frequently the young child also has a language problem. Plans for therapy will take into consideration the specific needs of each child. A great amount of attention may have to be given to the correct production of sounds. Sometimes this is to be approached directly by working for phonetic placement, and sometimes the remedial work must be approached indirectly. The speech therapist may experiment to a degree to see what works for a certain child but should consult with the specialists to make sure that nothing is done that may be harmful to the child. There are definite methods to be used in each case; and if the speech therapist feels unsure of the type of therapy to be applied, he may find it possible to ask for help at the nearest college or university speech clinic. Westlake (16) has prepared a set of procedures that are helpful in planning speech therapy, and Cruickshank (3) has an entire book that is devoted to the individual and community problems of the cerebral palsied child.

How THE PARENTS CAN HELP. Remedial procedures for the child with cerebral palsy begin long before he becomes school age. The parents have a great responsibility in the training of their child and should encourage him to make sounds and to talk at an early age. The parents should accept any kind of speech that he may happen to use in the beginning, even if this be only noises, babbling, and speech that cannot be understood. The parents should talk to the child, read him stories, and sing with him. It does not matter how the child sings; he may sing "la-la-la" or "da-da-da."

Sometimes it is possible to get certain sounds by this type of singing that cannot be accomplished in any direct manner of sound placement. Pictures, objects, a mirror, and electrical recordings may be helpful in developing speech. We often recommend that the parent make a speech scrapbook or a "speech box," filled with pictures that interest the child. "Lessons" can be the repeated "reading" of the book and new pictures can be added. The speech box can be filled with small objects and toys that interest the child and are related to his daily experiences. Play "speech games," but keep the material used on the level of the child's ability. The child should not be pressured in speech but should be encouraged in his efforts, whatever they may be. Encourage meaningful gestures. Keep speech play periods short in length and avoid fatigue. Enlist the help of the specialists and follow their suggestions.

It is important that we give the cerebral palsied child as many varied experiences as possible. He may be hungry for knowledge, and because of his physical handicap be limited in his opportunities for learning. Take the child visiting; introduce him to new friends, new ideas, new places and activities. Give him something to talk about and some need and reason for talking; and then listen to what he has to say, even if he cannot always be understood.

Those who are associated with the child should watch their own speech when speaking to the child or within the child's hearing. It is necessary to speak carefully and clearly. It may be wise to use short, simple phrases and words that the child understands, but do not neglect working for a larger vocabulary. Encourage speech, accept it as his best at the present time, but let him feel that he will surely improve. He should never suspect that it may be a long and tedious process.

Remember that there are many other things this child can be taught to do for himself. Too often, parents are likely to be overprotective and may do too much for the child. The child is being cheated in his personal development when he is not allowed and even urged to do all that he is capable of doing for himself, and this may be much more than the parent thinks he can do. The parent will have to be very patient and willing to devote many hours to the training process. Above all, the parent must accept the child. Over-protection may in some cases be only a case of rejection in disguise. At times, it is impossible for the parent to know whether or not he is honestly accepting the child. In case the parent is concerned about this, he should consult with a qualified psychologist. A little more understanding of himself and of the child may aid tremendously in helping the child to develop to the best of his ability. Cerebral palsied children, as do all children, need love, attention, guidance, and understanding. But most of all, they need to be accepted.

The Child with a Cleft Palate

Help for the child with a cleft palate and/or cleft lip begins with helping the parents to understand the problem when the child is very young. The first thing the parent usually asks is, "Why should this happen to my child?" The parent can honestly be told, "We don't know." Actually, there is no known cause of the malformation known as cleft palate and/or cleft lip. Research and clinical observation suggests that one or more causal factors may be related to the condition. These include genetic factors (related to heredity), dietary factors (in relation to the mother), febrile disease during early pregnancy, and the RH factor. The condition develops during the early prenatal period and is the result of the failure of the palate and/or lip to join in the midline. The parents should understand that personal blame can be placed on no one. The mother must be helped to understand this, if she has developed a sense of guilt and blames herself for the child's condition. A child with a cleft palate and/or lip can appear in any family. It occurs in approximately 1 of every 800 live births.

The cleft may appear as a complete or partial opening of the bones of the hard palate, the bones of the face that hold the upper teeth, the tissues of the roof of the mouth, the muscles of the soft palate, the upper lip, and the floor, bones, or septum of the nose. There may be a simple cleft of the lip alone (harelip); a simple cleft of the palate; or a complete cleft through the palate, lip, and nose; or any degree or combination of these clefts. A severe cleft may include a double cleft of the lip. Sometimes there is only a slight malformation such as a small cleft in the soft palate or perhaps only a shortening of the soft palate.

PROCEDURES AND CARE. The care of the child with a cleft palate and/or cleft lip is a problem for a team of specialists. This team includes the surgeon, the plastic surgeon, the dentist, the orthodontist, the prosthodontist, the speech therapist, the otolaryngologist, the psychologist, the educator, and at times the social worker. Since in most instances the need for surgery is apparent, it is important to understand the latest developments in cleft-palate surgery and the possibilities that may be achieved through the services of the prosthodontist and the orthodontist.

Attitudes of the specialists toward early surgery for the repair of the cleft palate have changed in recent times. It was formerly believed that in all cases the openings should be closed at the earliest possible moment. The resulting dental, speech, aesthetic, and psychological problems that often appeared were disregarded. Early operations on cleft palates may interfere disastrously with the subsequent growth of the facial skeleton. As a result, teeth may be disarranged and muscle relationships become abnormal. Scarred tissues may interfere with proper movement. Secondary deformities may result from improper surgical and dental treatment. There may be an arrested development of the head, face, mouth, dental malocclusion, and disturbed speech development.

The best time for surgical treatment must be decided by the plastic surgeon and the pediatrician trained in the treatment of cleft-palate children. Research during the past ten years at university speech clinics and at cooperating medical centers seems to indicate that in many cases the surgical repair of the cleft palate may be delayed in part or wholly until between the third or fifth year. This delay allows for more normal growth and development of the jaw, teeth, and facial bones. Consequently, the face is often less deformed, the teeth come in more normally, and speech is more adequate. The cleft lip is usually repaired early, but the decision for time of operation here also must rest with the specialists who understand the latest developments in cleft-palate and/or lip surgery.

In cases where the palate has been left open in order to encourage a more normal development of the facial bones, or if surgery has not been successful, or if there remains an opening or short palate, it is often possible for the prosthodontist to design a light palatal appliance known as an obturator (a false plate that covers the opening) that may encourage more normal speech development.

Each cleft-palate child should receive a thorough study as early as possible by the team of specialists suggested; and then a proper program of surgical repair, orthodontia, prosthodontia, dental care, and speech therapy can be outlined. There are several cleft-palate clinics connected with universities and medical and dental colleges in the United States where the team approach is practiced. When adequate study of the patient is undertaken early enough (in infancy), decisions can be reached that will reduce the number of unsuccessful surgical rehabilitation cases, which have been common until recent years.

When damage has already been done and the facial contour is abnormal, the orthodontist, the prosthodontist and the plastic surgeon can often be of help in bringing about a more satisfactory facial profile. Sometimes the repair work for the child with a cleft palate and/or lip may be continued over a period of years. The speech therapist, the teacher, and the parents must not assume that everything has been done for the child until adequate examinations have been made and recommendations have been carried through to completion.

PROGRAM OF SPEECH THERAPY. The case of the cleft-palate child does not end with surgical repair and with the work of the orthodontist, prosthodontist, or dentist. The speech therapist, the teacher, and the parents have a long-time program in speech therapy and personality development to plan and carry out. The speech therapist must work closely with the specialists and with the classroom teacher and parents. Successful therapy will endeavor to make the child acceptable in appearance, in speech, and in personal adjustment.

We frequently find a hearing loss in cleft-palate cases, because the child is more susceptible to throat and middle-ear infections. Periodic audiometric tests are essential, and referral should be made for an examination by a specialist when hearing losses are found. If the loss persists and is great enough to interfere with the development of speech, speech therapy should include procedures similar in some instances to those used in training the hard-of-hearing child.

In considering the speech difficulties of the child with a cleft palate and/or lip, we find that there is no such thing as "cleft palate speech." Each child is affected in speech development according to the degree of injury and according to a number of related factors such as adequacy of speech stimulation, degree of intelligence, and opportunities for normal development. The child may have only a slight speech difficulty, he may have very defective speech, or any degree of defect between these two extremes may exist. There may be a disturbance in the ability to produce many sounds, hypernasality of voice, and substitution or distortion of sounds.

It is important that speech be understandable and within as normal a range in voice quality and sound production as possible. Fortunately, the often inadequate speech of the child with a cleft palate can be improved. Responsibility for the actual speech program falls upon the speech therapist. Following the recommendations of the surgeon, the orthodontist, dentist, otolaryngologist, and prosthodontist, the speech therapist sets up the speech program for the child and adjusts the methods in articulation and voice procedures to suit the child's needs. To this end, many of the procedures used in correcting errors in articulation and in voice will be adaptable to the speech needs of the child with a cleft palate and/or lip. In addition, there will be muscle training of the lip and palate as need may indicate.

The results of recent research suggest that the speech therapist should not employ all the techniques mentioned in earlier literature concerning speech therapy for the child with a cleft palate. In the past, much time has been wasted on blowing exercises, which were supposedly for directing air through the mouth and strengthening the muscles of the soft palate. Since we do not speak as we "blow," more acceptable therapy is concerned with directing the flow of air through the mouth in a less forceful manner, and with teaching the proper use of the mouth and throat as resonators. The child may need to be helped to make an adequate oral-nasal closure by raising the soft palate and bringing the pharyngeal wall (back of the throat) forward. Sometimes the child can make the closure, but cannot use it in continuous speech. Unless a closure can be approximated, the voice is likely to remain nasal in quality. The use of an obturator may help some children who are unable to make a closure because of the organic defect. The ear must be trained to hear the difference between the nasal and the denasal sounds, and the muscles must be trained to feel the difference. It will also be necessary to work for adequate tongue and lip movements. The quality of the voice will depend to a great extent upon adequate production of the vowel sounds, and better production of the consonant sounds should also bring improved articulation and improved voice quality.

It may not be possible for the child to make all sounds exactly as the speech therapist thinks the sounds should be produced. Compensations should be accepted, but the therapist should be sure these are the best compensations possible for the particular child. The goal is the best possible acceptable speech. The therapist should accept each

stage of speech development as the best the child can produce at the present time. He should encourage the child
but should not place undue pressure upon him.

The child with a cleft palate should be given individual
speech training when this need is indicated and should also
be included in group therapy activities. Such a child often
needs to be encouraged in group participation. He can become inconspicuous in his efforts to gain better speech in
the creative-play activities and in the choral reading groups.
He will react favorably to criticism offered the group as a
whole, and speech development and improvement can become a pleasant program for him. Group activities in speech
development allow for situations in which the child can
practice and carry over the techniques taught to him in his
individual therapy sessions.

HOW THE PARENT CAN HELP. It is not hard to understand
the unhappiness of parents when they are first notified that
their child has a cleft palate. It is very important that the
parents receive proper counseling at this time. The disturbed muscular efficiency of the palate, lip, and other tissues
may bring problems of malnutrition and may upset the
functions of sucking, chewing, swallowing, and breathing,
as well as interfere with the speech and personality development of the child. The cosmetic results of a cleft may also
interfere with the adequate growth of the child's personality.
The speech therapist, the teacher, and the parents can help
the child develop a pleasing personality regardless of the
fact that he has a cleft palate and/or lip.

The child should be regarded as a normal child from early
infancy. His parents should help him to understand and
accept his difference. Their objective attitude can do much
to help him socialize with other children and adults. When
other children ask, "What's the matter with your face?" the
parents can teach the child to take such questioning without
emotion and have an explanatory response ready: "I was
born with an opening in my lip (or the roof of my mouth).
This happens sometimes and no one knows exactly why it

happens. But the doctor and the dentist are helping to make things better."

Delayed Speech and Speech Retardation

The terms *delayed speech* and *retarded speech* appear to be used interchangeably by many authorities in speech pathology and speech therapy. In his glossary of terms, Wood (18) defines delayed speech as a "failure of speech to develop at the expected age; usually due to slow maturation, hearing impairment, brain injury, mental retardation, or emotional disturbance" (p. 54), and retarded speech is described as "slowness in speech development in which intelligibility is severely impaired; often preceded by late or delayed emergence of speech" (p. 64). We prefer to make a more specific distinction between the two terms. We will consider *delayed speech* as a mode of speaking that does not meet the expected level of speech for a child of normal intelligence and of a given chronological age. *Retarded speech* shall be used to describe the abnormal speech of the child who is mentally retarded. In the words of Kirk (7):

The term *mental retardation* is used with many meanings. It does not describe a disease like tuberculosis; it describes a condition. It is a general term referring to all degrees of retarded mental development. . . . A child who is mentally retarded may be one who does not make normal progress in school. . . . Another child referred to as mentally retarded may be helpless all his life (p. 8).

According to our definition, the child with retarded speech may have articulatory problems and/or vocal difficulties but will also be retarded in language development to a greater or lesser degree. His lack of normal speech and language development is related to his mental retardation, but other causal factors may also be involved. When no other causal factors are present, a child can be expected to develop speech and language on a level related to his degree of mental maturity. It is quite possible, however, that factors other than mental retardation are to be considered. The mentally retarded child may be further handicapped by psychological, physical, or organic involvements. He may be entirely without speech, this condition being caused by severe mental retardation; at other times the degree of retardation may not be great enough to account for the total absence of speech.

The term *delayed speech* is a generality that leaves much to be desired in understanding the actual speech perform-ance of the child, the related causal factors involved in his speech deficiency, and the individual child's present speech needs. At times, the speech examiner may be prone to use the label "delayed speech" when he finds himself unable to analyze or diagnose more adequately the child's speech difficulties and the factors related to the problem. The term is so general and so all-inclusive that it tells us nothing much except that a given child's speech performance does not equal that which is expected of him. The child who is delayed in speech may retain infantile speech mannerisms. He may say, "Me no dot no woller kates," meaning, "I have no roller skates." He may be delayed in vocabulary and language usage but not for reasons of mental retardation. He may have a large vocabulary and sentences of adequate length but may use many sound substitutions, distortions, and omissions. In extreme cases, the child may be practically without speech and yet be normal in intelligence. Such a child, known as an "aphasic" child, may be brain injured but not in the sense that the cerebral palsied child is injured. The motor coordination may be normal, but the brain injury affects the speech centers in such a way that the child may neither receive and understand speech nor be able to express himself in speech.

Extensive damage to the brain may also result in mental retardation. When this happens, we will refer to the child as "retarded in speech." Some "aphasic" children can under-stand speech, but cannot express themselves in speech. Reading and writing difficulties may also be present. The "aphasic" child will require special training under the direc-tion of a qualified speech therapist. The classroom teacher rarely sees such a child because he is not enrolled in the public schools, at least not for any length of time.

THERAPY FOR THE CHILD WITH DELAYED SPEECH. Since almost any kind of abnormal speech used by the young child within the range of normal intelligence may come under the label of "delayed speech," we are scarcely able to outline a specific procedure of therapy applicable to any or all of the difficulties. In general, the principles used in speech development, improvement, and correction for the young child apply here, but related factors must also be carefully considered. One child may require treatment that is entirely different from that which another child may require. We may be quite sure that the child will improve in speech as he is ready to improve, physically, organically, emotionally, and intellectually. We may also be sure that his rate of improvement will be directly related to environmental conditions and to his personal adjustment and his motivation to speak. In most cases, it is important to provide for group participation with children of his age level. In the group situation, the approach to speech development and improvement should in most cases follow the nondirective methods, applying speech stimulation, criticism, and correction to the group as a whole in an unobtrusive manner along with the well-planned group activities. The speech therapist can watch the performance of each particular child during the group activities, and frequently cues can be accumulated that will aid in training the child during his individual sessions if these are necessary.

THERAPY FOR THE CHILD WITH RETARDED SPEECH. Under our definition of retarded speech, we can accept the fact that mental retardation is a related factor but not overlook the possibility of other related factors. We will recognize that there are children who are mentally retarded who have no perceptible speech defects and will study the retarded child as carefully as we study the child who is within the range of normal intelligence. The retarded child is a member of our society; and our teachers, schools, and society are under an obligation to help him live as useful and happy a life as possible. Mental retardation is, we know, a matter of degree; if the norm were an I.Q. of 145, many more of us would be considered "mentally retarded"! The degrees of mental retardation range from very low mental ability to almost normal ability. For convenience, we may separate the mentally retarded into three groups: the educable, the trainable, and the totally dependent individuals. The speech therapist is certainly justified in putting forth time and effort to help the educable mentally retarded child.

Questions are raised at times as to whether or not the speech therapist should spend time with children in the trainable group. It is possible that such a practice has been criticized because of the shortage of qualified speech therapists. It may be more important to help children with normal intelligence who have speech defects, but let us suppose we had available all the special teachers and speech therapists that were needed. Society's goals in helping the trainable mentally retarded child are to train him to be as self-sufficient as possible in caring for his personal needs; as socially adjusted as possible, in order that he may live as comfortably as possible with his associates; and as economically useful as possible, in order that he may to some degree contribute to his personal maintenance. Helping the trainable child gain as adequate speech as possible contributes to the attainment of these goals.

The totally dependent individuals are frequently without speech or are severely retarded in speech development. In these cases the work of the speech therapist might well be considered a waste of time and effort. Totally dependent individuals will need constant custodial care.

Speech development, improvement, and correction techniques for the first two categories will depend upon the individual child's ability to cooperate and upon the possibilities of alleviating any relating factors. The educable mentally retarded child's progress will be slower than that of the normal child and he will not be able to reach the academic level of the normal child. It is quite likely, however, that his speech will be normal, barring any physical, organic, or psychological abnormalities. When the educable mentally retarded child has speech difficulties, these can be corrected by using methods similar to the ones used in helping the child of normal intelligence. We can expect progress to be slow and we can expect his vocabulary and language usage to be more limited. It is important that we do not pressure him in his speech development beyond the limits of his present mental ability. Urging a child to perform in a manner that is beyond his capacity may bring complicating psychological problems that further impede his growth and development.

The speech and language development of the trainable mentally retarded child will be limited to a much greater extent than that of the educable child. The trainable child is more likely to have speech defects and is much less likely to respond to remedial treatment. Some corrective procedures are likely to be a waste of time and effort, but it will be profitable to provide opportunities for developing speech and for growth in language. This will mean that we will stimulate the child with speech; we will talk with him; arrange for him to work and play with other children in a sheltered-workshop situation; and develop as much speech as possible through the use of group speech activities, music, rhythmic movement, and group singing, utilizing objects and experiences within the child's understanding. The main objective is to keep the child interested and to help him to develop his potentialities to the utmost of his ability in speech as well as in his capacity to care for himself and to learn constructively to perform simple tasks.

How the Parents Can Help. The parent has three important responsibilities in relation to the retarded child: (a) to accept the child in the light of his present abilities, (b) to determine the degree of retardation of the child, with the cooperation of the psychologist, and (c) to love and care for the child and to carry out a recommended program of training procedures.

It is very difficult for parents to accept the fact that they have a mentally retarded child. If repeated psychological examinations administered by a qualified psychologist, over a period of time, definitely indicate that the child is mentally retarded, then the parents must be helped to accept the fact. In the case of the trainable child and the totally dependent child, the parents must be helped to understand and accept the type of program that will be the best for the child, even if this program will include institutionalization. A complete study of the family situation and of the child's capabilities is necessary in making final decisions. The psychologist, the physician, the social worker, and the minister can be of assistance in helping the parent to realize his responsibilities. Quite frequently the speech therapist is involved in these decisions and is called upon to assist in making recommendations. Unfortunately, parents of retarded children frequently think that everything would be quite adequate if only the child could "learn to speak correctly." They must be led to realize that the problems of mental retardation are not limited to speech problems. Although it is a shock to parents to be told that they have a retarded child, most parents, when they understand and accept the facts, rise to the situation and do their utmost to help the child adjust to his place in life.

Local, state, and national interest in the retarded child is expanding rapidly. The various specialists engaged in experimentation and research are trying to help this type of child as they search for methods of preventing retardation whenever possible. Only the future will show how much can be done, and the speech therapist and pathologist will have their part in the research and educational practices undertaken.

It may be a matter of time before there are enough trained teachers and speech therapists to meet the needs of children in relation to speech development, improvement, and correction. However, in our democratic society, emphasis is being placed upon giving service to the child according to his individual needs. As the Midcentury White House Con-

ference on Children and Youth (14) has stated, in part, in
its Pledge to Children:

To you, our children, who hold within you our most cherished hopes,
we . . . make this pledge: From your earliest infancy we give you
our love, so that you may grow with trust in yourself and in others.
We will recognize your worth as a person and we will help you to
strengthen your sense of belonging. We will respect your right to be
yourself and at the same time help you to understand the rights of
others, so that you may experience cooperative living. We will help
you to develop initiative and imagination, so that you may have the
opportunity freely to create. We will encourage your curiosity and
your pride in workmanship, so that you may have the satisfaction that
comes from achievement. We will provide the conditions for wholesome play that will add to your learning, to your social experience, and
to your happiness. . . . We will work to rid ourselves of prejudice
and discrimination, so that together we may achieve a truly democratic
society. . . . We will provide you with rewarding educational opportunities, so that you may develop your talents and contribute to a
better world. . . . We will intensify our search for new knowledge in
order to guide you more effectively as you develop your potentialities.
As you grow from child to youth to adult . . . we will work with you
to improve conditions for all children and youth (p. 28).

Realizing that this pledge to children is particularly applicable to parents and to all teachers of children, we now
turn our attention to the methods and materials that can be
used by the classroom teacher and the speech therapist in
their efforts to make it possible for all children to develop
speech to the best of their individual abilities.

Bibliography

1. AXLINE, V. M. *Play Therapy.* Boston: Houghton Mifflin Co., 1947.
2. BACKUS, O. L., and BEASLEY, J. *Speech Therapy with Children.* New
   York: Houghton Mifflin Co., 1951.
3. CRUICKSHANK, W. M., and RAUS, G. M. *Cerebral Palsy: Its Individual
   and Community Problems.* New York: Syracuse University Press, 1955.
4. FAIRBANKS, G. *Voice and Articulation Drillbook.* New York: Harper
   and Brothers, 1940.
5. JOHNSON, W. "Perceptual and Evaluational Factors in Stuttering,"
   Chapter 28 in Travis, L. E. (ed.), *Handbook of Speech Pathology.* New
   York: Appleton-Century-Crofts, Inc., 1957.

6. JOHNSON, W., BROWN, S. F., CURTIS, J. F., EDNEY, C. W., and KEASTER, J. *Speech Handicapped School Children*, rev. ed. New York: Harper and Brothers, 1956.

7. KIRK, S. A., KARNES, M. B., and KIRK, W. D. *You and Your Retarded Child*. New York: The Macmillan Co., 1958.

8. MCCARTHY, D. "Language Development in Children," Chapter 9 in Carmichael, L. (ed.), *Manual of Child Psychology*. New York: John Wiley and Sons, Inc., 1954.

9. MURRAY, E. "Speech Personality and Social Change," *Journal of Higher Education*, 12, No. 4 (April, 1941), 185-190.

10. PALMER, M. F. "Speech Therapy in Cerebral Palsy," *The Journal of Pediatrics*, 40, Nos. 3, 4, 5 (March, April, May, 1952). Reprint: Research Council of the United Cerebral Palsy Association, Inc., Second Symposium on Cerebral Palsy, pp. 68-78.

11. PHELPS, W. M. ."Description and Differentiation of Types of Cerebral Palsy," *The Nervous Child*, 8, No. 2 (April, 1949), 107-127.

12. ——. *The Farthest Corner*. Chicago: The National Society for Crippled Children and Adults, Inc., 1948, pp. 2-23.

13. ROGERS, C. L. *Counseling and Psychotherapy*. Boston: Houghton Mifflin Co., 1942.

14. RICHARDS, E. A., ed. *Proceedings of the Midcentury White House Conference on Children and Youth*. Raleigh, N. C.: Health Publications Institute, Inc., 1951.

15. THOMPSON, G. G. *Child Psychology*. Boston: Houghton Mifflin Co., 1952.

16. WESTLAKE, H. A. *System for Developing Speech With Cerebral Palsied Children*. Columbus, Ohio: Society for Crippled Children. Reprint of issues, *The Crippled Child*. Chicago: National Society for Crippled Children and Adults (June, August, December, 1951).

17. WOLFE, W. B. "A Comprehensive Evaluation of Fifty Cases of Cerebral Palsy," *Journal of Speech and Hearing Disorders*, 15, No. 3 (September, 1950), 234-251.

18. WOOD, K. S. "Terminology and Nomenclature," Chapter 2 in Travis, L. E. (ed.), *Handbook of Speech Pathology*. New York: Appleton-Century-Crofts, Inc., 1957.

PART II
Finding Individual Speech Needs

Section A

KEEPING INDIVIDUAL
RECORDS

Illustrating the Testing Method

In attempting to determine the individual child's speech problems, it is important that the examiner make as accurate a judgment as possible of the child's ability to produce sounds and combinations of sounds and evaluate the child's adequacy of voice production. If the child is too immature or if he does not respond adequately to the test sentences, the examiner may use the picture test to bring about a desired speech response. If the child can read, the test sentences or the test paragraphs may be used. The order of the test pictures and sentences follows the order of the sounds on the check sheet ("Record of Individual Speech Needs," pp. 146–47). In checking individual speech errors, check only one sound at a time. Note whether an error is made in the initial, medial, or final position of the word; check also the use of consonant blends. If a substitution is used for the sound being tested, place the substitution used in the space provided. If the sound is omitted, mark "omitted"; if the sound is distorted, indicate this.

An Example. Suppose "s" is the sound being tested.

The sentence read is: Sing a song of sixpence.

If the "s" sound is given correctly when the sentence is read by the pupil, leave the spaces blank under *Initial, Medial, Final,* and *Blends,* beside No. 15, sound "s."

Suppose the pupil should read: "Thing a thong of thickth-penth." The examiner would place the substituted sound *th*

RECORD OF INDIVIDUAL SPEECH NEEDS

Name _____ Age _____ Grade _____ Address _____ Phone _____

Abnormalities of:

Lips _____ Teeth _____ Tongue _____ Nose _____ Palate _____ Jaw _____

Throat _____ Facial muscles _____ Hearing _____ Mental maturity _____

Adjustment _____

Speech Problem: Articulatory _____ Voice _____ Nonfluency _____ Other _____

Production of Speech Sounds

No.	Sound		Initial	Medial	Final	Blends
1	p					
2	b					
3	m					
4	wh	(ʍ)				
5	w					
6	f					
7	v					
8	th(thin)	(θ)				
9	th(that)	(ð)				
10	t					
11	d					
12	n					
13	l					
14	r					
15	s					
16	z					

No.	Sound		as in
26	(i)		be
27	(ɪ)		it
28	(eɪ)		day
29	(ɛ)		get
30	(æ)		bat
31	(ʌ)		cup
32	(ə)		sofa
33	(ɑ)		star
34	(ɒ)		not
35	(ɔ)		saw
36	(ʊ)		full
37	(u)		too
38	(oʊ)		hoe
39	(aʊ)		now
40	(aɪ)		ice
41	(ɔɪ)		boy

146

17	(ʃ)	sh		___
18	(ʒ)	zh		___
19	(tʃ)	ch		___
20	(dʒ)	j		___
21	(j)	y		___
22		k		___
23		g		___
24	(ŋ)	ng		___
25		h		___

Consonant Combinations

___ ___ ___ ___

Voice Production and Control

Quality	Pitch	Loudness	Time
Nasal ___	Too high ___	Too loud ___	Too fast ___
(through the nose)	Too low ___	Too weak ___	Too slow ___
Denasal ___	Abnormal	Abnormal	Staccato (jerky) ___
(M,N,ng, through mouth)	variations ___	variations ___	Drawled ___
Hard-harsh ___	Monotonous	Monotonous	Broken fluency ___
Hoarse-husky ___	pitch ___	force ___	Monotonous rate ___
Breathy ___	Adequate ___	Adequate ___	Adequate ___
Infantile ___	Other ___	Other ___	Other ___
Adequate ___			
Other ___			

Date _____   Examiner _____

_____

147

(θ) in the columns marked *Initial, Medial, Final,* and *Blends,* beside No. 15, sound "s." If the "s" sound is omitted, the examiner would mark *omitted* in the proper spaces.

Check the adequacy of voice production and control during the sentence reading or in the oral response to the pictures, and also in spontaneous conversation with the child.

In completing the records of the individual speech needs, the assistance of the school nurse or physician may be obtained. An examination record form appears in Appendix A.

Section B

SPEECH TESTING
MATERIALS

Picture Test

The picture test is to be used with children who cannot read and with those who do not respond adequately to other test procedures. The order of the pictures follows the order of the record form (pp. 146–47). In most instances the consonants are represented by three pictures each, illustrating the sound in the initial, medial, and final position if it appears in these positions in the English language. Each vowel and diphthong is represented by one picture. The pictures may be presented directly from these pages or a filmstrip of the pictures may be used.* The response may be obtained by pointing to the picture or by asking "What is this?" A question may be necessary at times to encourage a response. Suggested questions are given under certain pictures.

Above each picture is given the number of the sound on the record sheet, the phonetic symbol of the sound, and an indication of the position of the sound in the word pictured (*i*—initial, *m*—medial, *f*—final).

* Lucile Cypreansen's "Speech Testing Filmstrip," a standardized filmstrip of these pictures in color, is available from the University of Nebraska Speech and Hearing Laboratories, Lincoln, Nebraska. Artists, Muth Williams and M. J. Brodie; photography, University of Nebraska.

1. (p) *i* pig

1. (p) *m* apple

1. (p) *f* cup

2. (b) *i* book

2. (b) *m* baby

2. (b) *f* tub

3. (m) *i* man

3. (m) *m* hammer

3. (m) *f* drum

4. wh(ʍ) *i* wheel

4. wh(ʍ) *m* pinwheel

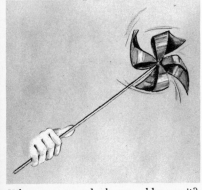

5. (w) *i* window

What goes around when you blow on it?

151

5. (w) *m* wristwatch

What kind of watch do you wear on your wrist?

6. (f) *i* fork

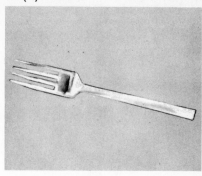

6. (f) *m* telephone

6. (f) *f* knife

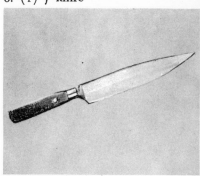

7. (v) *i* vacuum sweeper

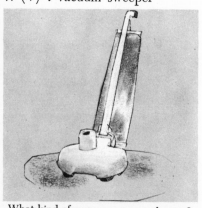

What kind of sweeper sweeps the rug?

7. (v) *m* oven

In what part of the stove do we bake the pie?

7. (v) *f* stove

8. th(θ) *i* thumb

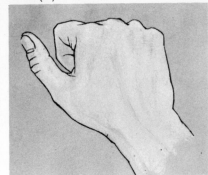

Which finger is this?

8. th(θ) *m* toothbrush

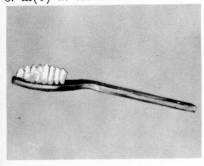

8. th(θ) *f* mouth

Where are your teeth?

9. th(ð) *m* feather

10. (t) *i* table

What does a lady wear in her hat?

10. (t) *m* butter

What do you spread on your bread?

10. (t) *f* hat

11. (d) *i* dog

11. (d) *m* candy

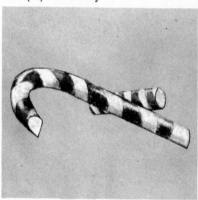

11. (d) *m* bird

12. (n) *i* nest

Where does the bird lay her eggs?

12. (n) *m* Santa Claus

12. (n) *f* chicken

13. (1) *i* lamp

What is this that gives us light?

13. (1) *m* policeman

13. (1) *f* candle

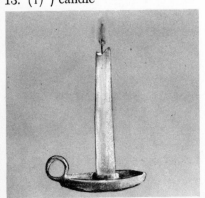

14. (r) *i* rose

What kind of flower is this?

14. (r) *m* carrot

14. (r) *f* chair

15. (s) *i* sun

What shines in the sky in the daytime?

15. (s) *m* pencil

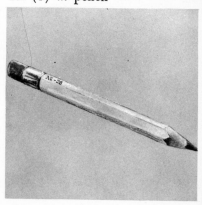

15. (s) *f* house

16. (z) *i* zipper

What do you pull to close the coat?

16. (z) *m* scissors

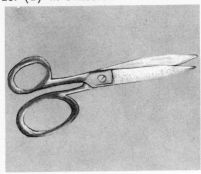

16. (z) *f* eyes

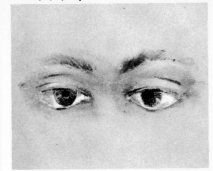

What do we see with?

17. sh(ʃ) *i* shoe

17. sh(ʃ) *m* fishing

Where is the boy going with his pole?

17. sh(ʃ) *f* brush

18. zh(ʒ) *m* television

18. zh(ʒ) f garage

Where do we put the car at night?

19. ch(tʃ) i chimney

Where does the smoke come from?

19. ch(tʃ) m highchair

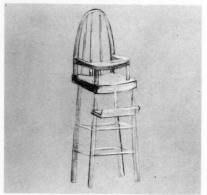

What do we call the baby's chair?

19. ch(tʃ) f match

What makes a fire when we light it?

20. j(dʒ) i jumping

What is the girl doing?

20. j(dʒ) m soldier

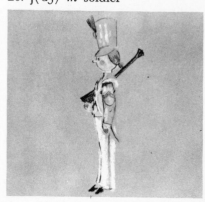

20. j(dʒ) f orange

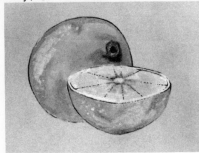

21. y(j) i yarn

What do we use when we knit a sweater?

21. y(j) m onion

What kind of a vegetable is this?

22. (k) i cat

22. (k) m basket

22. (k) f track

What does the train run on?

23. (g) *i* gun

What do we call the rifle?

23. (g) *ni* buggy

23. (g) *f* egg

24. ng(ŋ) *m* singing

What is the boy doing with the music book?

24. ng(ŋ) *f* swing

25. (h) *i* hand

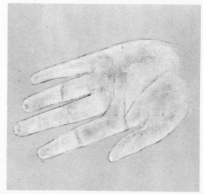

25. (h) *m* grasshopper

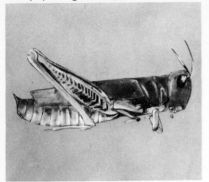

What jumps around in the grass?

26. (i) tr*ee*

27. (ɪ) Indian

28. (eɪ) c*a*ke

29. (ɛ) bread

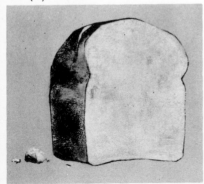

30. (æ) b*a*t

31. (ʌ) bug

What do we call a beetle?

32. (ə) banana

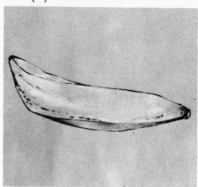

33. (ɑ) star

34. (ɒ) sock

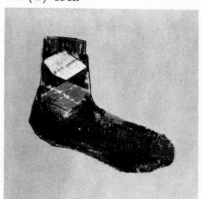

35. (ɔ) saw

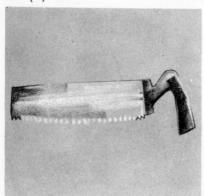

36. (ʊ) cookies

37. (u) broom

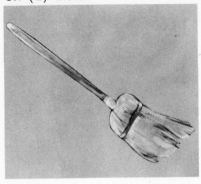

38. (ou) boat

39. (au) cow

40. (ɑɪ) ice cream

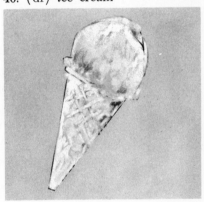

41. (ɔɪ) boy

Test Sentences for Checking Individual Speech Needs of Children Who Can Read

These sentences follow the order of the sounds on the Record of Individual Speech Needs.

(p) 1. Peter pulled Paul across the pond.
Papa will be home for supper.
Flip-flop, skip and hop around the shop.

(b) 2. Bobby called the baby bear Buster.
Bobby brought the baby to the table.
Rub-a-dub-dub, three men in a tub.

(m) 3. May gave us more milk.
Someone is coming to see Tommy.
Sam came home with Tom.

(ʍ) 4. The wheel whistles when it spins.
He saw a pinwheel somewhere in the shop.

(w) 5. We wear warm mittens in the winter time.
Everyone will use the sidewalk.

(f) 6. "Fee-fi-fo-fum," said the giant in the fairy tale.
Father had coffee for breakfast before going to the office.
"I'll huff and I'll puff," cried the wolf.

(v) 7. Van will visit Violet.
Seven covers are too heavy.
The bears live in a cave above the road.

(θ) 8. The third girl put a thimble on her finger.
Today is Arthur's birthday.
John will go north with Beth this month.

(ð) 9. The children will play with the marbles and then they will return them.
My mother, father, and brother will go together.
Bathe the baby with care.

(t) 10. He will tell the tale of Tiny Tim.
Peter likes potatoes and butter.
Put the cat in the boat.

(d) 11. Ding, dong, dell, pussy is in the deep, dark well.
The lady is ready to sing today.
Ted played with a red sled.

(n) 12. Ned needs a new knife.
He saw only a tiny pony.
Jane and Don can run fast.

(l) 13. Look at the little lake.
Lilly is playing alone with her dolly.
We will roll the ball down the hill.

(r) 14. Ruth called, "Run, Rover, run!"
Mary told a very good story.
Father saw the bear near the fire.

(s) 15. Sing a song of sixpence, and Sue will slip down the
slide.
Lucy bought a pencil at the grocery store.
Bess will meet us at the bus near her house.

(z) 16. We fed the zebra at the zoo.
It is easy to keep busy if you are not lazy.
The bees buzz around the rose.

(ʃ) 17. She will brush her shoes until they shine.
At the seashore we could see the fish splashing in the
sunshine.
I wish I could catch the fish that splash in the pool.

(ʒ) 18. To find the treasure, measure two feet from the tree and
dig.
The car is in the garage.

(tʃ) 19. Charles chose the red chair.
His teacher likes peaches.
The witch will reach for a match.

(dʒ) 20. Jack and Jill jumped down the hill.
The largest engine belongs to John.
The fudge is on the edge of the table.

(j) 21. You may use the yellow yarn.
The corn is in the field beyond the barnyard.

(k) 22. Katy can catch Kenneth.
The monkey ran across the tracks.
"Tick-tock, tick-tock," sang the old clock.

(g) 23. Grandfather gave the goat to Grace.
The boys are digging for worms again.
The big dog lies on the rag rug.

(ŋ) 24. Frank's fingers are longest, but John's are the strongest.
Red-wing sang a song the whole day long.

(h) 25. He hid the hat in the hall.
Perhaps the boys should not play behind the bee hive.

(i) 26. Each of you should eat slowly.
Please peel a peach for me.
We had tea under the peach tree.

(ɪ) 27. Isabel is ill.
The robin sings on the window sill.
This is a lovely May day.

(eɪ) 28. James is eight years of age.
Jane and Dale are playing in the rain.
Will you stay and play with May today?

(ɛ) 29. Edward may have eggs for breakfast any day.
Betty fed the red hen.

(æ) 30. An apple in the afternoon is good for Ann.
Jack put the cat on the mat.

(ʌ) 31. It is upon the shelf or under the sofa.
Cut a cup of butter into the sugar.
Run and jump over the mud puddle.

(ə) 32. The twins look alike when awake and when asleep.
Dora is sitting on the sofa eating a banana.

(ɑ) 33. Are you going to carry your arm bag?
My father has a large garden on his farm.

(ɒ) 34. The odd-numbered oxen were sold on Thursday.
Molly cannot stop the spinning top.

(ɔ) 35. Paul always is gone all day.
Mary may fall over the rug in the hall.
See-saw, Majorie Daw eats potatoes when they are raw.

(ʊ) 36. The horse pulls a full load.
The bull chased the wooly sheep.
He should look where he puts his foot.

(u) 37. The school room was not cool at noon.
You can wear your blue shoes, too.

(ou) 38. On the cliff overlooking the ocean grows a great oak tree.
Hold your coat close or you will be cold.
The wind will blow the snow so high that it will go over the fence.

(au) 39. Take an ounce of flour out of this sack.
The clown has a frown between his eyes, but a smile about his mouth.

(aɪ) 40. I like ice cream.
I can tie my white tie all by myself.
Why does Billy cry for another piece of pie?

(ɔɪ) 41. Oysters may be fried in oil.
Joyce has a pretty voice.
The boy pointed to the toy wagon.

Consonant Combinations

At times it will be noted that there is difficulty in combining consonant sounds. Checking with the following sentences will help to discover where the difficulty lies in the case of older children who are able to read the sentences. Younger children will have to be checked in consonant combinations through the use of the less complicated sentences, conversation, or the picture test.

1. What is the width of the ninth small spool?	*dth nth sm sp*	
2. The enthusiasm of his sneeze startled his host.	*zm sn st*	
3. Skating was a task for the slow twin.	*sk sl tw*	
4. She dwells in a blue playhouse in the glade.	*dw bl pl gl*	
5. The crow flies through the clear sky.	*kr fl kl*	
6. The fresh prairie breeze blew through the trees.	*fr pr br tr*	

7. The queen's dress was sprinkled with splendid diamonds.   *kw dr spr spl*

8. The street car screeched as it swung around the turn.   *str skr sw*

9. Three baby squirrels were in the nest in the shrubs.   *thr skw shr*

10. Perhaps the pig eats corncobs.   *ps ts bz*

11. The winds blew the nests of two doves from the roofs of the houses.   *dz sts vz fs*

12. The moths ate the wool cloths.   *thz ths*

13. Elsie asked the men to drill wells on both farms at once.   *ls lz mz ns*

14. When the bell rings, close your books.   *ŋz ks*

15. Ann's mother told her to buy two dozen eggs.   *nz gz*

Test Sentences for Older Children

Each of the following paragraphs is loaded with a particular consonant in its many positions, combinations, and blends. The phonetic order of these paragraphs follows that of the sounds on the Record of Individual Speech Needs.

1.   (p)   The wasp whispering near his ear gave Philip a sharp surprise. Perhaps that's why he spilled the printer's purple ink while helping to place the paper on the press. He could not help but turn the bottle topsy-turvy.

2.   (b)   It will disturb Herbert and Bob to learn that Barbara blames them for breaking her umbrella. They will feel obligated and will go to the trouble of buying her a new one.

3.   (m)   Miriam likes pumpkin pie, but when she had the mumps at the summer camp her head thumped and she was so temperamental at times that it took much prompting even to get her to drink skimmed milk.

4.　(ʍ)　The bobwhite whistled awhile in the garden, but when the cat came near, he flew away somewhere.

5.　(w)　"Work quietly between and during the air raids," the Queen warned her people. "Swarms of planes will sweep the skies from dawn until twilight. Stay by your purpose unswayingly, or we must all suffer the consequences of defeat."

6.　(f)　Frank refused to go fishing off the wharf; with a refreshing laugh, he flung himself from his surf-board and, shuffling a trifle to get his balance, floated away in elfish glee.

7.　(v)　Vera did not swerve from her decision to solve the problem by wearing the velvet gown which was a survival of the gay nineties.

8.　(θ)　One of the myths concerned three thin Ethiopians south of camp who supposedly disappeared into the ether at the ninth hour.

9.　(ð)　The mother smothered the child in clothes until he could scarcely breathe, and when he cried in discomfort she soothed him with another blanket.

10.　(t)　As the doctor stopped to call the hospital, the man entreated him to hurry; the occupants of the wrecked train were twisting in agony. Thirty were hurt in the first car.

11.　(d)　Don dreamed that he dwelt in Eden. A bald and aged angel shooed away the bees that buzzed around his head. He heaved a sigh. Could this be paradise?

12.　(n)　"No," thundered the pint-sized man, "I'll not give an inch until she makes up her mind to do her stunts." And he lunged at Blanche, but she only munched her oats in silence and moved out of range.

13.　(l)　The jungle blazed. Great flames leaped to the clouds. The sly fox, glancing an instant back, slipped swiftly away. The deer splashed through the rippling stream, and twelve bears stumbled over crackling elm branches, struggling in the battle for life. The bulk of the elephant was no hinderance to speed, and though dazzled by the fire, he could help himself to safety. The babble of the native people was heard above the crackling of the trees, and yet the rattler lay asleep near the puddle.

14. (r) He ate the crumbling bread and drank the cool water. Soon it would be dark in the great forest. Suddenly he was afraid. He feared that he would shriek and scream in fright, but at last strength returned and hope sprang eternal. He was searching for the truth! They must not disturb him in that. Thrice the angry scoundrels were upon him. He swam the midstream, hatred in his heart. He could make it before daybreak. He did not discredit their power, but he was an Earl. They might overthrow him, harm him physically, but they could not warp his soul. He had nerve, he was hard, and once across the prairie they could never apprehend him.

15. (s) The splendor of the sunset across the sky spreads sweet peace as dusk caresses the sleepy western basin. A small child, whistling on the street, stops to whisper to a squirrel, but the frisky fellow screws up his nose, snaps his jaws and hastens on his way, unswayed by the wisp of a boy. Night falls; silence waits as the breath of the wind sweeps the trees and whisks the leaves. Perhaps the breaths of ghosts are the wind, or wasps stir the air at night. Who speaks of ghosts and wasps laughs at his fears this night.

16. (z) Abe's uncle bowls on Tuesday and goes to the zoo on Wednesday. He minds chickens and farms for a living. He gives eggs to his neighbors, and one neighbor brings him clothes in return.

17. (ʃ) She asked if the dress would shrink in washing; she did not wish to buy it if it would shrink when washed.

18. (ʒ) She smeared the rouge on in good measure.

19.   (tʃ)   He was richer than any other member of the church, but he watched that no one came within an inch of his purse.

20.   (dʒ)   "Judge not that ye be not judged, for the judgment is oft unjust."

21.   (j)   The youngster played the piano so loudly that it could be heard beyond the court.

22.   (k)   The floor creaked, the mouse squeaked and scampered to the cupboard, but a hand clapped across it and a voice exclaimed, "Now I have acquired the sulking scamp." Into a box he was whisked. A dog barked, a cat's eye twinkled as he drank his milk, but after dusk the mouse went to work and gnawed his way to freedom.

23.   (g)   The lawyer struggled with the angry witness in the legal court. His anger became greater when they examined his bags; he glared at the lawyer and banged his fist upon the table.

24.   (ŋ)   She said "thanks" as he placed the ring on her finger; she blinked at its size but said, "I'm thinking I'd rather have minks." His only reply was, "I'll be hanged if I'll buy you mink."

25.   (h)   Perhaps you will be happy to hear that this is the end. Hip-Hip Hurrah!

NOTE: The twenty-five sentences above were originally prepared for Leroy T. Laase's *Speech Project and Drill Book*, 1954, pp. 204–206, and are reproduced here with the special permission of the William C. Brown Company, Publishers, Dubuque, Iowa.

PART III
Methods and Graded Materials

Section A

TEACHING THE PRODUCTION OF SPEECH SOUNDS

Refer to the test results (pp. 146–47; 325–34) to discover the individual needs of each child. In individual corrective work, it is sometimes wise to teach only one sound at a time. When one sound has been comparatively well learned, the teacher may proceed with the next sound to be taught. Some children may be able to learn the production of more than one sound at a single session.

Corrective work should be discontinued during a session if a child shows the slightest sign of fatigue. A twenty-minute practice period is usually long enough for individual work. In group work, the time may be extended. The first teaching may at times need to be individual. After the formations of the sounds have been learned, it is often helpful to work in small groups. Supplement or substitute the individual work with group work as soon as possible.

Since (s), (z), (r), (l), (ʃ), (tʃ), and (dʒ) are usually more difficult to learn, other misused sounds should be taught first. The teacher will usually wish to start on the sound which the child can produce most readily. Carry on the work in a quiet atmosphere. Allow no observers until the pupils are ready to work in groups. Even at this time, it will be wise to have observation through the means of a one-way vision window. Sound equipment can be used in relation to such a window so that observers may see and hear the corrective procedures.

Procedures in Teaching Individual Sounds

1. Speak the sound so that the pupil may *hear* it correctly.

2. Call attention to any movement or vibration that may occur with the sound so that the pupil may *feel* how the sound is made.

3. Let the pupil watch the teacher form the sound in order that he may *see* how the sound is correctly produced. Let the pupil use a mirror while forming the sound himself.

4. Use the stimulation-imitation method first, as in (1) above. If this fails to get the proper sound production, it may be necessary to teach the formation of the sound specifically. Do not dwell too long on the nonsense-syllable practice. Carry over as soon as possible to the use of words, phrases, sentences, and to the group work in speech games, creative play, and choral reading. *Always present the practice of sounds to young children through methods related to play activities.*

5. It is quite possible, and often advisable, to eliminate most individual instruction. Start, instead, with the stimulation of sounds and carry through steps 1, 2, 3, and 4, using the group structure. The children who can produce certain sounds correctly gain a feeling of security, and those who have difficulty do not feel conspicuous in the group situation, since correction and instruction can be given to the group as a whole.

SAMPLE LESSON—TEACHING AN INDIVIDUAL SOUND TO YOUNG CHILDREN. *Error:* the (θ) and (ð) are used in place of (s) and (z).

Procedure of correction:

Teacher: Have you ever been on a farm?
Response:
Teacher: There are many animals on a farm. Some of the animals talk. What kind of animals are on the farm?
Response:
Teacher: What does the cow say?
Response: (Probably) Moo!
Teacher: And what does the dog say?

Response: Bow-wow (or) woof-woof!

Teacher: That's right, and do you know that the snakes talk, too? (It doesn't really matter whether they do or not, the children are quick to make believe!)

The snake says "s-s-s." What does the snake say?

Response: S-s-s.

Teacher: That's quite good! (Even if it is not!) Do you know that the snake lives behind a white fence? We do not want to let him out. Let us play that our teeth are the white fence and our tongue is the snake. Now let us keep the snake back of the white fence. S-s-s. (The teacher may wish to use mirrors at this point. Let each child see where he should keep his tongue. The snake game may continue with the practice of the nonsense syllables.)

Teacher: Sometimes many snakes live in a nest back of the white fence. Once there was a whole family of snakes, the father snake, the mother snake, and lots of little baby snakes. One day when the baby snakes woke up, they were very hungry. They wanted something to eat. They said, "Soo-soo-soo," and they meant "We are hungry!" What did the baby snakes say when they were hungry?

Response: Soo-soo-soo!

Teacher: That's right. Then the father snake said, "Sah-sah-sah," and he meant, "I'll go to the garden and get you some breakfast." What did the father snake say?

Response: Sah-sah-sah!

The game can continue as long as the teacher in her creative cleverness can keep the interest of the group. The teacher may remind the children to "keep the snake behind the white fence," and she may have to help some of the children in getting the correct sound placement. At times the teacher may wish to use a sound-discrimination game before attempting to get the sound formation.

Sound Discrimination Game

A sound discrimination game can help the children in developing the ability to discriminate between the correct sounds and the sound substitutions which may be used.

Illustration of the Sound Discrimination Game.

Teacher: Now we are going to play another game. You are to tell me when I make a good snake sound (s) by clapping your hands. When I make the "angry goose" sound (th), you will tap your toes.

All right, are you ready? S-s-s. Yes, that was a good snake sound, so clap your hands! Now listen carefully: tha, tha, tha. That was not a snake sound; that was the angry goose sound, so tap your toes. Listen again: soo-soo-soo! Clap your hands. Tho, tho, tho; that's right, tap your toes!

The game continues with other nonsense syllables and with words and short phrases until the children can begin to distinguish quite easily between the (s) and the (th).

Encourage the carry-over of correct sound placement through the use of the various speech games and activities, and with the use of creative play and choral reading. The teacher should remember to watch for signs of fatigue. The speech correction work is approached as play, but the teacher should remember that the play is for the purpose of good speech development. If the play element becomes too great, the speech element may be neglected. *At no time,* however, must any child feel that pressure is being placed upon him for a better standard of speech. The development of better speech must be fun. Children, as do adults, learn faster those things which they like to do. Thus speech development, improvement, and correction should be presented through pleasurable activities. With this in mind, use the nonsense syllables not as drills, but in speech activities in games such as ring toss, bouncing the ball, tenpins, tossing the beanbag, climbing the ladder, and other word-action games.

Section B

TEACHING SOUND
FORMATIONS

Sounds which the child misuses in words often appear correct to him. The nonsense syllables are not words and therefore present a new experience to the child. The correct sound placements are often more easily learned if nonsense syllables are presented before words and phrases. This type of experience, however, should not be prolonged. More natural speech activities should replace anything which even suggests a drill technique as soon as possible.

The teacher should be aware of the fact that certain sounds are not always produced in exactly the same way by everyone. For instance, it is quite possible to make a good (s) sound with the front of the tongue up. It is equally possible to produce this sound with the front of the tongue down.

DESCRIPTIONS OF SOUNDS. The following descriptions of sounds are presented in simple terms in the hope of helping the teacher and the older child understand how the various sounds may be produced. The order of these sounds follows the phonetic order of the checking sheet. This is not intended to mean that the sounds must be taught in this order. Follow the teaching of the individual speech sounds with speech activities games, creative play, and choral reading to help in establishing new habits.

Nonsense Syllables

1. P (p)
   The lips are closed. The breath explodes lightly between the parted lips, making the sound. No vibration is felt when the hand is placed on the throat.

   p p p
   poo po pah
   po puh puh-po
   pa-po puh-poo
   pu-pah paw-po
   ip eep opp op
   ap aup ep sep
   lape teep nop foop

2. B (b)
   On (b) the lips are closed and the breath explodes between parted lips. The hand on throat feels the vibration of the sound.

   buh buh buh
   boo boo boo
   bo bo bo
   bah bah bah
   be-bay be-bo
   bah-bo bah-boo
   ob abe ab
   tobe tabe tab
   sib lob koob

3. M (m)
   The lips are closed and the breath passes through the nose with a slight hum. Vibration is felt with the hand on the nose and throat.

   m m m
   moo moo moo
   mome maib maheem
   mah-mo mah-moom **mah-mi**
   eem im ome om
   oom um bin nom
   fam soom bome

4. Wh (ʍ) as in "what," "when," "where." The breath passes between the lips, which are slightly puckered. First teach the (h) as in Number 25 (below), then teach blowing lightly through the lips. Try blowing against the edge of a piece of paper. Blow a feather or a small piece of paper easily off the hand.

   h h h
   hwuh hwuh hwuh
   whay whee whah
   whes whit whuf
   whay-whoa whay-whee
   whoe-whuf whah **whuf**
   whiz-whee whit-**whah**

5. W (w) as in "one," "wear," "we." The breath passes between the lips. Vibration is felt with the hand against the throat.

oo oo oo
oo-ah oo-ah oo-ah
wah wah wah
ahwo awah ahwoo
eewi eewah eewo
wa-wo wa-wah wo-we
twee twah twoh
swee swah swoe
kwee kwah kwoe

6. F (f)
The lower lip is placed slightly under the upper teeth and the breath escapes between the teeth and lip. The hand on the throat feels no vibration.

f f f
foo foo foo
fae fae fae
fah fah fah
fee-fay fee-fah
fah-fo fah-foo
fah-fay fah-fee
oaf aif af
ahf oof eff
tof sif nuf

7. V (v)
The lower lip is placed slightly under the upper teeth and the breath escapes between the teeth and lip. Vibration is felt with the hand on the throat.

v v v
voo voo voo
voe vah vay
vee vi vaw
vah-voe vah-voo
vah-vay vah-vee
oov bov av
ove iv teve
tav soov nuv
dev bav kiv

8. Th (θ) as in "thin." The front of the tongue is placed lightly against the upper front teeth and the breath escapes between the teeth and the tongue. No vibration is felt with the hand on the throat.

th th th
thoo thoo thoo
thace thooce thit
theet thid thun
thub thape thope
ooth-aw eethah
eth ith aithee
nooth kawth deeth

9. Th (ð) as in "that."
This sound takes the
same formation as the
"th" without vibration,
Number 8. The vibra-
tion is felt on the (ð)
with the hand on the
throat. Try for the "th"
with "noise."

th th th
thah thah thah
thut thut thut
thoo theh thoot
theet thid thun
ooth aith ith
aith-o ath-oo
ath-a ath-ee
eeth-ah ooth-oh
oth ath ith

10. T (t)
The tip of the tongue is
placed against the upper
teeth ridge. The breath
is stopped by the tongue
tip for an instant, then
escapes over the tongue
to form the (t). No vi-
bration is felt by the
hand on the throat.

t t t
tuh tuh tuh
toop toop toop
tofe tofe tofe
tah-to tah-tee
tah-too tah-tay
lat-to nit-too
oot aht ite
sate fot doot
vit lut keet

11. D (d)
The tip of the tongue is
placed against the teeth
ridge back of the upper
teeth. The breath is
stopped by tongue tip
for an instant, then es-
capes over the tongue to
form the (d). The hand
on the throat feels the
vibration of the sound.

d d d
duh duh duh
dee dee dee
doop doop doop
dah dah dah
do-do do-dah
dah-do dah-doo
ode-ad ode-ood
od-oo od-ee
tod sid fud

12. N (n)
The front of the tongue
is placed against the up-
per teeth ridge and the
breath passes through
the nose. Vibration is
felt with the fingers on
the nose and the throat.

n n n
noo noo noo
nah-noo nah-no
nay-no noo-nay
nee-noe nee-noo
nah-nee nah-nie
bon ain een
un oon aun

13. L   (l)

The front of the tongue is against the upper teeth ridge and the breath escapes over the sides of the tongue with more or less friction. The beginning (l) uses more force and the tongue comes quickly down, whereas the final (l) is unstressed and somewhat longer. To get the initial (l) sing "ah," lifting the tongue tip to the upper teeth ridge while singing "ah-la" as the tongue plays "teeter-totter" up and down. A medial (l) sound may be either an initial (l) or a final (l) sound. The final (l) may be placed in various positions according to the preceding vowel sound.

ah ah ah
ah-lah ah-lah
ah-lo ah-lay
ah-loo ah-lee
o-lay o-lee o-loo
lob luf los
lib laz loog
vil zal pel
tol beel kal
ool o-nal ah-pal

14. R   (r) as in "run." The breath trips over the tongue tip. The front of the tongue is raised toward the roof of the mouth near the teeth ridge, but does not touch the ridge. The lips are slightly rounded. Let the tongue drop down as the sound is produced. Keep the lower lip away from the upper teeth. If the sound proves exceptionally difficult to teach, have the pupil insert the

ruh ruh ruh
roo roo roo
rike ras rab
roo-ro roo-rah
ree-ro ree-rah
ba-ra bo-roo do-re
bra bro broo
prah pro pree
tro trah treek
dro dree druh
kra kre kruh
gri gree gruh
troo frah fro

knuckle of his index finger under his tongue and try for the sound. If the sound still remains difficult, try for the soft (ʒ), then try jer-ah, jer-oh, jer-oo (dʒɛru).

(ɚ) as in "mother." The final "r" may be formed with the tongue slightly raised in the back, or it may be produced with the tongue raised in front as in (r) in Number 14. Start with the sound "ah" with the mouth well open, then slowly bring the mouth to a near closed position. The "er" sound should follow if the tongue is brought up in front just back of the teeth ridge.

ah-er ah-er
pah-er bah-er
tah-er mah-er
sah-er kah-er
fah-er gah-er
oor ire ai-er
jore keer nire
sahr koor zehr
erd irt urs
arsh urch arth
irst urm oorm

15. S (s)
The tongue is against the upper teeth ridge and the teeth are nearly together. The breath escapes over the groove in the center of the tongue. No vibration is felt with the hand on the throat. If the position is difficult to attain, an orangewood stick or a toothpick may be used to help the pupil form the groove of the tongue. Often if a (t) is given first, the (s) sound follows more readily.

s s s
soo soo soo
sah sah sah
seh seh seh
saf sab soob
sim sib sif
oose ose eesoo
sah-soo sah-seh
kes dis tusah
nase pahsa feesah
smi smo sme
spa spe spo
ste stah stob
skoo skeh skah
slee sloo slah
ose bees nas
hes ves dos

Keep the tongue away from the teeth; do not let it push against the teeth. It is also possible to make the (s) sound with the tongue front down behind the lower front teeth. Air, however, must not escape over the sides of the tongue.

16. Z (z)

The tongue is against the upper teeth ridge. As in (s), the (z) may also be made with the tongue front down behind the lower front teeth. It is usually easier to teach the (s) and (z) with the tongue front up. The breath must not escape over the sides of the tongue, and the tongue must not push against the upper teeth. The teeth are nearly together. The breath escapes over the groove in the center of the tongue, as in (s). Vibration is felt on the (z) with the hand on the throat. Use more "noise" on the (z) than on the (s).

z z z
zah zah zah
zee zee zee
zay zoe zaw
zeh zeep zehp
muz-o meez-ah kooz-o
ah-zah ah-zoo
o-zuh o-zum o-zee
oz oz oz
uz ez dooz
taiz tez tiz
tiz kooz daz-oz

17. Sh (ʃ)

The tongue is nearly flat in the mouth, slightly raised in the middle and back. The teeth are to-

sh sh sh
shay shay shay
shah shuh shawm
shibe shan shoof
shoo-shah shoo-sho

gether, the lips parted and slightly protruded. The breath rushes over the tongue surface and out between the teeth, with friction. No vibration is felt with the hand on the throat.

shay-shuh shay-shee
ah-shie ah-shoo ah-shah
ish ush esh
oosh oash ahsh

18. Zh (ʒ) as in "vision" and "measure." It may be well to teach the (ʃ) as in Number 17 first, then try making the "sh" sound with more "noise" or with vibration. The tongue is nearly flat in the mouth, slightly raised in the back. The breath rushes over the tongue surface and through the teeth with friction. Vibration is felt with the hand on the throat.

sh sh sh
zh zh zh
oozh-er ezh-er
azh-ah awzh-ah
izh-ah izh-on
eezh-ah eezh-er
oozh ezh azh
ohzh izh ahzh

19. Ch (tʃ)
If the (t) and the (ʃ), Numbers 10 and 17, are not properly used, the teacher may wish to teach these sounds first. For the (tʃ) the tongue begins in the position of the (t) sound and slips to the (ʃ) position instantly. Teach the (t), then the (ʃ), then combine the two sounds. Imitate the sound of a starting engine. Practice a sneeze, "at-choo."

t t t
sh sh sh
t-sh t-sh t-sh
at-choo at-che at-chah
ch ch ch
chuh chuh chuh
chay chay chay
chee cheh chi
cho-chi cho-che kitchoo
choo-chay choo-chee
chi-cho chi-chaw
ooch aich atch
och utch meech
kooch daich fatch
moch putch

20. J (dʒ) as in "John" and "engine." The sound begins like the (d), Number 11. The teeth are close together and the lips are parted. After the tongue-front touches the teeth ridge back of the upper teeth for the (d), the tongue flattens and allows the breath to escape over the flattened tongue on the (ʒ) sound, as in Number 18. It may be helpful to teach (d), Number 11, (ʃ), Number 17, and (ʒ), Number 18, before teaching (dʒ).

d d d
duh duh duh
sh sh sh
zh zh zh
zhuh zhuh zhuh
duh-shuh duh-zhuh
juh juh juh
jee jee jee
jop jun jik
jah-ji je-jo
jah-jee jah-ji
poj-paj puj pooj
ij uj oj ahj
nuj haj soj

21. Y (j) as in "yet" and "yawn." Teach the (i), as in Number 26, first, then combine with the following vowel sound. The exact placing of the (j) sound depends upon the vowel following the sound. The breath passes through the mouth with friction over the raised tongue. Vibration is felt with the hand on the throat.

ee-ah ee-ah ee-ah
ee-oh ee-oh ee-oh
ee-ih ee-aw ee-eh
ee-ahf ee-od ee-uhm
ee-oop ee-ehb ee-ehk
ee-elk ee-ope ee-en
yee yoo yah yoh
be-yah kee-yah fee-yoh
yo yi yeep
yik yat yon
ayook ayak ayant

22. K (k)
The tip of the tongue is down and the back of the tongue is raised. The breath is stopped at the back of the tongue and lightly "explodes"

k k k
koo koo koo
ko ko ko
kah kah kah
kay kay kay
kah-ko kay-kee
ack tok kock

through for the (k)
sound. The hand on the
throat feels no vibration.
If the sound is difficult
to learn, keep the tongue
in the proper position
and try for a light
"cough" from the back
of the tongue, not from
the throat.

puk loke neek
fek bick fauk
sook fick nahk

Q (kw) as in "queen"
is a combination. Teach
the hard (k), Number
22, first, then teach the
(w), Number 5. Next,
combine the two sounds.
Vibration is felt with the
hand on the throat for
the (w) part of the (kw)
combination, but the (k)
is without vibration.

k k k
wuh wuh wuh
kuh-wuh kuh-wuh
kwee kwee kwee
kway kwoo kwah
kwo-kwee kwi-kway
kwas kweed kwin
kwode kwap kwen
akwee acqwi inqwi
qo qu qi
qah qoo qa

X (ks) as in "six" is
also a combination. If
the (k) and the (s)
sounds, Numbers 22 and
15, are not used cor-
rectly, teach these sounds
first. The "x" is a com-
bination of the (k) and
(s) sounds. It is actually
the two separate sounds
combined. Teach the
hard (k), then the (s),
and then combine the
two sounds. No vibra-
tion is felt on the (k) and
the (s) sounds.

k k k
s s s
ks ks ks
ixer oxah axer
oox oox oox
awx foox bix
soox deex spox
eex feex ix
tox moox nux
spix bux boox

23. G (g) as in "go" and
"girl." If the (k) is also
misused, you may wish

guh guh guh
goo goo goo
gope gope gope

to teach (k) first. The
tip of the tongue is down
and the back of the
tongue is raised. The
breath is stopped at the
back of the tongue and
explodes through for the
(g) sound. The hand on
the throat feels the vi-
bration of the sound.

gah gah gah
gah-gay gah-goo
gee-go gee-go
ahg-go ahg-gi
og aig ag
sog teeg fag
hig pag nug

24. NG (ŋ)
There is no (g) sound
here. "Ng" is an (n)
formed with *the back of
the tongue*. The back of
the tongue is raised to
the roof of the mouth
and the front of the
tongue is down. The
breath is stopped at the
back of the tongue and
then passes through the
nose. Vibration is felt
with the hand on the
nose and the throat.

ng ng ng
inkah ankah unkah
inker unker ankee
ing ing ing
ung ung ung
ong ang bing
bung bong boong
fing fung fong
ning nang nung
kang kung kong

NK (ŋk) as in "think"
is a combination. Teach
the (ŋ) as in Number
24, first, then teach the
(k) as in Number 22.
The first part of the "nk"
is formed like the (ŋ).
The back of the tongue
is raised and the front of
the tongue is down. The
breath passes through
the nose on the first part
of (ŋk). The (k) sound
follows immediately
after the (ŋ), with the

ng ng ng
ngk ngk ngk
inkah ankah unkah
inker unker ankee
eenk unk onk
oink oonk ank
awnk bink konk
soink poonk teenk
fank sawnk tunk
bonk dink doonk
fink funk nink

(k) exploding over the back of the tongue, which is raised to touch the roof of the mouth. The breath passes through the mouth on the (k) part of the sound, with a slight explosion. Vibration is felt with the hand on the nose and throat on the (ŋ), the first part of the sound, but no vibration is felt on the (k) part of the sound.

25. H (h)
This is merely a breath exhaled with a slight friction at the throat. No vibration is felt with the hand on the throat. The usual misuse of (h) is in using it when it should not be used, or in omitting it when it should be used. If (h) is not used, practice this first group.

hay hi ho hoo
he-hah ho-hoot
hote hile hobe
heen herk hon
hap hus huf
han hipe haup
hop-hob hed-hed
hon-hit his-hab

If (h) is used when it should be omitted, practice these exercises as well as the first group. Explain how the (h) sound is made and teach that it must be left off at certain times.

ema ena ila
ope uka ata
ot id ess
oko eko ano
abah aibah atah
ubah opah okah

In teaching the vowel sounds, make definite use of imitation and discrimination between the undesired sound and the desired sound. The use of the recorder can be helpful in this. Remember that these sounds may be adequately produced in a number of slightly varied positions. Let the ear judge the adequacy of the production.

26. E (i) as in "me." The tongue is raised slightly in the center, the sides touching the upper side teeth. The jaws are rather close together and the lips are drawn back, slightly smiling in position. Vibration is felt with the hand on the the throat. The breath passes through the mouth.

ee ee ee
eep eef eeg
eek ees eem
een eeb eed
ee-nee ee-dee
ee-gee ee-tee
bees keef seeb
dee dee dee
gee ree vee

27. I (ɪ) as in "sit." The tongue may be slightly raised at the center, the breath escaping over the tongue through the mouth. Vibration is felt with the hand on the throat.

ih ih ih
ik ith iv
id ip ig
bik mik mib
nif id ik
pif-nif sib-fin
tib-dis kib-nit
bih bih bih
fih sih hin

28. A (eɪ) as in "Jane." The sound has two movements, from (e) to (ɪ), as in Number 27. The tongue is slightly raised in the center. The lips are parted and the mouth slightly open. The jaws are more closed on the (ɪ) sound and the lips may be slightly smiling in position on this last part of the sound.

aee aee aee
a-i a-i a-i
bafe kafe dafe
fabe kabe dabe
tane tace tabe
pake sape fape
fay-gay ga-tay
nay-bay pay-das
abee adah atoo
oota odoo ahta

The breath escapes through the mouth. Vibration is felt with the hand on the throat.

29. E (ε) as in "let." The jaws are farther apart than for the long (i), as in Number 26. The tongue is slightly raised in the center and the breath passes through the mouth. Vibration is felt with the hand on the throat.

eh eh eh
beh beh beh
keh feh meh
teh peh seh
et-fet ed-meh
eb-seh ef-teh
ek ep et
es em ez

30. A (æ) as in "math." The tongue is flat in the mouth. The mouth opens slightly more than in sounding the (eɪ), as in Number 28. The breath escapes through the mouth. Vibration is felt with the hand on the throat.

a a a
ag af ab
aj ap av
fal bam paf
ta-fal sa-gam
fa bam lo dal
fa ta ga
la gan taf

A (a) soft as in "ask." If the child uses Number 30 correctly, do not be concerned about the misuse of this short soft (a) sound. It is produced in like manner to Number 30, but is less tense, being a softer and more relaxed sound.

31. U (ʌ) as in "cup." The tongue is slightly raised in the center. The jaws are slightly open and the

uh uh uh
ub uk un
buh buh buh
dus fuh tuh

breath escapes through
the mouth. Vibration is
felt with the hand on
the throat.

puh kuh muh
duh suh guh
tuh-vuh mud-us
but-tuh nut-sud

32. A (ə) as in "sofa." The
position is similar to
Number 31, but the
sound is less tense. Use
the same nonsense sylla-
bles as in Number 31,
but a more relaxed form.

33. AH (ɑ) as in "father."
Sound "ah" with the
tongue flat in the mouth.
The jaws are opened
more than for the short
(a) as in Number 30. The
breath is released
through the mouth. Vi-
bration is felt with the
hand on the throat.

ah ah ah
bah lah fah
sah tah kah
ah-dah ah-pah
ah-mah ah-gah
ahp bahp tahs
tahk lahb lahf

34. O (ɒ) as in "not" and
"cot." This sound is
made very much like
Number 33, but the
tongue is slightly more
retracted and the sound
is more tense.

English use it

o o o
ok ok ok
op op op
do-to do-ko
do-to ko-do
ko ko ko
do do do

35. AW (ɔ) as in "Paul." The
tongue is slightly raised
and drawn toward the
back of the mouth. The
lips are more rounded
than for the soft (ɑ), as
in Number 33, and the
jaws are more apart. Vi-
bration is felt with the
hand on the throat. The
breath passes through
the mouth.

aw aw aw
awp awk awm
mawt sawg lawb
awpaw awbaw awtaw
faw faw faw
baw gaw kaw
taw-saw maw-daw

36. OO (ʊ) as in "put," "stood." The lips are puckered and slightly farther apart than with the (u) as in Number 37. This sound is formed farther back in the mouth than the (u). Vibration is felt with the hand on the throat. The breath passes through the mouth.

u u u
buh buh buh
tuh tuh tuh
cuh duh fuh
guh luh muh
uht uhk muhf
muh-fuh puh-tuh

37. OO (u) as in "spoon." The lips are puckered. The tongue is flat. The breath passes through the mouth. Vibration is felt with the hand on the throat.

oo oo oo
boo boo boo
foo goo poo
koo-moo boo-loo
doo-voo poo-too
ood koob poon
oot koos oop
ook-doo koo-doo
goo-soo too-voo

U (ju)
This is a combined sound of "y" (j), as in Number 21, and "oo" (u) as in Number 37.

38. O (oʊ) long as in "no." The lips are rounded. The breath passes through the mouth. The tongue is flat. Vibration is felt with the hand on the throat. The sound is often treated as a diphthong, gliding from (o) to (ʊ), as in Number 36.

o o o
om-ote ko-so
obe-oaf oan-oat
ko ko ko
mo-vo ob-do o-ko
bo-do vo-no
do-do fo-do
mo-go ko-po
to-po so-go

The diphthongs are made up of two combined vowels which glide together. Numbers 28 and 38 are often used as

diphthongs, or these may be short (o) and (e) as they often
appear between consonants.

39. OW OU (ɑʊ) as in "how"
and "mouse." Teach (ɑ)
as in Number 33 first,
then teach (u) as in
Number 37. Then short-
en to (ʊ) as in Number
36. Next, combine the
two sounds for the "ow"
or "ou." The breath
passes through the
mouth. The hand on the
throat feels the vibration
of the sound.

ah-oo ah-oo ah-oo
oud oub ouk
dow dow dow
fow gow pow
lowk powf sowt
now-dow fow-dow
gow-mow bow-pow

40. I (ɑɪ) as in "pie." First,
teach the (ɑ) as in Num-
ber 33, then teach the
(ɪ) as in Number 27;
next, combine the two
sounds. If the sound
is difficult to teach, teach
"ah-ee" (ɑi), then short-
en the last sound until
(ɑɪ) is achieved. The
breath passes through
the mouth and vibration
is felt with the hand on
the throat.

ah-ih ah-ih ah-ih
kih kih kih
bice bife bipe
kide pite mife
fide sipe nipe
tie-pie die-sie
ido itah iseh

41. OY, OI (ɔɪ) as in "toy"
or "boil." Teach (ɔ) as
in Number 35, then teach
(ɪ) as in Number 27; next,
combine the two sounds.
The breath passes
through the mouth. Vi-
bration is felt with the
hand on the throat.

aw-ih aw-ih aw-ih
oip oit ois
poy noy soit
soik oid oim
doys koys loit
doy doy doy
foy hoy moy

Nonsense Syllable Practice on Consonant Sound Combinations

In teaching the correct usage of sound combinations, teach the individual sound first and use simple nonsense syllable practice, then follow with practice in the combination of sounds. Give only a short time to such work, proceeding to words and sentences through speech games. This type of practice is often too difficult and confusing to use with young children, therefore do not emphasize it with young children, but use short-time sound games instead.

dth	nth	sp	sm	zm	sn	st		sk	
odth	anth	spee	smee	izm	snee	stee	est	skee	esk
idth	enth	spa	sma	azm	sna	sta	ast	ska	isk
	inth	spi	smi	ozm	sni	sti	ist	ski	osk
		spo	smo	oozm	sno	sto	ost	sko	oosk
		spoo	smoo		snoo	stoo	oost	skoo	ahsk

sl	tw	dw	pl	bl	gl	fl	kl	kr	fr
slee	twee	dwee	plee	blee	gleh	fleh	klee	kree	freh
slah	taw	dwa	plah	bla	gla	flah	klah	kra	fra
sli	twi	dwi	pli	bli	gli	fla	kli	kri	fri
slo	twoe	dwo	plo	blo	glo	flo	klo	kro	fro
sloo	twoo	dwoo	ploo	bloo	gloo	floo	kloo	kroo	froo

pr	br	tr	dr	qu	spl	spr	str	skr	sw
pree	bree	trah	dree	quee	splee	spreh	stree	skree	swee
prah	brah	trah	drah	qua	spla	sprah	strah	skra	swah
pri	bri	tri	dri	qui	spli	spri	stri	skri	swo
pro	bro	tro	dro	quo	splo	spro	stro	skro	swoo
proo	broo	troo	droo	quoo	sploo	sproo	stroo	skrah	swi

squ	thr	shr	ps	bz	ts	dz	fs	vz	sts
squee	thrah	shre	ops	abz	ats	adz	afs	avz	asts
squa	thri	shra	aps	obz	ots	odz	ofs	ovz	osts
squi	threh	shri	ips	ibz	its	idz	ifs	ivz	ists
squo	throo	shro	oops	oobz	oots	oodz	oofz	oovz	oosts
squoo	thro	shroo							

ths	*thz*	*ls*	*lz*	*mz*	*ns*	*nz*	*ngz*	*ks*	*gz*
aths	athz	els	alz	amz	ans	anz	angz	oks	agz
oths	othz	ols	olz	amz	ins	onz	ongz	aks	ogz
iths	ithz	ils	elz	imz	ens	inz	ingz	iks	oogz

MEDIAL POSITIONS

adtho	ostee	aplah	okree	adro	askree	avza	angza
anthi	uskee	opli	ofre	equee	eskri	ethze	agza
aspo	asko	oblee	apri	oquah	aswee	olzo	
ospi	eslee	obloo	abre	esplee	oswo	amzo	
osma	itwo	aglee	etre	ospli	esquee	enze	
osnee	etwee	aflee	atroo	aspree	ithrah		
esta	adwa	aklee	adra	ostree	ahsree		

Section C

SPEECH GAMES IN GRADED SEQUENCE

In using games, the teacher must keep in mind their main purpose. Much can be accomplished in the way of speech development, improvement, and correction if the teacher is aware of the purpose and gently guides the children into better speech habits. No child must be made to feel self-conscious. No child should stand out as being different in speech. A clever teacher encourages good speech in all, sets a good example, and when correction is needed gives it unoffensively—and preferably to the whole group. Under good leadership, the children soon get the idea of accepting constructive criticism, and everyone tries for good speech and likes doing it because the teacher makes the learning of good speech habits fun.

The children should be encouraged to speak well at all times. The teacher should watch for any errors which may be made in speech and may suggest correct forms if incorrect formations of sounds are used. Suggest to the whole group, and let everyone try the correct production if any sounds are misused by any child. The children should be encouraged to keep conversations natural and easy. The teacher must avoid a critical attitude.

The attempt to use the correct form should not be made under pressure. If the child does not get it after the first or second try, the teacher should say "That's fine," or "That's a good try," and go on with the game.

Games for Relaxation and Free and Easy Movement

The teacher may wish to begin each class period with the use of one or more of these simple games. Use games appropriate to age and grade level. The games are presented in more or less graded arrangement, from the easiest to the more difficult. The teacher, however, will soon learn to use games of appropriate age and grade level. The games will help in getting the children in a cooperative mood and should aid in teaching them to follow directions.

FLOWER GARDEN. Each child chooses to be his favorite flower. The flowers grow in a beautiful garden. Soft breezes blow as the flowers sway back and forth. The children raise their arms and faces, as the flowers look toward the sun. Then the children slowly lower their arms and heads as the flowers droop and go to sleep.

THE BEAR WALK. The children stand, feet slightly apart, arms extended over the head. They drop forward from the waist, and with head, arms, and hands swinging easily, walk slowly about the room.

YAWNING. Ask the children to yawn, making deep, long, slow yawning motions, getting the mouth open, then stretching the arms slowly.

LAZY-AH. Sitting comfortably in chairs, the children drop their arms loosely at their sides. Falling forward from the waist, they let their heads drop to their knees, saying slowly, "Lazy-ah-h." They try to be completely relaxed. Then they return to the upright position slowly, chests out, chins in, heads up.

SIGHS. Ask the children to give three long sighs. Next, have them vocalize the sighs with vowel sounds: ah-ah-ah-ah-ah-ah, ee-ee-ee-ee-ee-ee, o-o-o-o-o-o, oo-oo-oo-oo-oo-oo. Next vocalize the sighs with ho-hum, ho-hum.

BREATHING WHILE INSTRUCTOR COUNTS. Ask the children to inhale quickly through the mouth on a count of 1-2. They try to hold their breath easily without strain, on a count of

1-2-3. They exhale very slowly on a count of 1-2-3-4. Work for low and middle chest breathing. Ask them to avoid high chest breathing and the raising of the collar bone and shoulders.

BLOWING GAMES. Blowing games may be used to encourage well-sustained breathing habits, to gain interest, and to show how the breath may be sent through the mouth. Remember that speech sounds are not made with blowing effort and do not overdo this type of exercise. Work for easy, low or middle chest breathing. Let the children blow lightly against the edge of a piece of paper. Place a small piece of paper on the back of the hand and let each child try to gently blow it off. Let them blow a feather afloat in the air.

SOAP BUBBLES. The children may blow real soap bubbles if the necessary equipment is available; otherwise they may pretend to blow bubbles. Get them to blow easily and slowly as long as one breath can be sustained. See how large a bubble can be blown with one gentle, easy breath. Bubble blowing rings and a prepared solution can be found at dime stores.

BALLOONS. Blow up real or imaginary balloons. See how large a balloon can be blown in one slow, easy breath.

PIN WHEELS. Blow on homemade pin wheels or upon ready-made pin wheels which may be purchased at the ten-cent stores. See how long and steadily the pin wheels may be blown in one long breath.

WHISTLES. Blow upon homemade whistles. Use whistles and horns which may be purchased from the ten-cent stores.

Speech–Action Games

In the following speech games, be sure that the sounds, words, or phrases are produced *with action*.

THE FIRE ENGINE GAME. The children stand. As they take deep breaths, they slowly raise their arms and swing them back; they let the breath out slowly, singing up the scale on an unbroken "Oh." As their arms come slowly down, they sing the descending scale on the unbroken "Oh." Repeat on a new breath. This game may be carried through with any sound or combination of sounds, or with words or phrases.

BALL TOSS. A ball is tossed from one pupil to the next. Use a large ball. Nursery rhymes may be used. The pupil with the ball may speak one word or one line on the toss of the ball. If the word or line is spoken incorrectly, the entire action and speech may be tried again. The second try is "better" even if not correct. Do not insist upon perfection, but get on with the game. The pupil who catches the ball tosses it to the next pupil as the next word or line of the rhyme is spoken. The teacher may speak the line first and then the child may imitate the teacher as he tosses the ball.

BALL BOUNCE. The ball may be bounced on a cement walk or on the classroom floor. Use spoken words or lines as in Ball Toss. Again be sure to use *constructive criticism*: "That was pretty good; let's try it again and try for a clear 's' sound. That was better" (even if it is not).

BALL ROLL. The ball may be rolled from one pupil to another on spoken words or lines as the children sit in a circle on the floor.

The teacher may write lists of words on the blackboard, if she wants certain sounds practiced. For the younger children who cannot read, the teacher may pronounce the words and have the children repeat them after her, or she may use a variety of simple pictures to get word responses. The teacher may wish to use the nonsense drills, poems, and sentences listed elsewhere in this book in playing these speech games.

HORSESHOE OR RING TOSS. Two or more children can play this game. If scores are kept, the game is more interesting. A set of rubber horseshoes can be obtained in almost any toy department. The children may make their own horseshoes out of heavy cardboard, or they may be cut from wood or wallboard. Rubber jar rings may be used in place of horseshoes. The peg may be fastened to a flat piece of board so that the game may be played indoors or out-of-doors.

As the shoes or rings are tossed at the peg, one word, phrase, or sentence is spoken. A child throws only a certain number of horseshoes or rings at one time, and then the next child has his fun. A ringer counts three points. When the peg is touched, but a ringer is not made, two points are given, and when the horseshoe or ring falls within the circle drawn around the peg, one point is given.

This game may be varied by having squares marked off and numbered at different values instead of using the peg. A large board may be covered with a variety of pictures, or one large picture with numerous details may be used. Large nails or screw hooks may be placed at various points and the board may be set up against a wall. Sets of pictures may be prepared which emphasize certain sounds. These may be pasted on light cardboard and holes may be made to slip over the nails, then the same board may be used in practicing on various desired sounds. When one makes a ringer, one tries to say correctly the name of the picture.

TENPINS. Set up the tenpins. The ball is rolled at the pins as words or phrases are spoken. The children take turns at rolling the ball and score is kept. If the words or phrases are given incorrectly, the child is encouraged to try for the correct form, but a second chance at rolling the ball is not given until the next turn comes around.

THE FISHING POND. Small magnets may be purchased at the ten-cent store. A string is tied to a fishing pole, which is made from a stick. The magnet is fastened to the end of the string. The teacher will prepare small slips of paper with words, phrases, or sentences written on each. A pin is fastened to each slip of paper. The paper slips are then placed in a large box and the children take turns fishing. As a fish is caught, the catcher reads aloud the writing on the paper. Variety may be added to the game by numbering the fish and by keeping score of the poundage caught. The fish may be of different colors, size, and shape. Small pictures of fresh-water fish and salt-water fish may be cut out and words and phrases and poundage may be typed and pasted on the backs of the fish. Press a wire staple along the mouth of the fish and the magnetic fishing line catches the fish like magic. Use a large round hatbox for the pond. Color it with blue waves and paint on jumping fish.

THE TEA PARTY. The tea party is a "must" for groups of young children because it allows for speech practice in a real life situation. The tea party should be a daily affair, coming near the close of the speech practice period. Provide real tea things if possible, or at least small paper cups, napkins, and a teapot. Orange juice or a cool drink add to the festivities, and cookies or crackers are an added treat. Let one child invite the others to a tea party. Conversation should flow naturally and easily. "Would you like to come to my tea party?" "Thank you, I'd like to come." "Would you like to pass the tea?" "Yes, thank you." "Would you like to pass the cookies?" "Yes, thank you." "Will you have some orange juice?" "Yes, thank you." "Would you like a cookie?" "Yes, thank you." The teacher encourages conversation. When speech help is given, it should be unobtrusive and addressed to the *group*, not to the individual child. "I like the way every one says 'Yes, thank you,' with a good 'snake sound' on 'yes'!"

THE GROCERY STORE. If possible, set up the "store" for more or less permanent use. The children may be asked to bring clean empty bottles and containers. Tables and benches may be used as store counters, or apple boxes may provide excellent storage space. Paper money may be made by the children. Different children may be given an opportunity to play the store manager, the clerk, and the customers. The customers ask about the quality of the food and about the prices. Perhaps they make purchases. Perhaps they talk about the weather or discuss the affairs of the town with the other customers or with the storekeeper. The teacher encourages the children to use good speech. When necessary, she can make suggestions for improvement, addressing these suggestions to the whole group.

PICTURE, DRAWING, AND CUTOUT BOOKS IN SPEECH TRAIN-ING. Much can be accomplished in corrective speech work with small children through the use of colorful picture books which can be purchased at the ten-cent stores. Mother Goose books, cutout books, animal books, drawing books, and coloring books can all play an important part in speech training. Pictures may be discussed, poems spoken or acted out, or stories may be told about the pictures. The children enjoy looking at the books, cutting out the pictures, and pasting or coloring, and at the same time the teacher can give the children speech training. This type of training is of great value because the children are not resentful of corrections, if these are addressed to the group and are given constructively. The clever teacher can keep the children busy and happy, encourage free and easy conversation, and make corrections almost an unconscious procedure on the part of the children. In this type of procedure the teacher must be quick to grasp an opportunity to give speech training in an unoffensive manner. She must not let the play activity become so predominant that she forgets the purpose of the play period. Always the teacher is watching speech development, although the children must not be aware of this. The clever speech teacher stimulates good speech production and makes her corrections a part of the play situation in a very unobtrusive manner. "What color are you making the house, Mary?" "Wed." "Oh, red! That is fine! Can you hear the 'r' sound there? 'Red' has a 'grr' sound like in 'run,' 'right,' and 'race,' and like in 'rah, rah, rah.' Try it . . .'red.' That's a good try!"

DOWN ON THE FARM. The teacher asks the children if they have ever been on a farm. She asks them what kind of animals there are on the farm. Some of the animals "talk." What do the different animals say? By questioning and suggesting the teacher will get a variety of responses similar in content to the following:

Suggested Animals	*Suggested Sounds*
Little Pig	Oink, oink
Big Pig	Grunt, grunt
Cow	Moo
Dog	Bow-wow, woof
Cat	Meow
Sheep	Baa-aa
Rooster	Cock-a-doodle-doo
Hen	Cluck-cluck
Baby chick	Peep-peep
Duck	Quack-quack
Owl	Whoot-to-who
Snake	Sssssssss
Bee	Buzzzz
Frog	Yawp-yawp
Donkey	Aw-hee-aw-hee hee-haw
Dove	Coo-coo
Crow	Caw-caw
Whippoorwill	Whip-poor-will
Chickadee	Chic-a-dee-dee
Turkey	Gobble-gobble

Now the children are ready to play the Farm Game. Who would like to be the farmer? Who will be the dog? The cat? The cow? Each child selects the animal he wishes to be. The farmer places his animals about his farm, each in his proper place. Then the farmer feeds the animals one at a time and each animal says, "Thank you" in his own language. The children may take turns at playing the farmer; they may choose to be different animals at different times. The wise teacher may suggest that the child who is working for a good (s) sound may wish to play the snake because he is learning to make such a good "snake" sound. Other special sound practice may be worked into this game.

THE CLOCK STORE. The children discuss the different types of clocks with the teacher. She asks for suggestions as to the appearance of the different clocks and then discussions follow regarding the sounds that each clock makes.

Suggested Clocks	*Suggested Sounds*
Grandfather Clock	A slow, heavy "TICK-TOCK." The arms swing, with the hands clasped, from left to right, in rhythm to the "TICK-TOCK." This clock strikes a deep, slow "BONG-BONG."
The Cuckoo Clock	A quick, light "tick-tock, tick-tock." This clock calls the hour with "cuckoo-cuckoo."
The Alarm Clock	This is a quick, sharp "tick-tock." The clock rings the time set with a "brrrinnng!"
The Chime Clock	Tick-tock, tick-tock. The clock strikes a chime for the hours. Use a three- or four-tone chord. The child may say "chime, chime, chime, chime," or "la, la, la, la," or use other sounds.
The Watch	A fast "tick-tick-tick" is made for the watch.

China clocks, electric clocks, kitchen clocks and other types of clocks may be suggested.

"Let's have a clock store," is the next suggestion made. So a clock store is planned. Who would like to be the storekeeper? A storekeeper is chosen from the volunteers. Then at the suggestion of the teacher, the children volunteer to be the different clocks. The storekeeper arranges the clocks, dusts them, and winds them. A customer enters the store; the clocks are displayed. The customer may wish to hear the clocks tick and call the hour. He may buy a clock after talking of prices and values. The game may be repeated with a change of characters and variation in the procedure. The class may offer constructive criticism which may improve the production; criticism must be offered only after each production is finished. Follow the suggestions for criticism given in the discussion of creative play.

GAME OF COMPARISONS. This game should help to develop tone strength and variation and aid in developing a ratio of values. The first item is small, the second large, and the voice is changed according to size and meaning. The children may make up their own words for comparisons.

Suggested Comparisons

A fly	An eagle
A penny	A million dollars
A printed page	A library
A brick	A ten-story building
A rowboat	A ship
A blade of grass	A tree
A poster	A signboard
An ant hill	A mountain
A goldfish	A whale
A kite	An airplane
A match	A streak of lightning
A thread	A chain
A moment	A century
Sand	Rocks
A drop of water	A cloudburst
Kindergarten	College
A baby	An old man
The New Year	Father Time
A stepladder	An escalator
A paint box	A rainbow
A paper fan	A cooling system
A cup of water	An ocean
An inch	A mile
A newsboy	The president
A kitten	A lion
A box	A warehouse
A cube of ice	The Arctic Ocean
A pin	A bolt
Tin	Platinum
A mule	A streamlined train
A pigmy	A giant

Glass . . . . Diamonds
A spark . . . . A star
Soft . . . . Hard
Light . . . . Dark
Small . . . . Large
Weak . . . . Strong
Cowardly . . . . Brave
Sweet . . . . Sour
Left . . . . Right

Comparisons may be used for a "stand up and sit down" game. Place the children on two sides. One side starts the game by giving the original word for comparison. The first person on the other side must supply a suitable comparison immediately or drop out of the game.

Singing Games

Singing games may be stimulating and helpful in establishing and maintaining good speech habits. There are many children's song books which suggest good singing action games. The old traditional singing games should not be overlooked. These can be played to recorded music or with piano accompaniment or just to the joyous accompaniment of the teacher's and children's voices. With an aim toward improved voice and articulation, try the old favorites: *London Bridge Is Falling Down, Here We Go 'Round the Mulberry Bush, This Is the Way We Wash Our Clothes, Here We Go Looby Loo,* and *The Farmer in the Dell.* These singing games and many others can offer an opportunity for the practice of correct speech habits. Look over the children's song books at local music stores for other possible songs which may be used in singing games. Use a song to start the group work with little children: "Hello, hello, and how are you? How are you? How are you? Hello, hello, and how are you? I'm fine, I'm fine, I'm fine!" Use a song also to close the period: "Now we're going home, now we're going home, goodbye, goodbye, goodbye, goodbye; now we're going home!"

Emphasizing Consonant Sounds

FOR USE IN GROUP READING WITH OLDER CHILDREN

1. P (p) "Peter Piper picked a peck of pickled pepper;
A peck of pickled pepper Peter Piper picked;
If Peter Piper picked a peck of pickled pepper,
Where's the peck of pickled pepper Peter Piper picked?"

He pleaded for a trap, a trap, a trap,
And the Pied Piper tapped a gentle tap.

"Speak the speech, I pray you, as I pronounced it to you trippingly on the tongue."
—Shakespeare

2. B (b) The big black bug bit the big black beetle.

Bitter butter makes bitter batter,
But better butter makes better batter.

Big, better, best, never let it rest,
'Til your big be better and your better best.

3. M (m) Many men want more money;
Most men might make more money.

The moonbeams shimmer among the murmuring leaves.
The mist upon the mountain summits remained many months.

4. Wh (ʍ) The whippoorwill whistled somewhere in the garden.

5. W (w) The wicked witch went away on a windy winter day.

"From my wings are shaken the dews that waken
The sweet buds every one."—Shelley

6. F (f) "Fee, fi, fo, fum, huffy, huff, puff,
Enough is quite enough," puffed the giant in a huff.

"Fiddle, dee, dee; fiddle, dee, dee,
The fly has married the bumble bee."

"Fair is foul and foul is fair
Hover through fog and filthy air."
                              —Shakespeare

"The fair breeze blew, the white foam flew,
The furrow followed free."—Coleridge

7. V   (v)   Violet Virginia flavors liver with vinegar.
               The modest violet lives not in vain.

               "Wherever I wander, wherever I rove,
               The hills of the Highlands forever I love."
                                           —Burns

8. Th   (θ)   First of this thing and that thing, and t'other
               thing think.

               "The wind bloweth where it listeth, and thou
               hearest the sound thereof, but canst not tell
               whence it cometh or whither it goeth; so is
               everyone that is born of the spirit."—St. John

9. Th   (ð)   "Come hither, come hither, come hither!
               Here shall he see
               No enemy
               But winter and rough weather."—Shakespeare

10. T   (t)   "How they tinkle, tinkle, tinkle,
               In the icy air of night! . . .
               Keeping time, time, time
               In a sort of Runic rhyme."—Poe

               " 'Tis some visitor," I muttered, "tapping at my
               chamber door."—Poe

               "Tick-tock, tick-tock," the tiny clock ticked the
               time.

11. D   (d)   Deedle deedle dumpling, my son John.
               Ding dong dell, the donkey's in the deep, dark
               well.
               "Hey diddle diddle, the cat and the fiddle."
               "Ho! For the pirate Don Durk of Dowdee!"

               "Double, double, toil and trouble;
               Fire burn and cauldron bubble!"—Shakespeare

12. N   (n)   Nellie needed new needles and pins.
               The noble knight sings 'neath her window at
               noon.
               Nine nimble nymphs danced near the fountain.

13. L   (l)   Little Lilly likes licorice lollipops.

"The splendor falls on castle walls . . .
The long light shakes across the lakes,
And the wild cataract leaps in glory."
—Tennyson

"Some fly light as a laugh of glee,
Some fly soft as a long, low sigh;
All to the haven where each would be,
Fly!"—Swinburne

14. R   (r)   Around the rugged rocks the ragged rascal ran.

"I bring fresh showers for the thirsting flowers,
From the seas and the streams."—Shelley

"Roll on, thou dark and deep blue ocean, roll!"
—Byron

"The rain is raining all around,
It falls on field and tree;
It rains on the umbrellas here
And on the ships at sea."—Stevenson

15. S   (s)   Sing a song of sixpence.
Silly Sally sat selling seashells by the seashore.
Simple Simon sang a song of silver sails.

"I slip, I slide, I gloom, I glance
Among my skimming swallows;
I make the netted sunbeam dance
Against my sandy shallows."—Tennyson

16. Z   (z)   The busy bees buzz around the rose.
The man's nose was zig-zag on his face.

"Hear the loud alarum bells—
Brazen bells! . . .
Oh, the bells, bells, bells!
What a tale their terror tells
of Despair!"—Poe

Zera saw the zebra at the zoo.

17. Sh   (ʃ)   Hush, Shirley, hush. She shall eat the mush.
The dog shivers and shakes in the shade of the
    ash.
They shot once at the odd-shaped ship.
She brushed the wool of the sheep.

18. **Zh** (ʒ) It is a pleasure to search for the treasure.
Rouge is not of azure hue.

19. **Ch** (tʃ) "To sit in solemn silence in a dull, dark dock,
In a pestilential prison with a lifelong lock,
Awaiting the sensation of a short sharp shock,
From a cheap and chippy chopper on a big black block!
A big black block,
A short sharp shock,
From a cheap and chippy chopper on a big black block!"—Gilbert

"How much wood would a woodchuck chuck, if a woodchuck could chuck wood? Just as much wood as a woodchuck would if a woodchuck could chuck wood."

Cheerful Charles chartered a ship to China.

20. **J** (dʒ) Jingle, jangle, jungle joys.
Jumping, joyful girls and boys.

John was joking when he urged Jimmie to jump over the juniper hedge.

"Judge not that ye be not judged.
For with what judgment ye judge, ye shall be judged."—New Testament

21. **Y** (j) The youngster yelled as the yelping hyena leaped into the barnyard beyond the fence.
This beautiful canyon is peculiar because it yields a crop of a million onions.

22. **K** (k) Klopity-klop, klopity-klop, klopity-klop, klop,
Klop, trotted the horses before the cart.

The cat can catch the kingfish;
The King can catch the cat.

"For you are called plain Kate,
And bonnie Kate and sometimes Kate the curst;
But Kate, the prettiest Kate in Christendom,
Kate of Kate-hall, my super-dainty Kate!"
—Shakespeare

Q   (kw)   The quail quickly flew away when the queer
duck quacked.
The Queen quilted a quaint quilt.
The arrow quivered through the quiet air.

X   (ks)   It took six weeks to wax the floors.
What makes the snakes cross the lakes?
Mary bakes cakes until her head aches.

23. G   (g)   The grumpy gray goat gobbled grapes in the
grove.
The green grass grew at the garden gate.
"Grr," growled the dog with an angry grin.

24. Ng   (ŋ)   Spring brings the King of England to the coun-
try.
The bird is on the wing early in the spring.
I take a fling at hunting in the morning.

"The cock is crowing,
The stream is flowing, . . .
The cattle are grazing,
Their heads never raising; . . .
Small clouds are sailing,
Blue sky prevailing;
The rain is over and gone!"—Wordsworth

Nk   (ŋk)   "Robert of Lincoln is telling his name:
Bob-o-link, bob-o-link,
Spink, spank, spink."—Bryant

"I think," he said with a knowing wink, "our
work was done at the river's brink."—Poe

He blinked his eyes at the twinkling light.

25. H   (h)   Ha-ha-ha, ho-ho-ho, how he hopes his hops will
grow!
Happy Harry hops hoppity hop, hoppity, hop,
hop!

"Oh, who is so merry, heigh-ho, heigh-ho,
As the light hearted fairy, heigh-ho,
She dances and sings to the tune of her wings,
With a hey, and a heigh, and a ho, ho, ho!"

Section D

IMPROVEMENT THROUGH CREATIVE PLAY*

General Suggestions

Choose short, simple stories and fables. Use rhymes and poems with action and with two or more characters. Tell or read the story or rhyme to the children. Encourage the children to discuss the characters and scenes and imagine what might be said by the characters. Allow the children to volunteer to play the different characters and choose the cast for the first scene. An announcer and a stage manager may also be chosen.

Work with only one small unit or scene at a time. The dialogue should be original and spontaneous. It will, of course, constantly change and should improve as constructive criticism is given *after* each scene is completed. Thus, after the first scene, the children may discuss the production and decide how it could be improved, then a second cast may be chosen and the first scene repeated. Change the cast with each repetition. Repeat the first scene until it is well done, before the second scene is attempted.

The children should not be interrupted while the play is in production. Criticism by the teacher and by the children must always be constructive. "I think it would have been better if the dog had been ready to come in at the crash of

---

* Selected references concerning creative play and group activities will be found in Appendix B.

the dish" is much more helpful than to say, "I don't think the dog played his part right." As the play develops, one scene at a time, the interest grows. When the play is completed any child in the group should be willing and able to play any part.

In working with creative dramatization for the purpose of speech improvement, little attention need be given to stage setting and costuming. The stage may be a raised platform or just one end of a room. A table and a few chairs will be sufficient to set any scene. The children's imaginations will carry them to any country and place them in almost any situation. There are no costumes, no properties, no light changes, no curtain pullings. The children sit in chairs before the stage, whatever it may be, and when characters are chosen from the volunteers, the players proceed to the stage and improvise their lines and carry out their own ideas of the action.

The suggested selections for creative play which follow are arranged according to graded levels from easy and simple material to the more difficult. In use of the material, however, such an arrangement is flexible. Only the teacher is able to judge when her group will demand material more or less mature in content.

It is suggested that the story be read or told to the children first. In some instances, the children may want to read the stories themselves. The dramatizations as presented here are not presented for use as formal dramatizations. It has been found helpful, however, after the story has been studied, to read to the group the dramatizations as they have been worked out by other children through the use of creative play. The reading of such dramatizations often proves to be stimulating and will usually inspire better production through creative play by the children themselves. Under no circumstances should the children memorize the lines of the dramatizations as they are presented here because such formalization defeats the purpose of creative play. Read these dramatizations only after the children have studied the original story and discussed the characters and scenes. Then the reading of the dramatizations may stimulate the children to create a better performance themselves.

In using creative play for the purpose of speech correction, the teacher must keep in mind a few basic principles. First, correction should be given to the children as a group. No child should be made to feel conspicuous by having his speech errors pointed out to him personally. The announcer may say, "Thith ith the thtory of Thimple Thimon." The teacher will let the dramatization continue *without interruption*. After the children finish the scene, the teacher may comment. "That was quite well done. I liked the way the Pieman cried 'Pies for sale,' and the way Simple Simon spoke. He was so clear we could all understand him very well. What did you like about it?"

When the good things have been pointed out, the teacher may ask, "How can we improve upon the play? Would it be better if————" and then constructive criticism is given by the teacher and the children.

To correct individual errors by using group stimulation, the teacher will use a technique such as, "There are a great many (s) sounds in this play. Can you find some (s) words? That's right, 'Simple Simon,' 'Pies for sale,' and 'alas.' Let's all try these words and remember to get a good (s) sound with the tongue away from the teeth." When the class makes the attempt, the teacher tells them, "That is fine! Now let's all be the announcer and try: This is the story of Simple Simon and the Pieman. Let's all watch that we get good (s) sounds."

The teacher may watch the children who need to develop a correct use of the sound. She may at this point let a number of the children try the announcer's line alone. She will offer suggestions and comment favorably as the children try for the good (s) sound. This type of constructive criticism will go on continually through the process of the group work, but will be given only after a scene is finished and after the children have returned to their chairs.

Illustration of the Development of Creative Play

How the Story of Simple Simon May Be Developed Through Creative Play. The teacher will read the rhyme or perhaps the children will read it in chorus:

> Simple Simon met a pieman
> Going to the fair;
> Says Simple Simon to the pieman,
> "Let me taste your ware."
> Says the pieman to Simple Simon
> "Show me first your penny."
> Says Simple Simon to the pieman,
> "Indeed I have not any."

The teacher may ask how many characters there are in the rhyme.

"Two," the children will likely reply. "Simple Simon and the Pieman."

The discussion may continue as follows:

"What is Simple Simon like?"

"He is slow, rather lazy, and good natured."

"What is the Pieman like?"

"He is a large, jolly, kind man."

"Where is Simple Simon going?"

"He is walking along the street on his way to the fair."

"Whom does he meet?"

"The Pieman, who is selling pies."

"I wonder what the Pieman might be saying."

"He might be saying, "Pies for sale! Pies for sale! Cherry pie! Pumpkin pie! Apple pie! All kinds of pies!' "

"When Simple Simon sees the Pieman, what would he likely say?"

"He would probably say, 'Good morning, Mr. Pieman.' "

"To which the Pieman would likely reply in what manner?"

"Good morning, Simple Simon, where are you going?"

"I am going to the fair. I'm very hungry, however, and I should like to taste one of your wonderful pies."

"That, I fear, will cost you a penny, my friend."

"Alas, alack! Indeed, I have no penny!"

"Alas and alack! Then you can have no pie! Pies for sale! Pies for sale! Cream pie! Blueberry pie! Chocolate pie! All kinds of pie!"

Someone may suggest: "I think the Pieman will feel sorry for Simple Simon and call him back and give him a small pie."

Thus the dramatization grows and is continued as long as the children's interest lasts. When interest lags, new material must be introduced.

Traditional Rhymes—Selections for Creative Play

LITTLE MISS MUFFET

Little Miss Muffet
Sat on a tuffet
Eating her curds and whey;
There came a big spider
And sat down beside her,
And frightened Miss Muffet away.

PUSSY-CAT, PUSSY-CAT

Pussy-cat, Pussy-cat, where have you been?
"I've been up to London to look at the Queen."
Pussy-cat, Pussy-cat, what did you there?
"I frightened a little mouse under the chair."

OLD KING COLE

Old King Cole was a merry old soul,
And a merry old soul was he;
He called for his pipe, and he called for his bowl,
And he called for his fiddlers three.
Every fiddler he had a fine fiddle.
And a very fine fiddle had he;
Tweedle deedle dee, went the fiddlers.
Oh, there's none so rare as can compare
With King Cole and his fiddlers three.

OLD MOTHER HUBBARD

Old Mother Hubbard
Went to the cupboard,
To get her poor dog a bone;
But when she came there,
The cupboard was bare,
And so the poor dog had none.

She went to the fruit store,
To buy him some fruit;
But when she came back
He was playing the flute.

She went to the hatter's
To buy him a hat;
But when she came back,
He was feeding the cat.

She went to the barber's
To buy him a wig;
But when she came back,
He was dancing a jig.

She went to the cobbler's
To buy him some shoes;
But when she came back,
He was reading the news.

The dame made a curtsy,
The dog made a bow;
The dame said, "Your servant";
The dog said, "Bow-wow."

THE OLD WOMAN AND HER PIG

One day when an old woman was cleaning her house, she found a little crooked sixpence.

"What," she said, "shall I do with this little sixpence? I know! I shall go to market and buy a little pig!"

As she was coming home, she came to a stile. The pig was stubborn and would not go over the stile.

She went a little farther, and she met a dog. She said to the dog:

"Dog, dog, bite pig!
Pig won't go over the stile,
And I cannot get home tonight."

But the dog would not.
She went a little farther,
And she met a stick. So she said:

"Stick, stick, beat dog!
Dog won't bite pig;
Pig won't go over the stile,
And I cannot get home tonight."

But the stick would not.
She went a little farther,
And she met a fire. So she said:

"Fire, fire, burn stick!
Stick won't beat dog;
Dog won't bite pig;
Pig won't go over the stile,
And I cannot get home tonight."

But the fire would not.
She went a little farther
And she met some water. So she said:

"Water, water, quench fire!
Fire won't burn stick;
Stick won't beat dog;
Dog won't bite pig;
Pig won't go over the stile,
And I cannot get home tonight."

But the water would not.
She went a little farther,
And she met an ox. So she said:

"Ox, ox, drink water!"
Water won't quench fire;
Fire won't burn stick;
Stick won't beat dog;
Dog won't bite pig;
Pig won't go over the stile,
And I cannot get home tonight."

But the ox would not.
She went a little farther,
And she met a butcher. So she said:

"Butcher, butcher, kill ox!
Ox won't drink water;
Water won't quench fire;
Fire won't burn stick;
Stick won't beat dog;
Dog won't bite pig;
Pig won't go over the stile,
And I cannot get home tonight."

But the butcher would not.
She went a little farther,
And she met a rope. So she said:

"Rope, rope, hang butcher!
Butcher won't kill ox;
Ox won't drink water;
Water won't quench fire;
Fire won't burn stick;
Stick won't beat dog;
Dog won't bite pig;
Pig won't go over the stile,
And I cannot get home tonight."

But the rope would not.
She went a little farther,
And she met a rat. So she said:

"Rat, rat, gnaw rope;
Rope won't hang butcher;
Butcher won't kill ox;
Ox won't drink water;

Water won't quench fire;
Fire won't burn stick;
Stick won't beat dog;
Dog won't bite pig;
Pig won't go over the stile;
And I cannot get home tonight."

But the rat would not.
She went a little farther
And she met a cat. So she said:

"Cat, cat, kill rat!
Rat won't gnaw rope;
Rope won't hang butcher;
Butcher won't kill ox;
Ox won't drink water;
Water won't quench fire;
Fire won't burn stick;
Stick won't beat dog;
Dog won't bite pig;
Pig won't go over the stile,
And I cannot get home tonight."

"Well," said the cat, "if you will give me a saucer of milk, I might attempt to kill the rat."

So the old woman went to a farmer near by and asked him for a saucer of milk.

"Well," said the farmer, " if you will fetch some hay for the cow, I will give you a saucer of milk."

So the old woman fetched some hay for the cow, and the farmer gave her a saucer of milk. She gave the cat the milk and then—

The cat began to kill the rat;
The rat began to gnaw the rope;
The rope began to hang the butcher;
The butcher began to kill the ox;
The ox began to drink the water;
The water began to quench the fire;
The fire began to burn the stick;
The stick began to beat the dog;
The dog began to bite the pig;
The pig jumped over the stile;
And so the old woman reached home that night.

There Was an Old Woman as I've Heard Tell

There was an old woman, as I've heard tell,
She went to market her eggs for to sell;
She went to market all on a market-day,
And she fell asleep on the King's highway.

There came by a peddler whose name was Stout.
He cut her petticoat all round about;
He cut her petticoats up to her knees,
Which made the old woman to shiver and freeze.

When this little woman first did wake,
She began to shiver and she began to shake;
She began to wonder and she began to cry,
"Oh! deary, deary me, this is none of I!

"But if it be I, as I do hope it be,
I've a little dog at home and he'll know me;
If it be I, he'll wag his little tail,
And if it be not I, he'll loudly bark and wail."

Home went the little woman all in the dark,
Up got the little dog, and he began to bark;
He began to bark, so she began to cry,
"Oh! deary, deary me, this is none of I!"

Three Little Kittens

Three little kittens lost their mittens,
And they began to cry;
"Oh, mother, dear, we greatly fear
That we have lost our mittens."
"What! Lost your mittens, you naughty kittens!
Then you shall have no pie.
Mee-ow, mee-ow, then you shall have no pie."

The three little kittens found their mittens,
And they began to cry;
"Oh, mother, dear, see here, see here,
We all have found our mittens."

"Put on your mittens, you silly kittens,
And you may have some pie."
"Purr, purr, purr, oh, let us have some pie."

The three little kittens put on their mittens,
And soon ate up the pie;
"Oh, mother, dear, we greatly fear
That we have soiled our mittens."
"What! soiled your mittens, you naughty kittens!"
And they began to sigh.
Mee-ow, mee-ow, mee-ow, and they began to sigh.

The three little kittens washed their mittens,
And hung them out to dry;
"Oh, mother, dear, see here, see here,
We have washed our mittens clean."
"What! washed your mittens! You sweet litle kittens!
Shh! I smell a rat close by!"
"Mee-ow, mee-ow, mee-ow! We smell a rat close by."

DRAMATIZATION OF THE RHYME OF THE THREE LITTLE
KITTENS. *As it was developed through creative play by a
group of third-grade children.*

Mother	Kittens, kittens, kittens! Come and get ready for some pie.
Kittens	Meow, meow, meow! Oh, Mother dear, see here. We have lost our mittens!
Mother	What! Lost your mittens! You thoughtless little kittens. You shall have no pie until you've found your mittens. *(Kittens leave crying meow, meow!)*
Mother	Oh, my careless little kittens! If they find their mittens, I shall give them each a nice big piece of pie. *(She rolls out her pie and puts the crust in the tin.)* A pie for my kittens now I make; All brown and nice the pie I'll bake. A cup of berries fresh and neat, A little sugar makes kittens sweet; A bit of spice to make them nice, A bit of tart to make them smart, And now my pie is all complete. *(She puts the pie into the oven.)*

Kittens	*(They come running in.)* Oh, Mother dear, see here, see here. Our mittens we have found!
Mother	What! Found your mittens! You sweet little kittens! Soon you shall have some pie!
Bufty	Guess where we found our mittens!
Mother	I'll never guess. You will have to tell me!
Tiny Puff	We made a snow man, big and fat, and our mittens we could not find. The snow man must have swallowed our mittens.
Susie	We broke the snow man into a hundred pieces and then we found our mittens.
Mother	You found your mittens! You dear little kittens. Now, you shall have some berry pie!
Kittens	Berry pie! Yum, yum, yum!
Bufty	Oh, what good pie! I wish mother would make pie every day!
Susie	I am glad we were good little kittens.
Tiny Puff	So am I! But I think that I shall die! My mittens are covered with pie!
Kittens	Oh, Mother dear, see here, see here! Our mittens we have soiled!
Mother	What! Soiled your mittens! You naughty kittens! Think of the work you make for me. Now, I shall have no time for pie!
Kittens	Oh, Mother dear, we are sorry kittens. We did not mean to soil our mittens. Meow! Meow! Meow!
Susie	Let us wash our mittens, dear brother kittens!
Kittens	Oh, Mother dear, see here, see here! We will wash our mittens clean!
Mother	What! Wash your mittens. You sweet little kittens. Now Mother shall have some pie.
Kittens	Rub-dub, dub, six mittens to scrub.
Tiny Puff	Lick them and slick them and make them glow!
Bufty	Look at mine, as white as snow!
Susie	See my mittens are nice and clean!

Kittens	Three little kittens, they couldn't be mean. Meow, meow, MEOW! Oh, Mother dear, see here, see here, our mittens are nice and white.
Mother	What! Clean little mittens; you dear little kittens. You surely scrubbed them right.
Kittens	Meow, meow, MEOW!
Mother	My three little kittens are dear little kittens and so Mother will not sigh. But sh, sh, sh! I smell a mouse near by!
Kittens	A mouse! Oh Mother, we are full of pie!
Mouse	Ha, ha, ha! Ho, ho, ho! You can't catch me; I guess I know! Three little kittens so full of pie, they can't catch a mouse, though he's near by!
Mother	Go to sleep, kittens, so full of pie; When you awaken the mousey will fly, Let the mouse dance and let the mouse jest, Soon he will run and hide in his nest.

Stories and Fables for Creative Play

Stories suitable for use in creative play are innumerable. Short, simple stories are the best to use. The stories should be graded to the age and ability of the children. A wealth of material will be found in fables, folklore, and old fairy tales. The children in the youngest groups will enjoy working with *The Little Red Hen, Three Billy Goats Gruff, Peter Rabbit, The Three Little Pigs, The Three Bears, The Fox and the Crow, The Lion and the Mouse, The Tortoise and the Hare, The Elves and the Shoemaker, The Gingerbread Man, The Rabbit Who Wanted Wings, Little Sambo, The Town Mouse and the Country Mouse,* and *Mr. Wolf Makes a Failure.*

ILLUSTRATION OF THE DEVELOPMENT OF CREATIVE PLAY THROUGH THE USE OF THE STORY OF THE TOWN MOUSE AND THE COUNTRY MOUSE. The story is told or read to the class once without interruption.

Now you must know that a Town Mouse once upon a time went on a visit to his cousin in the country. He was rough and ready, this cousin, but he loved his town friend and made him heartily welcome. Beans and bacon, cheese and bread were all he had to offer, but he offered them freely. The Town Mouse rather turned up his long nose at this country fare.

"I cannot understand, Cousin," he said, "how you can put up with such poor food as this. Of course, you cannot expect anything better in the country. Come with me and I will show you how to live. When you have been in town a week you will wonder how you could ever have stood a country life."

No sooner said than done. The two mice set off for the town and arrived at the Town Mouse's residence late that night.

"You will want some refreshments after our journey," said the polite Town Mouse, and took his friend into the grand dining room. There they found the remains of a fine feast. Soon the two mice were eating up jellies and cakes and all that was nice. Suddenly they heard growling and barking.

"What is that?" said the Country Mouse.

"It is only the dogs of the house," answered the other.

"Only!" said the Country Mouse. "I do not like that music with my dinner."

Just at that moment the door flew open, and in came two dogs. The two mice had to scamper down and run.

"Good-bye, Cousin," said the Country Mouse.

"What! Going so soon?" said the other.

"Yes," replied the Country Mouse. "Better beans and bacon in peace than cakes and ale in fear."

The teacher may go over the story a second time, asking questions and encouraging suggestions as to where the story takes place, who the characters are, and what the characters may say and do.

The children will probably decide on two scenes: the first at the home of the Country Mouse, the second at the home of the Town Mouse. The characters may include the Town Mouse, the Country Mouse, at least one dog, and maybe a cat. A cat is often added to the story by the children.

One group of second grade children decided that the Country Mouse should telephone the Town Mouse and invite him to his home in the country. This accomplished, the Town Mouse arrived and dinner was served. The Town Mouse, in accordance with the fable, complained about the food and invited the Country Mouse to his town house. So the second scene opened across the room where a table and two chairs represented the home of the Town Mouse.

Arriving at the town house, they found a mouse banquet in the remains of a feast. As the play continued, the children developed the conversation. Often a new thought or a clever line was added as the play progressed. After being repeated dozens of times, any child in the group was able to play any part. The play finally developed as follows:

THE TOWN MOUSE AND THE COUNTRY MOUSE

(The stage has been set by the stage manager. There is a table on the stage with a chair at each end of the table.)

Announcer	This is the story of the Town Mouse and the Country Mouse. First, you see the poor home of the Country Mouse.
Country Mouse	*(He is talking over the telephone.)* Hello, hello. I wish to talk to Mr. Town Mouse, number six-eight-six-two. Hello, is that you, Cousin Town Mouse? Well, this is your cousin, Country Mouse, speaking. Why don't you pay me a visit? The flowers are in bloom, and it is very pleasant out here in the country. Oh, you will come right out? That is fine. I will be looking for you. Good-bye. *(The Country Mouse straightens a chair, sweeps the floor, dusts his furniture.)* I must set the table for dinner. *(He sets the table.)*
Town Mouse	*(Knocking at the imaginary door)* Yo ho! Yo ho!
Country Mouse	Come in, Cousin Town Mouse. I am very glad to have you here. Dinner is on the table. I imagine you are very hungry.
Town Mouse	I am hungry. It was a long run from the town to your house. What do you have for dinner tonight?
Country Mouse	I do not have much to offer, only bacon, cheese, and beans, but you are most welcome to all that I have. I only wish that I had more to give you.
Town Mouse	Tut, tut, I cannot understand, Cousin Country Mouse, how you can put up with such poor food as this. But I don't suppose you can expect anything better in the country. Come to the city with me and I will show you how you should live. When you

have been there for a few days you will wonder how you could ever have liked this life in the country.

Country Mouse   Do you have many good things to eat in the city?

Town Mouse   Why, we have a banquet every night. Cake and candy, strawberry jam, chickens, and nuts are always on my table.

Country Mouse   Cousin Town Mouse, I believe I would like to visit the city. I do get tired of this country life.

Town Mouse   Let us leave at once. I will show you a good time in the city. (*They leave the stage.*)

Announcer   The Town Mouse and the Country Mouse are on their way to the big city. In this second scene you must know that you no longer see the poor home of the Country Mouse, but only the beautiful home of Mr. Town Mouse.

(*The cat and the dog are sleeping in the background.*)

Town Mouse   (*Enters slowly, looks around, beckons to his cousin, whispering.*)

The coast is clear. Shh! Come in quietly. See the banquet on the table! What did I tell you? I am hungry; let us get something to eat now.

Country Mouse   Cats and fishes! What luck! Jam and pickles, nuts, chocolate candy, and chickens, too! For my part, I shall have some of this gingerbread.

Town Mouse   Help yourself, only do not make too much noise.

Country Mouse   Why are you afraid of making too much noise?

Town Mouse   We must not disturb Buster and Tabby.

Country Mouse   And who are Buster and Tabby, please?

Town Mouse   The dog and the cat of this house. They are my enemies.

Country Mouse   (*He knocks over an imaginary dish.*) Oh, mercy me! I have broken a fine dish.

Buster   (*Growling as he awakens*) Grrr! What can all this noise be? There must be robbers in the house!

Tabby   I think I smell a rat!

Country Mouse   (*Shaking*) What shall we do?

Town Mouse   Run for your life! (*He runs around the table.*)

Buster	Woof! Woof! Woof! (He chases the Town Mouse.)
Tabby	Meow! Meow! Meow! (He chases the Country Mouse.)
Country Mouse	Good-bye, Cousin Town Mouse! (*Buster and Tabby leave the stage.*)
Town Mouse	What! Are you leaving so soon?
Country Mouse	Yes, I don't like this music with my dinner. I would rather have cheese and bacon in peace, than have cake and be afraid.

It must be realized that a production such as this is worked out only over an extended period of time. The second-grade children who produced this dramatization heard the story read, talked about the characters, the action, the scenes, discussed what the characters might say, and then played out the scenes over and over again until any child could play any part. The characters were changed with each scene and the dialogue continually changed. Finally, after three weeks of practice, the second-grade children presented the dramatization for the kindergarten children. Even at the last minute, the children of the second grade did not know which child would play which part. They sat in a group and volunteered for parts exactly as they had during their creative play sessions, and even during this final production no properties or costumes were used.

ILLUSTRATION OF CREATIVE PLAY THROUGH THE USE OF THE STORY OF LITTLE SAMBO AND THE TIGERS.*

Once upon a time there was a little boy and his name was Little Sambo. His mother was called Mumbo and his father was called Jumbo. One day Mumbo gave Sambo a little red coat, a pair of beautiful blue trousers, a little green umbrella, and a lovely pair of purple shoes with crimson soles and crimson linings.

Then wasn't Sambo grand!

He put on his fine clothes and went for a walk in the jungle. By and by he met a tiger.

* From Helen Bannerman, *Little Black Sambo*, Happy Hour Books, The Macmillan Company. Used by special permission from the publishers.

The tiger growled at him and said, "Little Sambo, I'm going to eat you up!"

Little Sambo cried, "Oh, please, Mr. Tiger, don't eat me up, and I'll give you my beautiful little red coat."

Little Sambo took off his beautiful red coat and the tiger put it on, and off he went with his head in the air, saying, "Now I'm the grandest tiger in the jungle."

Little Sambo went still farther and he met another tiger.

The tiger growled at him and said, "Little Sambo, I'm going to eat you up!"

Little Sambo said, "Oh, please, Mr. Tiger, don't eat me up, and I'll give you my beautiful blue trousers."

Then the tiger said, "Very well, I won't eat you up this time, but you must give me your beautiful blue trousers."

Little Sambo took off his beautiful blue trousers, and the tiger put them on, and off he went with his head in the air, saying, "Now I'm the grandest tiger in the jungle!"

Little Sambo went still farther and he met another tiger.

The tiger growled at him and said, "Little Sambo, I'm going to eat you up!"

Little Sambo said, "Oh, please, Mr. Tiger, don't eat me up, and I'll give you my lovely purple shoes with crimson soles and crimson linings."

But the tiger said, "Oh, no, your shoes wouldn't do me any good. I have four feet, and you have only two. I'm going to eat you up."

Then Little Sambo said, "You could put them on your ears."

"So I could," said the tiger. "That's a very good idea. I won't eat you this time."

Little Sambo took off his lovely purple shoes with the crimson soles and crimson linings and the tiger put one on each ear, and off he went with his head in the air, saying, "Now, I'm the grandest tiger in the jungle!"

Little Sambo went still farther and he met another tiger. The Tiger growled at him and said, "Little Sambo, I'm going to eat you up!"

Little Sambo said, "Oh, please, Mr. Tiger, don't eat me up, and I'll give you my beautiful green umbrella."

The tiger said, "Oh, no, your umbrella wouldn't do me any good. I couldn't carry it. You see, I have to use my four feet to walk on. I'm going to eat you up."

"Oh," said Little Sambo, "I know what you could do. You could tie a knot in your tail and carry it that way."

"So I could," said the tiger.

He tied a knot in his tail and slipped the umbrella through it, and off he went with his head in the air, saying, "Now I'm the grandest tiger in the jungle."

Poor Little Sambo had lost all his fine clothes and he started for home, crying.

By and by he heard a terrible noise that sounded like: GrrrrRRR! It grew louder and louder.

"Oh dear," said Little Sambo, "what shall I do? Here come the tigers to eat me up!"

He ran and hid behind a palm tree. After a while he peeped around it to see what the tigers were doing.

There were all the tigers fighting. Each said that he was the grandest tiger in the jungle. At last they grew so angry that they took off their fine clothes and began to fight again.

They came rolling out tumbling right to the foot of the tree, one tiger with another tiger's tail in his mouth.

Little Sambo called out, "Tigers, don't you want your clothes any more? If you don't want them, say so, and I'll take them back."

But the tigers wouldn't let go of each other's tails. All that they said was, "GrrrrRRRR!"

Then Little Sambo put on his fine clothes and walked off.

When the tigers saw this, they were very, very angry, but they wouldn't let go of each other's tails. They ran 'round and 'round the tree, faster and faster, trying to eat each other up. Finally they ran so fast that they just melted away and there was nothing left of them but melted butter around the foot of the tree.

That evening Jumbo was coming home from work with a big brass bowl in his arms. When he saw what was left of the tigers, he said:

"Oh, what nice melted butter! I'll take some home to Mumbo."

So he filled up the big brass bowl and carried it home to Mumbo. When Mumbo saw the melted butter she was very much pleased.

"Now," she said, "we will have pancakes for supper!"

So she mixed up some flour and eggs and milk and sugar and the butter and made a huge platter of lovely pancakes.

Then they all sat down to supper. Mumbo ate twenty-seven pancakes because she made them. Jumbo ate fifty-five pancakes because he brought the butter home.

But Little Sambo ate one hundred and ninety-six pancakes because he was so hungry.

DRAMATIZATION OF LITTLE SAMBO AND THE TIGERS. *As it was developed through creative play by a group of third-grade children.*

| Announcer | The first scene takes place in Sambo's home. Mumbo has finished making new clothes for Sambo. He is putting them on while Jumbo watches. |

Mumbo	Now, you must be careful with your beautiful new clothes, Sambo. Do not get them dirty and do not lose them.
Jumbo	And stay away from the tigers in the jungle.
Little Sambo	My new clothes are lovely, Mumbo. Thank you so much for making them for me. Please, may I go for a walk in my little red coat, my beautiful blue trousers, and my lovely purple shoes?
Mumbo	Yes, but do not go too far into the jungle. Carry your new green umbrella to keep the sun from burning you.
Little Sambo	Oh, I will be very careful. Good-bye, Mumbo. Good-bye, Jumbo.
Announcer	The second scene is in the jungle. Sambo is walking with his head held high. He meets the first tiger.
Tiger I	Grrr, Little Sambo, I'm going to eat you up!
Little Sambo	Oh, please, Mr. Tiger, don't eat me up. I'll give you my beautiful red coat.
Tiger I	Very well, I won't eat you this time, but you must give me your beautiful red coat.
Little Sambo	I'll help you put it on. There!
Tiger I	Now I'm the grandest tiger in the jungle! (*He struts off with his head held high.*)
Little Sambo	Well, I have lost my beautiful little red coat, but I am still alive.
Tiger II	Grrr! Little Sambo, I am going to eat you up!
Little Sambo	Ohhh! Another tiger! Oh, please, Mr. Tiger, don't eat me up. I'll give you my beautiful blue trousers.
Tiger II	Very well, I won't eat you up this time, but you must give me your beautiful blue trousers.
Little Sambo	Here they are.
Tiger II	(*He struts off with his head high.*) Now, I'm the grandest tiger in the jungle!
Little Sambo	Well, I still have my new purple shoes with the crimson soles and crimson linings, and I still have my green umbrella, and I am still alive!

Tiger III	Grrrr! Little Sambo, I am going to eat you up!
Little Sambo	What! Another tiger? Oh, please, Mr. Tiger, don't eat me up. I'll give you my lovely purple shoes with the crimson soles and crimson linings.
Tiger III	Oh, no. Your shoes wouldn't do me any good. You see, you have only two feet, but I have four. I'm going to eat you up at once!
Little Sambo	Wait a minute! You could put my shoes on your ears and you would be very beautiful.
Tiger III	So I could. That is a very fine idea. I will not eat you this time.
Little Sambo	Oh, thank you, Mr. Tiger. I will help you put my shoes upon your ears. There! You are very handsome.
Tiger III	I'm the grandest tiger in the jungle!
Little Sambo	Alas, all I have is my little green umbrella, but I am very happy to be alive.
Tiger IV	Grrrr! Little Sambo, I am going to eat you up!
Little Sambo	Oh, oh! Please, Mr. Tiger, don't eat me up! I'll give you my beautiful green umbrella.
Tiger IV	Your umbrella will do me no good. I couldn't carry it. I have to use my four feet to walk. I shall eat you up right now!
Little Sambo	No, no! Not now! Wait a minute. Please wait just a minute!
Tiger IV	Not a second. I shall eat you right now!
Little Sambo	Wait! I have an idea. You can tie a knot in your tail and carry my beautiful green umbrella that way!
Tiger IV	Why, yes, so I could.
Little Sambo	I will help you tie the knot. There! Now slip the umbrella through it. My, but that is fine looking!
Tiger IV	I guess I'm beautiful all right. In fact, I'm just about the grandest tiger in the jungle!
Little Sambo	All my pretty new clothes are gone. I am almost afraid to go home and tell Mumbo. Perhaps Mumbo will be so happy to see me alive that she

	will not scold me for losing my clothes and my umbrella.
Tigers I, II, III, IV	I'm the grandest Tiger in the jungle!
Tiger I	Who says he is the grandest tiger in the jungle?
Tiger IV	I am, of course. See my beautiful new green umbrella?
Tiger II	Grrr! Who says he is the grandest tiger in the jungle?
Tiger III	I am, of course. See my beautiful new shoes on my ears?
Tiger I	You are both wrong! I am the grandest tiger in the jungle. I, with my beautiful red coat!
Tiger II	Ho, ho, ho! You are all wrong. I, with my beautiful blue trousers, I am the grandest tiger in the jungle!
Tigers I, II, III, IV	I am! I am! I am! I am!
	(*They take off their fine new clothes, lay them by the imaginary tree and chase each other around and around in a circle.*)
Little Sambo	Oh, Mr. Tigers, don't you want your nice new clothes anymore?
Tigers	Grrrr! Grrrr!
Little Sambo	Well, if you are really through with them, I'll take them home with me, if you do not object.
Tigers	(*Still chasing each other around the tree*) Grrrrr-rrrr! Grrrrrrrrrr!
Announcer	Scene III takes place at home again.
Little Sambo	Oh, Mumbo, they were the biggest tigers I have ever seen!
Mumbo	Oh, I am so happy that my little Sambo is safe! You were a bright boy to escape from the tigers. I am glad that you have your new clothes again. You must promise to stay away from the tigers.
Little Sambo	Mumbo, I do not want to have anything more to do with the tigers!
Jumbo	(*From outside*) Yo ho! See what I have found!
Little Sambo	It is Jumbo. Hurry! Let us see what you have found.

Jumbo	(*Entering*) As I was coming home through the jungle, I saw four very angry tigers running around a tree. They ran so fast that they just melted away. When I came to the tree I saw nothing there but melted butter. So I filled my brass bowl with the butter, and there you are, nice fresh butter for Mumbo's pancakes!
Mumbo	I will make them at once, and you shall have them for supper. I shall eat twenty-seven pancakes, because I shall make them.
Jumbo	I shall eat fifty-five pancakes, because I brought the butter home!
Little Sambo	And I shall eat one hundred and ninety-six pancakes, because I am so hungry!

It will be noticed that the dramatization of the story was limited to three scenes. At other times, different children have planned for four scenes in this story, using a scene just before the last, showing Jumbo as he finds the butter and fills his bowl.

How the Story of Hansel and Gretel Was Developed Through Creative Play. It will be noted in this dramatization that a number of details in the created play differ from the original fairy tale. When the story was studied by a group of fourth and fifth graders, they decided to make a number of changes which they believed would improve their play. Insofar as these changes were constructive, they were encouraged by the teacher.

First, it was desired that the mother be a good mother, rather than a cruel stepmother. To bring about this change, the parents were given a logical reason for abandoning their children. To dispel with any idea of cruelty on the part of the parents, they were made to return and search for their children. It was felt that Hansel should be given a just cause in carrying away the jewels, therefore the story of the family jewels was fabricated.

Since it was impractical in the play to have Hansel and Gretel ride home on the back of a white swan, the white bird was invented to lead the children home. To keep the witch from being burned to death in the oven, the children decided to have Hansel and Gretel throw cold water on the stove. The witch's bag of magic was baked away, so she had no magic power left and was only a poor old woman.

At the close of the play the parents were happy when their children returned home.

HANSEL AND GRETEL[*]

Announcer   Would you like to go into a great forest and look into the poor and humble home of a woodcutter? Here a kind man and his wife and two little children live. They are so very poor that there is not even porridge in the house for breakfast. It is early morning. The two little children have awakened. They are dressed, except for putting on their shoes.

Scene I

Gretel   (*Enters from the left, carrying her shoes.*) Oh dear, I am so cold and hungry. I just couldn't sleep any longer. Hansel, perhaps if we search the woods this morning, we may find a few berries to eat.

Hansel   (*Follows Gretel in. He also carries his shoes.*) What's that you say? Berries? Last night I dreamed of the finest roast goose all decorated with apple dumplings, and on the table were dressing and gravy and potatoes in jackets. Oh, I'm so hungry, I have pains!

Gretel   Poor Hansel. We might as well have stayed in bed. There is nothing to eat for breakfast.

Hansel   Shh! Mother and Father are coming. Let us finish dressing. (*They go out.*)

Father   (*Entering*) But we couldn't do it, mother, not with our two dear little children. However could you think of losing them in the thick, dark forest?

Mother   (*Follows Father in*) But what will become of them here? We cannot feed our children. Each day they grow more pale.

Father   But wife, I cannot find it in my heart to take my children into the forest and leave them there alone. The wild animals would soon come and devour them.

[*] From the story by the Brothers Grimm.

Mother	Then you had better think of another plan, quickly. Our little children will not live long at home where they must starve.
Father	Since our money and jewels were stolen four years ago, we have had little with which to buy food and clothing. Our poor children are cold and hungry and we can do nothing.
Mother	I thought perhaps if we should leave them in the forest another woodcutter who is more prosperous might find them and take them home with him. I feel certain that no harm will come to them, and it may be the only way of saving them from starvation.
Father	Perhaps you are right. There seems to be nothing else to do.
Mother	We will go far into the forest today, and you can build a great fire to frighten the animals away. Then we will go off to cut wood and leave the children asleep by the fire.
Father	Very well, we will do as you say. But I really pity the poor little children. Every night I shall pray for them.
Mother	Yes, that I shall do, too. Come, now, we must prepare to leave for the woods. (*They go out.*)
Gretel	(*Enters with Hansel. They still carry their shoes.*) Oh Hansel, Hansel, it is all over with us! I am afraid! Did you hear what our parents said? Oh, I know we shall be devoured by wild animals!
Hansel	Do be quiet, Gretel, and do not fret. I will find a way out of this.
Gretel	But how? We shall be alone and lost.
Hansel	I have a plan. This morning, when mother gives us our crust of bread for lunch, do not eat one bite of it, no matter how hungry you may be.
Gretel	I will do as you say, but I shall be very hungry.
Hansel	As we walk through the forest I shall break the bread into crumbs and drop them along the way, then we shall be able to get back home again by following the path of the bread crumbs. Be easy, little sister; I will not forsake you.
Gretel	Oh, Hansel, you are so clever! Now, I shall not be frightened at all.

Father	(*Enters*) Come, come, Hansel and Gretel. Are you not yet dressed? Today we go into the forest to cut wood.
Hansel	(*The children are putting on their shoes.*) We are almost dressed, father. In a second we shall be ready.
Mother	(*Enters*) How are my dear little children this morning?
Hansel	I slept well, mother, and I feel quite strong.
Mother	Bless you, my son. This morning you must both put on your woolen jackets, for it is chilly outside, and we must spend the day in the forest.
Gretel	We shall look for berries, mother.
Mother	Yes, indeed. And I have saved for each of you one crust of bread, but you must not eat it before lunch time, for you will get no more today.
Hansel	I will keep the bread in my pocket, mother. Gretel is so hungry, I fear that she will eat it at once.
Father	Poor little Gretel. Here, you may eat my piece of bread. I have no taste for it.
Gretel	No, no, father. You will need it for dinner when you have worked hard all morning cutting wood. I shall find wild berries in the woods; you will see.
Mother	Come, we must be on our way.
Hansel	We are coming. I just want to say farewell to my little white bird in the cage. Poor little fellow, he will be lonesome all day. Goodbye, little bird, goodbye!
Bird	(*A voice off stage*) Tweet, tweet, tweet, tweet!

Scene II

Announcer	What brave little children Hansel and Gretel are. Do you suppose a prosperous woodcutter will find them and save them from the dangers of the forest? I feel sorry for the mother and father, don't you? It is not easy for the mother and father to desert their children in such a manner. Now, they have gone a long way into the forest. Hansel and Gretel are gathering wood for a fire.
Father	That's a good girl, Gretel. You soon will have gathered wood enough for a great fire.
Hansel	Here is another armful of brushwood. Isn't that enough?
Mother	'Tis enough indeed! You have made a little mountain of wood. Touch a light to it, father. Now, children, lie

down by the fire and rest. Father and I must go to cut wood.

Father   (*Kneels to light the imaginary fire*) There, that is a good blaze. Gretel, make use of my jacket for a pillow. I shall not need it. I shall keep warm by exercise. Stay close by the fire and try to go to sleep.

Hansel   Yes, father. Goodbye, mother!
(*Time passes.*)

Gretel   Hansel, are you asleep?

Hansel   No, I cannot sleep. The fire is dying out, and I am getting cold.

Gretel   I think I hear father making strokes with his axe. Perhaps he is still near.

Hansel   'Tis only a dry branch hanging to a withered tree that the wind moves to and fro. Mother and father are far away by now. See, the sun is getting low.

Gretel   How shall we ever get out of this wood?

Hansel   Fear not, little sister. A full moon will be up tonight. We shall be able to find our way home by the crumbs of bread that I have scattered along the path by which we came.

Gretel   Let us start right away. Hansel, what are you waiting for?

Hansel   Alas, Gretel! I can find no crumbs of bread. The birds of the field and forest have eaten the crumbs.

Gretel   Now we are indeed lost. Oh Hansel, I am so very much frightened.

Hansel   Perhaps we can find our way back without the crumbs. Come, let us try.

Gretel   Was it from this way that we came?

Hansel   I think so; it seems to be right. I am sure of it. See, there is the blackberry bush that we passed.

Gretel   'Tis not the same berry bush, because that one has berries on it, and I am certain I stripped all the berries off the other one.

Hansel   Alas, I fear we are lost indeed! I know not which way to turn.

Bird   (*Voice off stage*) Tweet, tweet, tweet!

Gretel	Look, Hansel! Look at that little white bird! (*Points off left*) Oh, Hansel, it is your little bird!
Hansel	Perhaps father set him free so that he might show us the way home.
Gretel	He is calling to us!
Hansel	He wants us to follow him!
Gretel	Come, let us follow him!
Hansel	Oh, my dear little bird! Were you sent by father to show us the way? Where are you going? Wait, we will follow!
Bird	Tweet, tweet, tweet!
Gretel	We will follow, little bird; we will follow! (*Off left*)
Hansel	Where is he now Gretel? (*Off left*)
Gretel	(*Enters*) There, ahead on a branch of that old oak tree. Hurry, Hansel, we must not lose him.
Hansel	(*Enters*) Let us run! Go ahead, little bird. We are following you! (*Both children run off, right.*)
Bird	(*Voice off stage*) Tweet, tweet, tweet, tweet!
Gretel	(*Enters*) Oh, Hansel! The little white bird is leading us to safety. (*Hansel enters.*) Isn't that a little house that I see through the trees?
Hansel	It is indeed a house, and the bird is flying toward it. Soon we shall find shelter.
Bird	(*Voice off stage*) Tweet, tweet, tweet!
Gretel	(*Gazing off stage, left*) It is a beautiful little house, yet it seems a little queer. It is made up of so many colors. Our little white bird is perched on a tree near by.
Hansel	Perhaps someone there will give us food and shelter.
Gretel	It is such a funny house. I believe it is roofed with cake frosting. It looks like divinity candy!
Hansel	I believe the windows are of crystal sugar! (*They go off left.*)
Gretel	(*Off stage*) The door knob is a lollipop!
Hansel	The porch railings are of peppermint-stick candy!
Gretel	We shall make a fine meal of this!
Hansel	I will eat a piece of the roof, Gretel, and you can have the doorknob. How good this tastes!

(They enter. Hansel is eating a piece of cake, and Gretel is eating a lollipop.)

Gretel	It is most delicious! I can't eat fast enough!
Bird	*(In warning)* Tweet! Tweet! Tweet! Tweet!
Gretel	Wait a while, little bird. Wait until we have eaten, and then we will follow you. Oh, this doorknob is most delicious!
Bird	Tweet! Tweet! Tweet!
Witch	*(Off, left)* Grump, grump, grump! I hear something like a thump. Who into my house is breaking, Cake and candy both are taking?
Gretel	*(Runs to Hansel in fright)* Oh, Oh! What is that? Hansel, did you hear?
Hansel	Yes, but I see no one. Perhaps it was the wind.
Gretel	But the wind is not blowing!
Hansel	Oh well, perhaps if we give verse for verse it will be all right.
Gretel	But I cannot think of a verse.
Hansel	Well, I can. How is this? Just a taste or two we take Of your candy and your cake. We mean no harm, we are not vicious, But your house is most delicious.
Gretel	The door is opening! Oh! I am afraid!
Bird	TWEET! TWEET! TWEET!
Hansel	Silly, it is only an old woman. Maybe she will help us.
Witch	*(Enters from the left.)* Well, well, well, my dear little children. How came you here?
Hansel	We were lost in the woods and were cold and hungry. When my little white bird led us to your house, we could not resist the temptation to eat some of it.
Gretel	If you wish, we will work to pay for the damage we have done.
Witch	Ah, my dears, you must come inside and stay with me. You will be of no trouble. Inside I have a fine meal laid

out, and you shall eat of pancakes with syrup, and apples and nuts. Come inside, my dears.

Gretel Oh, thank you! We will be glad to come.

Witch Heh, heh, heh, heh, heh!

Bird TWEET! TWEET! TWEET!

(*Hansel and Gretel follow the Witch off, left.*)

Announcer That was a queer laugh the old woman gave when she led Hansel and Gretel into the house. I wonder what she intends to do with them. The night has passed and the little children have not come out of the house. Let us look inside and see what is happening. It is early morning and the old woman has built a fire in the kitchen stove.

Scene III

(*In the Witch's house. A large oven is supposedly at center. Cage left. Table and chair at right. The two cats are asleep near the oven. Gretel is asleep on the floor, right.*)

Witch Heh, heh, heh, heh, heh! Now, I have them. They shall never escape from me. My bag of magic power will not fail me. Aha, what a fine feast I shall have! Where is that lazy girl? Ha, sound asleep in the corner. I'll wake her soon enough. Here, you lazy bones, get up and fetch the water and cook something nice for your brother to eat. He is locked in my spare cage. He cannot escape from me. I shall fatten him, and when he is nice and fat I shall cook him for my breakfast! (*The Witch and the Cats dance with glee.*) For my breakfast, for my breakfast! A special treat for my breakfast!

Gretel Oh, oh, you are a cruel, wicked woman! I am afraid of you. I want to go home!

Witch You shall stay and work for me. Stop your crying; it will get you nowhere. Take the pail and fetch some water right away! Then we shall bake some ginger bread.

Gretel If we had been devoured by the beasts of the forest, we should have fared better.

Witch Out with you!

Gretel Yes, yes, I am going! (*Goes out*)

Witch Heh, heh, heh, heh, heh, heh! (*To Hansel*)
Now, little boy, let us see how you are growing. Put out

your finger that I may the better judge. Ugh! You are as skinny as a bone! But I will fatten you nicely. Just wait!

Oh, what a happy life I lead!
The bread dough I make, the girl shall kneed,
And kneed, and kneed, and kneed!
Into this bowl I put a small rock,
Then I add a tock from the clock;
Next the plum of little Jack Horner,
And a hair from my cat asleep in the corner,
A thimble of water from Pussy-in-the-well,
Plus a good wish flavored with pumpkin shell,
Then a handful of flour made from turnip-seed
And a pinch of ginger is all I need.
Ah, what splendid ginger bread this will make!

Why hasn't that stupid girl returned? (*Gretel enters*) Ah, there you are! Well, well, did you fetch the water from the well?

Gretel	Yes, here it is. Oh, will you please. . . .
Witch	Ask no favors of me. I grant none. We must hurry and get the bread into the oven. I have heated the oven and have already kneeded the dough. After this you must be here to kneed it. Now then, we must see if the oven is hot enough for the bread. Creep in and see if it is properly hot so that the bread may be properly baked.
Gretel	But I don't know how! However shall I creep into the oven?
Witch	You stupid girl! The oven door is large enough. Can't you see? Why, I could easily crawl into it myself. Here, I'll show you how.
Gretel	But you are only half way in. Must I get completely inside the oven?
Witch	Yes, completely in. Like this; see?

(*Gretel pushes the Witch into the oven and closes the oven door.*)

Witch   Stop it! Oh! Oh, oh, help! Help! What have you done? Let me out! Let me out!

(*The Cats jump against the oven door, squeal with pain, and run to the corner of the room.*)

Oh, bag of magic, hear my cry!
Help me out or I shall die!

Alas, alack, unlucky day!
My bag of magic baked away!

Gretel	I shall not let you out! You are a mean wicked old witch, and I shall not open that oven door!
Hansel	Gretel! Gretel!
Gretel	Oh, Hansel! Are you all right?
Hansel	Yes, Gretel, I am all right. Can you let me out?
Gretel	I will try. There is a huge bolt on the door, but if I pull hard I think I can open it.
Hansel	I fooled the old Witch. She wanted me fat, but I fooled her. I showed her a chicken bone when she asked to see my finger.
Gretel	She is now stuck so tight in the oven that she cannot open the heavy door. Hear her kicking against it? There . . . I have the bolt drawn on the cage. Push, Hansel, push! At last it is open. Oh, Hansel, my dear brother, let us dance! We are free!
Hansel	It is good to be out of that prison. Dear little Gretel, you were most clever . . . but the Witch! She will burn in that oven!
Gretel	Her magic power must be baked away by this time. Let us throw water on the oven to cool it.

(*They throw the water on the oven.*)

Hansel	Now, let us hurry away!
Gretel	If only we can get out of the woods.
Hansel	Wait! In my prison cage are many bags of gold and silver and many sparkling jewels. The old witch gave them to me to play with. She said I must be amused, because if I became of a sour disposition I would have a most sour flavor.
Gretel	But she did not mean for you to keep the jewels.
Hansel	The jewels were to be mine as long as I lived, so, as I am still living, there could be no harm in taking some of them home with us. Come, let us fill our pockets, and we shall be wealthy when we reach home.
Gretel	I can wrap some in my apron and carry it over my shoulder. Let us hurry!
Hansel	I wonder if my little bird is still waiting to show us the way home.

Gretel	Yes, yes! He is still there on a branch of the old oak tree. Come, come, let us be gone!
Bird	Tweet, tweet, tweet!
Hansel	Yes, little bird, we are coming. This time we will follow you closely, and we will not tarry on the way.
Bird	Tweet, tweet, tweet!
Hansel and Gretel	We are coming, little bird! (*Out right*)

Scene IV

Announcer	Are you not glad that the little white bird is taking Hansel and Gretel home? I'm glad that this time they are not going to stop on the way. Would you like to see them as they arrive at the woodcutter's little house? All right, let us take one last look at the children as they reach home.
Hansel	Let us surprise mother and father. We will call at the door and then run and hide in the bushes.
Gretel	All right. Yo ho!
Hansel	Is anyone home? Yo ho!
Gretel	Run, Hansel, run! (*They go off right.*)
Father	(*Enters, left*) Who is calling at our door? If it is a hungry wayfarer, let him come in. Why, there is no one here. Mother, did you not hear a call?
Mother	(*Enters from left*) I heard it distinctly, but I see no one.
Hansel and Gretel	Mother! Father!
Hansel	We have come home!
Mother	My little ones! Oh, my darling children!
Father	Hansel and Gretel, you have come back!
Hansel	Yes, yes, and we have had a great adventure.
Mother	Oh, my dears! We deeply regretted leaving you in the woods alone, and we went back that evening to find you, but you had gone.
Father	I let your little bird free, hoping he would find you and lead you home.
Gretel	He did! He did!

Father	We have not much more to give to you, but we will manage. A kind neighbor has moved near us, and he has kept us from starving.
Hansel	Oh, father dear, we shall starve no more!
Gretel	And all of our neighbors shall have more than enough to eat!
Hansel	See, we have brought home jewels and gold and silver enough to keep us well fed all of our lives. My pockets are full of precious things!
Gretel	And I have an apron filled with valuable stones!
Father	Let me see them . . . Upon my word! Mother! Look at these things!
Mother	They are beautiful! But wait . . . these things . . . I have seen them before!
Father	Do they not resemble the jewels that were stolen from us four years ago?
Mother	They are the very same!
Father	Our blessed children have returned to us with riches which will be more than enough to keep us contented and happy all of our lives.
Mother	Let us sing and rejoice. Call in the neighbors, and we will let the children tell of their adventures.
Father	Then we will have a feast for all, for good fortune is at last ours!

OLD PIPES AND THE DRYAD.* *As developed through creative play by a group of children in the fifth grade.*

Scene 1

(On the hill side)

(Characters: Old Pipes, First Child, Second Child, Third Child)

| Old Pipes | (He plays his pipes for a few seconds. We hear the cows moo and the cowbells ring off stage.) I am through with my piping for another day. I might as well go home. The cattle have come down the hill for the night. Even though I am |

* "Old Pipes and the Dryad," from *The Best Short Stories of Frank Stockton,* Charles Scribner's Sons, 1957. Used by permission.

an old man of seventy years, I can still pipe the cattle as well as ever. Mother will be glad to get my money for this week. (*He sits on an old tree stump and counts his coins.*)

One, two, three, four whole pieces of silver. Poor old mother! She is as deaf as a gate—posts, latch, hinges, and all! I have to yell to make her hear me, but then she is a good housekeeper, and I should not complain. (*Rises and begins the climb home*) Ah me, this path is so steep, and my rheumatism is bad this rainy weather.

First Child	(*Runs on stage from left*) Tag! You're it!
Second Child	(*Running on stage from left*) Run, run! You can't catch me!
Third Child	(*From left*) Oh yes, I can!
First Child	(*Stops and turns back*) Oh, look—an old man!
Old Pipes	Children, I am very tired tonight. I don't believe I can climb this steep path to my home. I think I shall have to ask you to help me.
Third Child	We will be glad to do that. I'll help on your right side.
First Child	And I'll help on the left side.
Second Child	I'll push from behind. Here we go!
Old Pipes	I am very sorry if I tire you too much.
First Child	Oh, this will not tire us. We have come far today after the cows, the sheep, and the goats. They rambled high on the mountain, and we never before had such a time finding them. (*The Second Child shakes her head, trying to silence the First Child, but the First Child does not heed her.*)
Old Pipes	You had to go after the cows, the sheep, and the goats! What do you mean by that?
Second Child	Oh hush, Patty, you talk too much!
First Child	You see, good sir, the cattle can't hear the old piper who tries to pipe the cattle home. Somebody has to go after them every evening to drive them down from the mountain, and the Chief Villager has hired us to do it.

Old Pipes	How long have you been doing this?
First Child	It is for about a year now. Well, there you are, sir, at the top of the hill. I think we will go home now. Good night, sir.
Old Pipes	I can get along home now by myself. Good night, my children. Thank you for helping me up the hill.
Second Child	Oh, we were glad to do that! (*Old Pipes leaves, right.*)
Second Child	Now, you have done it!
First Child	Done what?
Second Child	That was Old Pipes himself. You should be ashamed of yourself, hurting his feelings like that!
First Child	Old Pipes!
Third Child	Oh, how terrible!
First Child	Now, what can we do?

Scene II

(Inside the cottage of Old Pipes and his Mother)
(Characters: Old Pipes, Mother)

Mother	(*She is setting the table and preparing supper.*) I must hurry and get supper on the table. Old Pipes will be tired and hungry when he comes home. Now, just to finish this blueberry pie and then to get it into the oven. My, my, how my dear boy does like blueberry pie! There, all finished and ready for the hot oven.
Old Pipes	(*Off stage*) Yo, ho! Mother, I'm home!
Mother	(*She does not hear Old Pipes call.*) Dear me, it is about time for Pipes to come home. (*Old Pipes enters from the left.*) Oh, there you are! I did not hear you come in.
Old Pipes	Did you hear the children outside, Mother?
Mother	What? What's that you say?
Old Pipes	(*Louder*) Did you hear the children outside?
Mother	Children? What children? I don't see any children.

Old Pipes	(*Loudly*) There were some children outside. They were helping me up the hill. They said that they were paid to bring the cattle home every night because the cattle can no longer hear my pipes.
Mother	They can't hear you? Why, what is the matter with the cattle?
Old Pipes	Ah, me! I don't believe there is anything the matter with the cattle. It must be with me and my pipes that there is something the matter. But one thing is certain; if I do not earn the wages the Chief Villager pays me, I shall not take them. I shall go straight down to the village and give back the money I received today.
Mother	Nonsense! I'm sure you've piped as well as you could, and no more can be expected. And what are we to do without money?
Old Pipes	I don't know, but I'm going down to the village to pay it back.
Mother	Oh, you foolish old boy. Will you never grow old enough to know what to do? You stay right here!
Old Pipes	No, Mother, I must go down to the village. Goodbye. (*He goes out, left.*)
Mother	(*Calls at door, left*) Pipes! you come back here! Do you hear me? Oh, oh, he is gone! Now, what in the world will we do for money? We will starve to death! That is what we will do!

Scene III

(*On the hill side*)
(*Characters: Old Pipes, Dryad*)

Old Pipes	It seems steeper than ever down this hill. Oh, my poor back! I simply must sit down and rest. I believe I will go by the other path. It is not as steep as my usual path. I'll rest just a short while by this old oak tree.
Dryad	(*From within the tree*) Let me out! Let me out! Oh please, won't you let me out?
Old Pipes	What is this? Why, this must be a Dryad tree! If it is, I'll let her out. I know she can come

out if I find the key and let her out, because tonight the moon rose before the sun went down. At this time in the summer when that happens a Dryad can come out if anyone finds the key and lets her out. If I find that key, I shall certainly turn it. Ah, here it is behind this piece of bark. There, it turns quite around!

Dryad	(*She comes out of the tree.*) Oh, oh, lovely! Lovely! How long it has been since I have seen anything like this! How good of you to let me out! I am so happy and thankful, you dear old man. You don't know how doleful it is to be shut up in a tree. I am so thankful. What can I do to express my gratitude? (*She touches his arm.*)
Old Pipes	Now, now! That will do! Of course I was glad to let you out.
Dryad	I don't mind being shut up in the winter, for then I am glad to be sheltered, but in summer it is a rueful thing not to be able to see all of the beauties of the world. People so seldom come this way, and when they do come they either don't hear me, or they are frightened and run away.
Old Pipes	I must confess that I tried to find the key because I had a great desire to see a dryad.
Dryad	But you were not frightened, you dear old man! What can I do for you to show you how grateful I am?
Old Pipes	If you really wish to do something for me, you can, if you happen to be going down toward the village.
Dryad	To the village! I will go anywhere for you, my kind old man. (*She touches his other arm.*)
Old Pipes	Well, then, I wish you would take this little bag of money to the Chief Villager, and tell him that Old Pipes cannot receive pay for services which he does not perform.
Dryad	For what services?
Old Pipes	For piping the cattle home. Now for more than a year I have not been able to make the

	cattle hear me when I piped to call them home. I did not know this until tonight, but now that I know it, I cannot keep the money.
Dryad	I will take the money for you. Good night, and thank you over and over again! (*She leaves, left.*)
Old Pipes	Now that that is off my mind, I do not feel so old and tired, and my rheumatism is suddenly gone. I feel like playing my pipes now! I'll just play for my own amusement. (*He plays his pipes.*) Ho, hum! I guess I'm a bit sleepy. I'll just take a little nap. (*He lies down to sleep.*)
Dryad	(*Enters from the left*) Old Pipes, Old Pipes! Oh . . . he is asleep. This is a good and honest man, and it is a shame that he should lose his money. The Chief Villager will not take it from one who has served him so long. I'll give it back to him. (*She lays the money by his side, and then hides behind the tree.*)
Old Pipes	(*Awakens*) Ho, hum! I really did doze off. What a queer dream I had . . . or was it a dream? My money? Oh, there it is by my pipes, and I dreamed that I had seen a Dryad and had given her the money!
Dryad	(*Coming out from behind the tree*) You did see a Dryad. Don't you remember? You let me out of the tree. To be sure, you have your money. The Chief Villager would not take it because you have served him so faithfully.
Old Pipes	But I cannot keep the money. I can no longer pipe the cattle home.
Dryad	Oh yes, you can. Now your pipes are strong and clear.
Old Pipes	They did seem to be better a short while ago.
Dryad	Yes. You see, when a Dryad touches a human being he becomes ten years younger. I touched you once on each arm, so now you are fifty years old instead of seventy.
Old Pipes	So that's why I feel so spry! Hurrah! My rheumatism is all gone! I really have grown younger. I thank you, good Dryad, from the bottom of my heart.

Dryad	I am glad I have been able to help you.
Old Pipes	I wonder if I may ask one more favor of you?
Dryad	Anything you may wish, my good man.
Old Pipes	My mother is old and deaf. Could you arrange to touch her twice some time when she is asleep in her chair by the porch? She does not believe in Dryads, and she would never let you touch her while awake, but if you could sneak upon her sometime . . .
Dryad	I will do it. I will do it within the week. I promise.
Old Pipes	Thank you again and again! But there . . . do not touch me again! I have no desire to return to childhood.

Scene IV

(On the hill side, the home of the Echo Dwarfs)

(Characters: First Voice, First Echo Dwarf, Second Voice, Second Echo Dwarf, Main Echo Dwarf, Dryad, Old Pipes)

First Voice	*(Off stage)* Yo ho! Yo ho!
First Echo Dwarf	*(In cupped hands)* Yo ho! Yo ho!
Second Voice	*(Off stage)* Hello! Hello!
Second Echo Dwarf	*(Cupped hands)* Hello! Hello!
	(Off stage, the sound of the pipes)
First Echo Dwarf	What is that? We have not heard that sound for a long time!
Second Echo Dwarf	Is that not the music of Old Pipes?
First Echo Dwarf	To be sure! Awaken our brother the Echo Dwarf who must return the notes of Old Pipes. No longer can he spend his time in idleness.
Second Echo Dwarf	*(Shakes Echo Dwarf sleeping in the corner)* Wake up, brother, wake up! There is work for you to do.
Main Echo Dwarf	Stop! Leave me alone! What is the idea of disturbing my beauty sleep? Go away! I have no work to do!
Second Echo Dwarf	Oh yes, you have! Listen!
	(The pipes are heard again.)

Main Echo Dwarf	The pipes!
	(*He echoes back the pipes.*) Who played this trick on me? Old Pipes hasn't been piping for months. Just wait until I find out who is responsible for this!
Dryad	(*Enters from the right*) Oh ho! So the Echo Dwarf does not like a little honest work to do!
Main Echo Dwarf	Ho, ho! Mistress Dryad! And what might you be doing out of your tree?
Dryad	Doing! I am being happy. I was let out of my tree by the good old man who plays the pipes to call the cattle down from the mountain.
Main Echo Dwarf	And how does it happen that he is piping loud enough for the cattle to hear him?
Dryad	Why, I touched him twice so now he is young and strong enough to play his pipes as well as ever.
Main Echo Dwarf	So you are the cause of this great evil that has come upon me. You are the wicked creature who has started this old man upon his career of pipe playing again.
Dryad	For shame, Echo Dwarf!
Main Echo Dwarf	What have I ever done to you that you should make me echo back the notes of those wretched pipes?
Dryad	What a funny little fellow you are! Anyone would think you had to toil from morn till night, while what you really have to do is merely to imitate for half an hour every day the merry notes of Old Pipes!
Main Echo Dwarf	Yes, and miss my beauty sleep, that's what!
Dryad	Shame on you, Echo Dwarf. You are lazy and selfish. You should rejoice at the good fortune of the old man. Learn to be just and generous, and then, perhaps you may be happy. Good-bye! (*She leaves, right.*)
Main Echo Dwarf	Wicked creature! I'll make you suffer for this. You shall find out what it is to insult one like me.

First Echo Dwarf	Oh, come and have a game of ring-toss and forget the Dryad.
Main Echo Dwarf	No!
Second Echo Dwarf	Then perhaps you will go fishing with me?
Main Echo Dwarf	No!
First Echo Dwarf	You'd better go and sleep it off.
Main Echo Dwarf	No! I'll find that Dryad if I have to stay awake all summer. I'll shut her up in a tree again, that's what I will. The idea of making me work so hard!
First Echo Dwarf	Well, don't work too hard.
	(First and Second Echo Dwarfs go off, right.) *(Old Pipes enters from the left.)*
Main Echo Dwarf	Oh ho! And who might be this . . . this old man? The one with the pipes it is, to be sure. I'll pretend to be his friend. Hi ho! My good man. Have you seen the Dryad?
Old Pipes	No, but I have been looking everywhere for her.
Main Echo Dwarf	Have you indeed! And what might you wish with her?
Old Pipes	I want to tell her that my old mother is now asleep in her chair on the porch. The Dryad promised to make her younger, as she made me younger, and I thought now would be a good time to do it.
Main Echo Dwarf	Your idea is good, but you should know that a Dryad can make no person younger but the one who lets her out of a tree.
Old Pipes	Indeed?
Main Echo Dwarf	But you can manage that affair very easily. All you need to do is to find the Dryad and request that she step into a tree and be shut up for a short time. Then you can go and bring your mother to the tree. She can open it, and all will be as you wish. Is not this a good plan?
Old Pipes	Excellent! I will find the Dryad at once.
Main Echo Dwarf	Take me with you! You can easily carry me on your strong shoulders, and I shall help you all I can.

Old Pipes	Very well, but wait! I see the Dryad now . . . ahead near those bushes, look!
Main Echo Dwarf	Oh, in that case, I'll be going!
	(*He hides behind some rocks.*)
	(*The Dryad enters from the right.*)
Old Pipes	Oh, Mistress Dryad! Will you do one more favor for me?
Dryad	Why, 'tis the old man with the pipes! Yes, indeed! What do you wish?
Old Pipes	Will you step into your tree for just a little while so that I may bring my mother to let you out again?
Dryad	Do you really wish me to go into my tree again?
Old Pipes	Just for a short time so that you can make my mother younger. I am told that such a procedure is necessary.
Dryad	I should dislike to do it, for I don't know what might happen. It is not at all necessary, for I could make your mother younger at any time, if she would give me the opportunity. Several times I have waited outside your cottage, but she does not come out, and you know a Dryad cannot enter a house . . . I can't imagine what put this into your head. Did you think of it yourself?
Old Pipes	No, a little dwarf whom I met proposed it to me.
Dryad	Oh, now I see it all! It is the scheme of that wicked Echo Dwarf, your enemy and mine. Where is he? I should like to see him!
Old Pipes	I think he has gone away.
Dryad	Oh no, he has not! There he is behind the rocks! Seize him and drag him out, I beg of you!
Old Pipes	I say, wait a minute! Come here! (*He grabs the Echo Dwarf.*) There I have you by the neck! What do you mean by running away?
Main Echo Dwarf	Let me go! Help! Help!

Dryad	Now, then, just stick him in this great oak tree, and we will shut him up! Then I will be safe from his mischief for the rest of the time I am free!
	(They put the Echo Dwarf in the tree.)
	There, now we need not be afraid of him!
Main Echo Dwarf	Let me out!
Dryad	Pay no attention to him. I assure you, my good Piper, that I shall be glad to make your mother younger as soon as I can.
Old Pipes	She is asleep now in her chair outside of the cottage. Will you come now?
Dryad	Of course, I will. At once. I'll touch your mother three times. That will make her thirty years younger, and she will be as spry as a woman of sixty. Wouldn't you like to have me make you ten years younger, also?
Old Pipes	Well, maybe, since Mother will be sixty, I might like to be forty again. But touch me only once more, as I have no wish to return to childhood! Just once, you understand? *(She touches his shoulder.)*

Scene V

Dryad	Winter is coming on. I do not like to be out in the cold. I would like the shelter of this tree for myself. I think the Echo Dwarf has been punished enough. I shall turn the key and let him out. *(She turns the key.)* Come out, Echo Dwarf. The cattle have come down the mountain for the last time this year. The pipes will no longer sound, and you can go to your rocks and have a holiday until next spring.
Main Echo Dwarf	Humph! It is about time you let me out! It would serve you right if I should break off the key so that no one can let you out next spring!
Dryad	Break it off if you like. Another will grow next spring. And although the good piper made me no promise, I know that when the warm days arrive next year, he will come and let me out again. Goodbye . . . until spring!
	(She steps into the tree.)

EAST OF THE SUN AND WEST OF THE MOON.* *As dramatized through creative play by a group of sixth-grade children.*

Scene I

(In Lassie's home. A simple room with rough furniture. Mother and children are seated about the fire. The two boys, Olaf and Sigvart, are carving ships.)

(Characters: Lassie, Father, Kristin, White Bear, Gerda, Mother, Olaf, Sigvart)

Father	*(Brushing the snow off his clothing)* 'Tis bitterly cold and cruelly dark, and a hungry man I am.
	(Children gather around their father.)
Gerda	Oh father, did you trap a rabbit for our supper? We have had no lunch you know.
Mother	Hush! Children, do not worry your father. He is tired and cold.
Lassie	Come, father, sit by the fire and dry your boots.
Father	Alas! Not a single trap was sprung today!
Lassie	Do not despair, father. We are not really hungry. We had breakfast this morning. Tomorrow you will trap a rabbit. I know you will.
Father	'Tis hopeless, dearest daughter. We must find some other way. *(Jokingly)* Now if, as in days of old, a handsome prince should ask for your hand, my charming daughter, our problems would be solved.
Mother	Nonsense, father. Why put such foolish thoughts into her head?
Kristin	But, mother, we are all so hungry and a real prince would be fun.
Olaf	Don't be silly, Kristin; a prince wouldn't come to this house.
Sigvart	*(Holding up a finished ship)* Perhaps I can sell one of my boats and buy us something to eat.
	(A knock is heard at the door.)
Gerda	What is that?

* From Scandinavian folklore.

Mother	'Tis only the wind.
	(*A second knock is heard.*)
Father	No, someone is knocking at the door. Quickly, Olaf, let the stranger in. 'Tis a bitter cold night for lingering outside.
	(*Olaf opens the door.*)
White Bear	(*Enters. The children scream and run to their mother.*) Good evening to you, my good friends. Do not be afraid, I beg of you.
Father	Good Evening, sir. This is rather an unexpected visit. What can we do for you?
White Bear	I have heard that your oldest daughter is both kind and beautiful and that you and your family are in great need.
Father	That, my friend, is true.
White Bear	I am a creature of vast wealth. I live in a great palace beyond the horizon, but 'tis lonely there, and I desire company. Let your daughter come with me and I will make you as rich as you are poor.
Lassie	No, no, Father! Do not ask me to go!
Kristin	(*Whispers aside to Gerda*) Perhaps it's a prince in disguise.
Father	I will not ask you to go. If you leave, it must be of your own free will.
Mother	(*Concerned*) Would you treat my daughter kindly?
White Bear	She shall have everything her heart desires. No prince could give her more. No harm shall befall her. That I promise.
Lassie	Keep your promise to my father, and I will go with you.
White Bear	I will make your father the wealthiest man in the land.
Lassie	Very well, let us go.
White Bear	It is a long, tiresome journey to my palace. Are you not afraid?
Lassie	No, I have no fear. I will get my cloak. Then let us go quickly.
Kristin	(*Bringing Lassie's cloak*) Here is your cloak, sister.

Gerda	May we come to visit you in your beautiful new palace?
Lassie	Later, perhaps.
Father	Good-bye, dear daughter. My blessing goes with you.
All	Good-bye, Lassie, good-bye, sister.

Scene II

(*The living room at the Bear's palace*)
(*Characters: Lassie, White Bear*)

Lassie	(*She is weeping as she spins.*) I know I should not weep. The White Bear does everything in his power to make me happy. He has given me robes of silk and velvet and food that is fare for a princess, but I am lonesome and homesick, and I cannot help but weep.
White Bear	(*Entering*) Are you busy and happy, my dear?
Lassie	(*Brushing away her tears*) Oh, yes indeed! I am happy, of course I am happy!
White Bear	Then why are there tears in your eyes? Alas, my dear, you have been weeping! Why?
Lassie	I guess I have been sad—a little.
White Bear	I have tried so hard to make you happy. Tell me what your heart desires. Anything you wish, I shall grant. Only do not weep. It breaks my heart to see you unhappy.
Lassie	Oh, my dear friend, you have been so very kind. I am ashamed of my tears, but the truth is that I am lonely. I long to go home and visit my family.
White Bear	Well, well, perhaps there is a cure for all this. I shall be very lonesome without you, but if it is to your home you wish to go, I shall grant your wish.
Lassie	(*Delighted*) Oh thank you! May I leave at once?
White Bear	First, you must promise to return in two days.
Lassie	I promise, I promise!
White Bear	And second, you must promise not to talk alone with your mother. For she will likely talk you into not returning. Do you promise?
Lassie	Oh yes, I promise to talk to my mother only when the rest are near.

White Bear	Very well. Go to your room and sleep well tonight. When you awaken tomorrow, you shall find yourself at home.

Scene III

(The beautiful new home of Lassie's Father)
(Characters: Lassie, Mother, Father, Kristin, Gerda, Olaf and Sigvart)
(Kristin is spinning by the fireside as Lassie enters.)

Lassie	Surprise! Surprise! I have come home!
Kristin	Oh Lassie, dearest sister! You nearly frightened me out of my wits. Mother! Father! Lassie has come home.
Mother	*(Enters)* My daughter! *(Takes Lassie in her arms)*
Father	*(Enters)* Dear little Lassie! Have you been happy?
Kristin	Is the White Bear a prince?
Gerda	*(Entering)* Is he? Is he?
Lassie	He is as good as a prince. That I can truly say.
Kristin	Your gown is gorgeous!
Gerda	But look at mine! *(She turns around.)*
Father	The White Bear has kept his promise. We want for nothing. I am working now, too. The townspeople have elected me Mayor-in-Chief.
Mother	So we are not only rich, but we are famous also!
Olaf	And Sigvart and I are studying with the good priest.
Sigvart	Soon we shall be able to read and write.
Lassie	What eager little students you are. We shall be proud of you I know.
Father	I must go to the village now, daughter. Will you remain with us for long?
Lassie	I must return soon; I promised.
Father	Farewell, dearest one, for now.
Lassie	Good-bye, my father, the Mayor!
Sigvart	Come Olaf, we must not be late for our lessons.
	Good-bye, Sister!
Lassie	Good-bye, little brothers!
	(The brothers leave.)

Gerda   Come, come, Lassie—we will show you our linen chests, filled with fine linens.
(Gerda and Kristin leave.)

Mother   A moment, dear daughter, I would have a word with you.

Lassie   Later perhaps, Mother?

Mother   No, no, I would talk with you now, at once!

Lassie   *(Hesitating)* Now, alone?

Mother   Yes, yes, alone!

Lassie   But, Mother, I—I—

Mother   Tut, tut, child! Is it too much for a mother to ask for a moment's word with her eldest daughter?

Lassie   *(Ashamed)* No, no, of course not, dear mother. What is it you wish?

Mother   Only this: to know if you are truly happy.

Lassie   Oh yes, indeed, the White Bear is wonderfully kind! But the evenings—they are so long and lonely. Never once have I seen the White Bear after sunset. Always he leaves me alone in the evenings.

Mother   My! That is bad! It may well be a troll you are living with! A troll must not be seen by human eyes after dark. But now I'll teach you how to set eyes on him. I'll give you a bit of candle which you can carry home. Just light it and look into his room after he's asleep. Take care not to drop any of the tallow on him.

Lassie   Very well, Mother, I will do as you say.

Kristin   *(Off stage)* Lassie, are you coming?

Lassie   Yes, yes, I am coming! *(She leaves.)*

Scene IV

(The White Bear's room)
(Characters: Prince, Lassie)

(The Bear's skin is on the floor, center. The Prince sleeps on a couch draped with a beautiful velvet cover. Lassie enters with a lighted candle.)

Lassie   I must be very careful. What is this? A white bear skin on the floor—but the bear—what—oh—(*She sees the prince.*) A handsome prince! (*She leans over him to get a better view.*) He is the prince of my dreams! Dare I awaken him? No! I am afraid! But no, I'm not afraid! Oh, oh, the candle—it drips. Three drops of tallow have fallen on his shirt. Alas, he awakens! Now what!

Prince   (*Awakens and arises*) Lassie, what have you done? Now you have made us both unlucky. Had you waited but this one year, I would have been free. For I have been bewitched by a wicked troll, so that I am a white bear by day and a prince by night. Now, I must leave you.

Lassie   No, no! Please do not leave me.

Prince   Alas, my dear, I have no other choice. I must go to the troll's palace which stands east of the sun and west of the moon. There I must marry the troll's daughter, Princess Long Nose. She has a nose three ells long, and she is the one I must now make my wife.

Lassie   May I not go with you?

Prince   No, I must go alone.

Lassie   Tell me the way then, and I will search you out! That surely I may have leave to do.

Prince   Yes, you may do that. But it will be difficult to find the place. It lies east of the sun and west of the moon, and thither you must find your way. Farewell, my dear.

Lassie   (*Weeping*) I shall search you out if forever I must wander.

Scene V

(*A scene in the woods. Dark skeletons of trees are in the background. A large rock is at left side. Lassie sits on the rock, tired and frightened.*)

(*Characters: Lassie, First Hag, Second Hag, Third Hag, East Wind, West Wind, North Wind, South Wind*)

Lassie   I have come such a long way and I am so very tired. 'Tis good to rest here for a while. I am hungry and cold and lost. Never shall I find my prince unless good fortune befalls me soon.

First Hag	(*Enters*) Golden apples, one, two, three, Grow upon my apple tree. Toss them far and toss them near; Toss one to the Lassie here.
Lassie	(*Catches the apple*) Oh—oh—thank you! Thank you very much!
First Hag	So you have caught my apple! 'Tis good luck it will bring you. Good luck indeed!
Lassie	I could use a little luck!
First Hag	Why are you so disgruntled, my dear?
Lassie	I am searching for a prince. He has gone to the troll's palace which lies east of the sun and west of the moon. There he must marry the princess with a nose three ells long.
First Hag	Maybe you are the lassie who should have had him?
Lassie	Yes, I am.
First Hag	So, so, it is you, eh? Well, all I know about him is that he is at the palace that lies east of the sun and west of the moon, and thither you'll come, late or never. But you may keep my golden apple. It will bring you luck. (*She leaves.*)
Lassie	Oh thank you; thank you very much.
Second Hag	(*Enters*) Wooly wool of the sheep I card With this my golden comb, I'm well known as a singing bard, As o'er the hills I roam. What ho! A lassie in distress, I trow.
Lassie	I am on my way to the troll's palace which is east of the sun and west of the moon.
Second Hag	And thither you shall come, late or never. But you shall have the use of my golden carding comb. Since you, no doubt, are the lassie who should have had the prince, it may help you. Good luck, my dear. (*She leaves.*)
Lassie	Oh thank you! Thank you so very much!
Third Hag	(*Enters*) As a spinster I shall spin Upon my golden wheel; Such honest work is not a sin, Though it's not quite my ideal.

	How now, my little lady! You with the golden apple and the carding comb, I see that my sisters have passed this way. Good luck those treasures will bring you, I'm sure.
Lassie	Your sisters were most kind, but still I do not know the way to the troll's palace which lies east of the sun and west of the moon.
Third Hag	I've heard of the place. Why do you wish to go there?
Lassie	It is I who should have had the prince who has gone to the palace to marry the princess with the nose three ells long.
Third Hag	Ah! Indeed! Well, thither you'll come late or never. Perhaps I can help you.
Lassie	Oh! Could you?
Third Hag	Yes, I will add my spinning wheel to your treasures.
Lassie	Oh thank you! Thank you so very much.
Third Hag	If you really wish to go to the troll's palace, my friend, East Wind, may be able to help you. (*Calls with her hands cupped around her mouth*) Yo—ho—Yo—ho.
East Wind	(*Enters blusteringly*) Whe—eee—ee! Did you call me?
Third Hag	Yes, my little friend here wishes to go to the palace that lies east of the sun and west of the moon. Can you tell her the way?
East Wind	I've heard of the place, but I don't know the way. I've never blown so far. I'll call my brother, West Wind. He is much stronger than I, perhaps he can carry you thither. Whe—eee—ee.
West Wind	(*Enters with a long drawn out whistle*) At your service, brother East Wind!
East Wind	Is it within your power, brother West Wind, to carry this lassie to the palace that lies east of the sun and west of the moon?
West Wind	Nay! So far I have never blown. But if you wish, I'll call brother South Wind. He is much stronger than either of us. Maybe he can carry you thither. (*He whistles for South Wind.*)
South Wind	(*Enters, speaking gently*) Shoo-oo-oo-oo! Who-oo-oo-oo calls the South Wind?

West Wind	I did, brother South Wind. This lassie wishes to go to the palace that lies east of the sun and west of the moon.
South Wind	You don't say! Well, I have breezed about in most places in my time, but so far I have never blown. But if you wish I'll call our brother, North Wind. He is the oldest and strongest of all of us, and if he doesn't know where it is, you'll never find anyone in the world to tell you.
Lassie	If it wouldn't be too much trouble.
South Wind	No trouble at all! Shoo-oo-oo!
West Wind	(*He whistles a long drawn out whistle.*)
East Wind	Whee-ee-ee-ee-ee!
North Wind	(*Brr-rr-rr-oo, noisily*) BLAST YOU ALL! WHAT DO YOU WANT! (*All shiver as the North Wind roars.*)
South Wind	You needn't be so very nasty for here we are—your brothers, and here is the lassie who ought to have had the prince who dwells in the palace that lies east of the sun and west of the moon. Can you take her there?
North Wind	YES, I KNOW WELL ENOUGH WHERE IT IS. Once I blew an oak leaf thither, and I was so tired I couldn't blow a single puff for many days after. If you really wish to go and aren't afraid, I shall blow you thither.
Lassie	Oh, with all my heart I wish to go!
North Wind	Very well then, but we must stay here tonight, for we must have a whole day before us if we are to get there at all.

Scene VI

(*At the palace that lies east of the sun and west of the moon. Lassie sits on the stump, left stage. The spinning wheel is at her feet and the carding comb in her lap. The palace window opens and Princess Long Nose leans out.*)

(*Characters Lassie, Princess Long Nose, Prince, Mother Troll*)

Princess Long Nose	Hi—you down there! What will you take for your golden apple?
Lassie	It's not for sale for gold or money.

Princess Long Nose	If it's not for sale for gold or money, what will you sell it for, then? You may name your own price.
Lassie	If I mav see the prince who lives here, you may have the golden apple.
Princess Long Nose	Give it to me at once, and I will send him out.
Lassie	Very well. (*She gives Long Nose the apple.*)
Princess Long Nose	(*Cackles*) Heh-heh-heh-heh. (*She slams the window shut.*)
Lassie	(*Runs to the door; knocks upon it*) You said I could see the prince. You took my golden apple and you have not kept your promise. (*Weeps; goes back to sit on the stump*) Perhaps the golden carding comb can tell me what to do. (*The window opens again and out comes the head of Princess Long Nose.*)
Princess Long Nose	Hi there! What do you want for the golden carding comb?
Lassie	It's not for sale for gold or monev.
Princess Long Nose	Well, if it's not for sale for gold or money what will you take for it?
Lassie	Well, if I may see the prince who lives here, you may have it.
Princess Long Nose	Give it to me then and I will send him out.
Lassie	Very well, here it is.
Princess Long Nose	Heh-heh-heh-heh. (*She slams the window down.*)
Lassie	(*Runs to the door and knocks*) Let me in. Let me in! You said that I might see the prince. (*Goes back to the tree stump and weeps. Takes up the spinning wheel and starts to spin*) Maybe the spinning wheel will bring me luck.
Princess Long Nose	(*Raises the window and thrusts out her head*) Hi there! What do you want for the golden spinning wheel?
Lassie	It's not for sale for gold or money.
Princess Long Nose	Well, if it's not for sale for gold or money, what will you take for it?
Lassie	If I may see the prince, you may have it.

Princess Long Nose	Give it to me then, and this time you shall see him. (*Lassie gives her the spinning wheel.*)
Princess Long Nose	(*Cackles*) Heh-heh-heh-heh (*Slams the window shut again.*)
Lassie	(*Goes to the door; pounds and knocks*) Let me in! You promised to let me see the prince. Let me in! (*The door opens and out steps the prince.*)
Lassie	(*Steps back*) OH! She *did* send you to me!
Prince	My dear, you have come just in time. For this afternoon I was to marry the Princess Long Nose.
Lassie	Oh no! NO!
Prince	The commotion in the court yard awakened me from a drugged sleep.
Lassie	OH! My prince! That is why you did not come before?
Prince	I will not have the Long Nose. You are the only woman in the world who can set me free.
Lassie	But how?
Prince	I'll say that I want to see what my wife is fit for. I'll ask the Long Nose to wash my shirt which has the three spots of tallow on it.
Lassie	That is work for a gentlewoman. No troll can remove the tallow spots.
Prince	I'll have no other for my bride than the woman who can remove the spots.
Mother Troll	(*Enters*) OH! Here you are, my dear prince. (*Smirking*) 'Tis almost time for the wedding, you know.
Prince	First of all I'd like to see what my bride is good for.
Mother Troll	Yes?
Prince	I have a fine shirt which I want to wear for my wedding, but it has three spots of tallow on it. I have sworn never to take as a bride any woman except the one who can wash it clean.
Mother Troll	Well, that is no great thing. My daughter can do that.
Prince	Very well, let her try.
Mother Troll	(*Goes to the door*) Long Nose, Long Nose! Bring a tub, some soap, and water out here.

Prince	I'll bring the shirt at once. Remember, if she cannot remove the spots, I will not marry her. (*Leaves.*)
Mother Troll	Oh, she will do it all right. Never you worry about that.
Princess Long Nose	(*Enters, bringing the tub, soap, and water*) What do you mean, mother, asking *me* to bring a tub of water? What are servants for, I'd like to know!
Mother Troll	Sh—sh, my dear. The prince wishes it. He has a little task for you by which you may prove your worthiness.
Prince	(*Enters with the shirt on which three red spots have been pinned*) Princess Long Nose, I would have my future wife prove her worth.
Princess Long Nose	(*Pretending to be sweet*) Oh yes indeed! My prince.
Prince	I would have you remove these spots from my wedding shirt.
Princess Long Nose	Huh! That's easy enough. Give it to me. (*She puts it in the tub, rubs, rubs, and rubs. She finally holds up a gray shirt. It also has three red spots.*)
Mother Troll	(*Pushes Long Nose aside*) Aw, you can't wash! Let me do it.
Princess Long Nose	That horrid soap hurts my hands (*wipes hands disgustedly*).
Mother Troll	(*She rubs, rubs, and rubs. Finally holds up the shirt which is now black. Screams*) Cats and witches! The thing is bewitched.
Prince	Oh! You are neither of you worth a straw! You can't wash. My, I'll be bound that this beggar lass can wash better than either of you. Come here, Lassie.
Lassie	Yes, Your Highness (*curtsies*).
Prince	Can *you* remove these spots, my lass?
Lassie	I don't know, but I will try. (*She bends over the tub, rubs a bit, holds the shirt up to view—spotless!*)
Prince	Oh! You are the Lassie for me.
Mother Troll	(*Screams, tears her hair in rage*) She washes well; that breaks the spell! (*Runs off stage, wildly.*)
Princess Long Nose	(*Follows her mother, screaming*) Ma, wait for me. If the spell is broken, I've lost the Prince.
Prince	Oh! Lassie, Lassie, your faith has set me free! Now we can return to my palace and rejoice forever.

A MAD TEA PARTY.* *As dramatized through creative play by a group of children in the seventh grade.*

(*Characters: Alice, March Hare, Hatter, Dormouse*)

(*The Dormouse is seated at center behind a table, asleep with his head on his arms. The March Hare and the Hatter each lean an elbow on the head of the Dormouse. Alice enters.*)

Alice	Very uncomfortable for the Dormouse. It's asleep, so I suppose it doesn't mind.
March Hare and Hatter	No room! No room!
Alice	There's plenty of room!
March Hare	Have some wine.
Alice	I don't see any wine.
March Hare	There isn't any!
Alice	Then it wasn't very civil of you to offer it.
March Hare	It wasn't very civil of you to sit down without being invited.
Alice	I didn't know it was *your* table. It's laid for a great many more than three.
Hatter	Your hair wants cutting.
Alice	You should learn not to make personal remarks. It's very rude.
Hatter	Why is a raven like a writing desk?
Alice	Oh, you are going to ask riddles! I believe I can guess that.
March Hare	Do you mean you think you can find an answer to it?
Alice	Exactly so.
March Hare	Then you should say what you mean.
Alice	I do; at least I mean what I say, and that's the same thing.
Hatter	Not the same thing a bit! Why you might just as well say that "I see what I eat" is the same as "I eat what I see!"

* From *Alice in Wonderland,* by Lewis Carroll.

March Hare	You might as well say that "I like what I get" is the same as "I get what I like!"
Dormouse	You might just as well say that "I breathe when I sleep" is the same as "I sleep when I breathe!"
Hatter	It *is* the same with you! What day of the month is it?
Alice	The fourth.
Hatter	Two days wrong! (*Sets his watch.*) (*To the March Hare*) I told you butter wouldn't grease the works!
March Hare	It was the *best* butter.
Hatter	Yes, but bread crumbs got in. You should not have put it in with the butter knife!
Alice	What a funny watch! It tells the day of the month and doesn't tell what hour it is.
Hatter	Why should it? Does your watch tell what year it is?
Alice	Of course not, because it stays the same year for a long time.
Hatter	Which is just the case with mine!
Alice	I don't quite understand you.
Hatter	Never mind. Have you guessed the riddle yet?
Alice	No, I give up. What's the answer?
Hatter	I haven't the slightest idea.
March Hare	Nor I.
Alice	I think you might do something better with your time than wasting it in asking riddles that have no answers.
Hatter	If you knew Time as well as I do you wouldn't speak of *it*. It's *he*.
Alice	What do you mean?
Hatter	I dare say you've never even spoken to Time.
Alice	Perhaps not, but I beat time in music.
Hatter	Ha! That accounts for it. He won't stand beating. Now if you had kept on good terms with him, he'd do anything you liked with the clock. For instance, if it were nine o'clock and time for lessons, you'd only need to whisper a hint to Time and 'round goes the clock—twelve o'clock and time for lunch!
March Hare	I only wish it were.

Alice	That would be grand, only I wouldn't be hungry, you know.
Hatter	Not at first, but you could keep it noon as long as you liked.
Alice	Is that the way *you* manage?
Hatter	No, I quarreled with Time last March. That was just before the Hare went mad, you know. At the concert of the Queen of Hearts I had to sing,
	Twinkle, twinkle, little bat,
	How I wonder where you're at?
	You know the song, perhaps?
Alice	I've heard something like it.
Hatter	It goes,
	Up above the world you fly,
	Like a tea-tray in the sky!
Dormouse	Twinkle—Twinkle—Twinkle—Twinkle. . . .
Hatter	Stop it! (*Pinches the Dormouse.*)
	Well, I finished the first stanza when the Queen cried out, "Off with his head! He is murdering Time!"
Alice	How dreadfully savage!
Hatter	Ever since that, Time won't do a thing I ask. It is always three o'clock now.
Alice	Is that why these tea things are here?
Hatter	Yes, it is always tea-time. And we have no time to wash the things between teas.
Alice	Then you keep moving around the table I suppose?
Hatter	Exactly so, as things get used up.
March Hare	Let's change the subject! I vote the young lady tells us a story!
Alice	I'm afraid I don't know one.
March Hare	Then the Dormouse shall! Wake up, Dormouse.
Dormouse	I wasn't asleep. I heard every word you fellows were saying.
March Hare	Tell us a story!
Alice	Please do!
Hatter	Be quick about it and don't go to sleep before it is done!

Dormouse	(*Quickly*) Once upon a time there were three little sisters who lived at the bottom of a well—
Alice	What did they live on?
Dormouse	On molasses—it was a molasses well.
Alice	They couldn't have done that, you know; it would have made them ill.
Dormouse	So they were—very ill.
March Hare	Have some more tea?
Alice	I've had nothing yet, so I can't take more!
Hatter	You mean you can't take *less*. It is easy to take *more* than *nothing*.
Alice	Nobody asked your opinion!
Hatter	Who is making personal remarks now!
Alice	I'm sorry. (*To Dormouse*) Why did they live at the bottom of the well?
Dormouse	It was a molasses well.
Alice	There's no such thing!
Dormouse	If you can't be civil, you'd better finish the story for yourself.
Alice	No, please go on. I won't interrupt again.
Hatter	I want a clean cup! Let's move up one! (*They all move.*)
Alice	They were in the well, you say?
Dormouse	Yes—well in! Well in.
Alice	But I don't think—
Hatter	Then you shouldn't talk.
March Hare	He is asleep again.
Hatter	Twinkle—twinkle—little bat—
March Hare	Let's put the Dormouse in the tea-pot!
Alice	This is the queerest tea-party I have ever been to in all my life! If you will excuse me, I'll be going!
March Hare	No need to hurry back. We will still be at tea when you get here!

BLUEBEARD.° *As dramatized through creative play by a group of seventh-grade children.*

(*Scene: The living room of Bluebeard's home*)

(*Characters: Bluebeard, Jeanne, Jean, Marie, Henri, Mother*)

Bluebeard	Now, my dear wife, we are at last home after our beautiful wedding. I hope you will be very happy here.
Jeanne	Oh! I know I shall be happy, because you will be so good to me.
Bluebeard	I am sorry to have to tell you that I must go away for several weeks.
Jeanne	Oh! Must you go?
Bluebeard	Yes, I beg you to amuse yourself during my absence.
Jeanne	I will have all my dear friends and my family come to visit with me.
Bluebeard	Yes, indeed, invite your family and your friends to make merry with you.
Jeanne	Thank you, my dear husband; you are very kind.
Bluebeard	I will leave you all my keys, and you may go about as you please. Here is the key to the room of silver and gold.
Jeanne	Oh, thank you! How I shall love to show my friends your room of silver and gold.
Bluebeard	And here is the key to the room of magic mirrors.
Jeanne	The magic mirrors!
Bluebeard	This is the key to my Dresden china closet.
Jeanne	I can give a wonderful dinner.
Bluebeard	Yes, yes, do that, and this is the key to all of the other rooms—the one with the diamonds and rubies, the one with the pearls and emeralds, and all else.
Jeanne	Oh, thank you! You are so generous, my dear husband. I shall guard your keys carefully.
Bluebeard	But this little gold key is the key to my closet at the end of the drawing room.
Jeanne	You have never told me of that room.

° From the French folktale, as told by Charles Perrault.

Bluebeard	You may open all the doors, go into all of the rooms, but you must not enter that little closet! I absolutely forbid it.
Jeanne	But my dear husband—
Bluebeard	If you so much as unlock the door, I shall be very angry! Do you understand? You must not enter that closet!
Jeanne	Yes, Yes. I will do as you say.
Bluebeard	That is good. And now, goodbye, my dear wife.
Jeanne	Goodbye, Bluebeard. . . . Now that I am alone, I am very much frightened. Bluebeard was so very cross about that closet. Yet he left me the key. I wonder what can be in that closet. Of course, I must not open the door. Bluebeard forbade me to enter. Oh, of course, I shouldn't think of disobeying him—but I wonder what is in there—I just cannot help but wonder.
Sister Marie	(*Off stage*) Sister Jeanne, Sister Jeanne!
Jeanne	(*She looks out of the window.*) Oh, it is Marie. Yoho! Marie!
Sister Marie	(Enters) You are all alone? Where is Bluebeard?
Jeanne	He has gone away for several weeks.
Marie	Oh, how nice!
Jeanne	Well, really, Marie!
Marie	I didn't really mean that, dear sister. I just meant what fun! Now brother Henri and dear friend Jean can come and see your beautiful palace. They would not come before, you know, because they do not approve of Bluebeard. I will run and tell them to come now.
Jeanne	Please do. (*After Marie has gone*) I don't understand why they should dislike Bluebeard. He is very kind to me. Of course, he is not handsome. I shall have a fine time showing my family and friends all of Bluebeard's precious things. I shall not show them that closet of course—but I should like to take a little peek into it myself. (*She goes to the closet.*)
	(*Henri, Mother, Jean and Marie enter.*)
Henri	Marie says you are alone, how jolly!
Mother	We rushed right over as soon as we heard.

Jean	Madam, it is kind of you to ask us to come. I hope you are well.
Jeanne	Thank you, dear Jean, I am very well.
Jean	You are as beautiful as ever, dear Jeanne.
Jeanne	Thank you kindly, my friend.
Marie	We are hoping you will show us all the lovely things in your home, sister.
Jeanne	I will be delighted to do that. You see, Bluebeard left all his keys with me.
Marie	I am glad that Bluebeard is not at home. His beard frightens me.
Mother	Such foolish talk, Marie! I am sure Bluebeard is most kind.
Jeanne	Yes, mother; he left me the keys which open the rooms containing all his treasures.
All	Oh! Show us the treasures!
Jeanne	You'll love the room of the magic mirrors.
Marie	Magic mirrors! What an interesting place that must be.
Jeanne	And I'll show you the room in which Blubeard keeps his beautiful Dresden china.
Marie	How wonderful! Real Dresden china. I shall love to see that.
Mother	How very fortunate you are to have such a wonderful husband, my dear daughter.
Marie	Let us get started. I want to see these treasures.
Jean	I am curious about the door at the end of the hall, Jeanne. What is in that room?
Jeanne	(*Frightened*) Oh! That is the door to Bluebeard's closet! We dare not enter there. I know not what is behind that door.
Jean	Skeletons, perhaps!
Mother	Oh, Jean, do not say such terrible things. Of course, Bluebeard does not keep skeletons in his closet.
Henri	The rugs of this room are rich and deep.
Jeanne	Come! Now I will show you the treasure rooms. After we have seen them all—we will dine before you leave.

(*Later*)

(*Bluebeard's wife is alone. Her guests have departed after
a very fine dinner.*)

Jeanne	I must know what is in that closet. The temptation is too strong for me. (*She opens the door and sees three heads hanging by the hair. She screams and drops the key on the floor.*) Oh, there is blood on the key! It will not wipe away! I shall scrub it well with sand. (*She goes out and comes back with a bowl and sand. Scrubs the key with a brush*) It will not come off. This must be a magic key. When I clean the blood from one side, it appears on the other side. Oh, I am afraid! What shall I do? I hear Bluebeard coming, now! (*She covers the bowl with Marie's scarf which has been left on the table. Bluebeard enters.*)
Jeanne	(*Hesitatingly*) Oh! Bluebeard, I was frightened. I— I didn't expect you so soon.
Bluebeard	I did not have to take the long trip after all. I received news at the very last minute that the business that I was to see about had been satisfactorily finished by my partners. So it was not necessary for me to be gone so long.
Jeanne	I am glad to see you back, my husband.
Bluebeard	You must bring me my keys the first thing in the morning. (*He leaves.*)
Jeanne	Yes, of course.

(*Next Morning*)

Jeanne	Good morning, Bluebeard.
Bluebeard	Have you brought my keys?
Jeanne	Yes, of course, Bluebeard.
Bluebeard	Then give them to me at once.
Jeanne	Oh, I must have dropped them. I will look for them. (*Leaves.*)
Bluebeard	Such stupid carelessness. (*Marie enters.*)
Marie	Oh, good morning, Bluebeard. I did not know you had returned.

Bluebeard	It was not necessary for me to stay away. I came back last night.
Marie	I came for my scarf. We were visiting with Jeanne last evening and I went away without it. Oh, here it is.
	(*She takes her scarf from the table.*)
Jeanne	(*Enters with the keys*) Good morning, Marie.
Marie	Good morning, sister. I came for my scarf.
Jeanne	Oh—yes, of course! (*Frightened as she sees the bowl uncovered*)
Bluebeard	Well, did you bring me my keys?
Jeanne	Here they are.
Bluebeard	There is blood on this little gold key!
Marie	Blood!
Jeanne	You must be mistaken!
Bluebeard	You have disobeyed me! You have entered the closet! Very well, Madam, you shall go in again and take your place among the other ladies whom you saw there.
Jeanne	Oh, no! No! I beg of you. Never again will I disobey you.
Bluebeard	You have had your chance at obedience. Now you shall pay the penalty. Prepare to die.
Jeanne	(*On her knees*) No! No! I beg of you, spare my life!
Bluebeard	Never!
Marie	My sister, what is the meaning of this?
Bluebeard	I have spoken!
Jeanne	If I must die, give me a little time in which to say my prayers.
Bluebeard	(*Looking at his watch*) I grant you exactly half of a quarter of an hour.
	(*Bluebeard goes to the closet, unlocks the door, takes out a great sabre, and tries the edge with his tongue. Goes back into the closet.*)
Marie	(*Screams*) Look, his wives! (*Marie runs to Jeanne.*)
Jeanne	Sister, dear sister, go, I beg of you, to the top of the tower and wave your scarf. If our brother or dear friend Jean see it, they will know of my distress.

	Hurry, hurry, perhaps they will come in time to save me.
Marie	Yes, I will go at once (*Leaves*).
Jeanne	They promised they would come if I ever needed them. (*Falls to her knees; after a few seconds calls*) Sister Marie, do you see anyone?
Marie	I see nothing but the sun, the dust, and the green grass.
Bluebeard	Wife, come now! (*Off stage*).
Jeanne	One moment longer, if you please. Marie, do you see anyone coming?
Marie	I see a great cloud of dust coming this way.
Jeanne	Is it Jean and my brother?
Marie	Alas, no my sister! It looks more like a flock of sheep!
Bluebeard	Wife, if you do not come this second, I shall come after you.
Jeanne	I am coming! Sister, do you see anyone?
Marie	I see two horsemen coming this way.
Jeanne	Praise be! It is my brother and Jean! Signal for them to hasten!
Marie	I am waving frantically! It is they!
Bluebeard	(*Enters*) Now, you shall die!
Jeanne	Yes, yes, of course, but wait a minute, just a minute.
Bluebeard	No wife shall disobey me and live to tell the tale! Stand up! (*Pulls her up by the hair.*)
Jeanne	Yes, yes. (*She staggers to her feet.*)
Bluebeard	Now! (*Raises his sabre. At this moment Henri and Jean enter and rush at Bluebeard who screams and runs around the table. He dashes to the closet where he stumbles and falls upon his own sabre.*)
Jean	Ha! Pierced through the heart with his own sabre!
Henri	Dear sister, at last you are safe!
Jean	My dearest friend, how you must have suffered!
Marie	Has Bluebeard any heirs, sister?
Jeanne	I am his only heir, and I shall put all of his wealth to good use. Sister Marie, you shall have a dowry large

enough so that you can marry the poor gentleman you have loved for so long.

Marie   Oh, my dear sister, that will make us both very happy.

Jeanne   And I shall buy a Captain's Commission for my dear brother Henri.

Henri   You are most generous, dear Jeanne.

Jeanne   And with the rest I shall help the poor and needy in all the land. . . . Friend Jean, is there something you wish?

Jean   I do not care for wealth, dear friend. But if you think you could marry a man who will try to make you forget your unhappy experiences with Bluebeard, I would ask you for your hand in marriage, my dear lady.

Jeanne   And I accept, dear Jean. We shall sell this great palace and find our happiness in a simple little cottage.

A MIDSUMMER NIGHT'S DREAM.* *An adaptation arranged by a group of eighth-grade pupils.*

The story of the play may be read from *Tales From Shakespeare* by Charles and Mary Lamb. The dramatization of the play may be done through creative play, or a formal dramatization of the following cutting may be used. In this case, let the pupils read the lines; do not waste time by asking the pupils to memorize lines.

Scene I

(*At the Edge of the Forest*)

Theseus   (*Enters from the right, following Hyppolyta*)
Now, fair Hyppolyta, our wedding hour draws near; we have but four happy days to wait.

Hyppolyta   Four happy days will quickly pass.

Theseus   I have bidden all Athenian youth to stir up merriment. I shall wed thee with pomp and triumph.

Hyppolyta   The palace is decorated. The cooks are preparing a banquet. I am certain it will be the finest wedding in the land.

* From the drama by William Shakespeare.

Theseus	Not a thing will be left undone.
Hyppolyta	Good Theseus, look who comes hither. Are these friends of yours?
Theseus	Friends, indeed, they are.
Egeus	(*Enters from the left with Hermia, Demetrius, and Lysander*) Happy be Theseus, our beloved Duke!
Theseus	Thank you, good Egeus. What's the news with thee?
Egeus	I am very angry with my daughter, Hermia. She refuses to marry Demetrius, who hath my consent to marry my daughter. But, my gracious Duke, this Lysander has stolen the heart of my child, bewitched her, I do believe. She would marry him against my wishes. I beg of you, Duke, decree that my daughter shall marry the man I choose or be put to death, according to the Athenian law!
Theseus	What say you to this, Hermia? Demetrius is a worthy gentleman.
Hermia	I do beg your grace to pardon me, but I love Lysander. I will not marry Demetrius. Let the law do whatever it may to me.
Theseus	Take time to think, my good Hermia. In four days time either prepare to die for disobedience to your father or to wed Demetrius.
Demetrius	Sweet Hermia, do as your father bids.
Hermia	Alas, Demetrius, I cannot.
Hyppolyta	Oh, my good Theseus, is there not some way that we can change the law. I do not like to see the sweet Hermia die, and I do think she should be allowed to marry the man she loves.
Theseus	There is no other way. Come, my Hyppolyta, we must go. Egeus and Demetrius, if you will come with me, also, I would talk to you about some other business.
Egeus	With duty we follow you.
	(*Theseus, Hyppolyta, Demetrius, and Egeus leave, left.*)
Hermia	Alas, Lysander, what now?
Lysander	Hear me, sweet Hermia. I have a widowed aunt who lives some distance from Athens. There the cruel law

of Athens cannot be put in force against you. If you love me, steal from thy father's house tonight and go with me to my aunt's house. There we will be married. I will meet you in the wood where we have so often walked. You know the place.

Hermia   My dear Lysander, tonight, truly, I will meet with thee.

Lysander   Look who comes here. Good-day, fair Helena.

Helena   (*Enters from the left*)
Do not call me fair. Call Hermia fair. Demetrius loves me not, but loves only Hermia. Oh, Hermia, teach me how to win the heart of Demetrius.

Hermia   Be comforted. He shall never see me again.

Lysander   Tonight Hermia and I will steal away and meet in the wood where we have so often walked among the primrose beds. Farewell, sweet Helena. When we are gone Demetrius may smile on you.

(*Lysander and Hermia go out, right.*)

Helena   How happy some can be! Once, Demetrius did smile on me, but now he loves only Hermia, and alas, she runs from him. I will go and tell him of Hermia's flight. Then he will follow her to the wood tonight. Perhaps he will thank me for this information and will like me a little more. Besides, I will guide him to the meeting place, and I shall be happy in his company.

Music

Scene II

(*Within the Forest, the bower of the Fairy Queen is at the right.*)

Fairies   (*They are dancing.*)
Over hill, over dale,
Through bush, through brier,
Over park, through gale,
Through flood, through fire,
We wander everywhere.

Puck   (*Enters from the left*)
Ho, ho! Ho, ho! Hear ye, hear ye!
The King will hold a meeting here tonight.
Take heed that the Queen comes not within his sight;

For Oberon, King of Fairies, is full of wrath,
Because the Queen for her servant hath
Taken a little Indian boy,
And King Oberon wants the child
To be his page and run the forest wild.
But she will not let him have the boy;
Instead, she crowns him with flowers and makes him
All her joy. And so the King and the Queen
Of Fairies do heartily disagree.

First Fairy   Either I mistake your shape and color quite,
Or else you are that spry and happy sprite
Called Robin Goodfellow. Are you not he?

Puck   I am that merry wanderer of the night.
Some call me hobgoblin, some sweet Puck;
I play pranks on people and bring them luck.
But wait . . . make room! Here comes the King!

First Fairy   And here the Queen! Oh, woe! We would the King
were gone!

King Oberon   (*Enters from the left*)
Ill met by moonlight, proud Titania!

Queen Titania   (*Enters from the right*)
What, jealous Oberon, is it you? Fairies, skip hence!
I have sworn not to be seen in his company!

King Oberon   Tarry, rash Queen. Am I not your King? Why does
Titania refuse to please her Oberon? I beg you, give
the little Indian boy to me to be my page.

Queen Titania   Set your heart at rest. All of the fairy kingdom cannot buy the boy from me. His mother was my dear
friend, and when she died, I promised that I would
care for her child. I will not part with him, and
he cannot be your page. If you will dance with us,
come; if not . . . . away!

King Oberon   Give me the boy, and I will go with thee!

Queen Titania   Not for thy kingdom! Come fairies, away!
I will quarrel further, if I stay!

(*The Fairies and the Queen leave, right. Puck remains.*)

King Oberon   Puck, a moment with you!

Puck   Yes, my King?

King Oberon	Puck, fetch me the flower which we call Love in Idleness. The juice of that flower, if laid upon the eyelids of those who sleep, will make them, when they awaken, love the first thing they see. Some of the juice I will drop on the eyelids of Titania while she sleeps, and when she opens her eyes, the first object which comes within her sight she will fall in love with, even though it be a bear or a monkey! And before I take the love charm from her, and I can do that with another charm I know, I'll make her give the little Indian boy to me. Now, get thee gone!
Puck	At this moment I am gone (*leaves left*).
King Oberon	'Tis well. I shall have things my way henceforth. . . . . But look, who comes here? A man and a maid. Quick! I'll make myself invisible.
	(*The King hides behind the Queen's bower.*)
Helena	(*Enters, following Demetrius*) Demetrius, wait for me! I implore you!
Demetrius	Helena, I do not love thee; therefore, do not follow me. Where are Lysander and fair Hermia? You told me that they were in this wood. Helena, get thee gone! Follow me no longer. I do not love thee!
Helena	Ah, but I love you the more. I would follow you and serve you.
Demetrius	You weary me. I do not want to look upon you.
Helena	But I do want to look upon you!
Demetrius	I will run from thee and hide and leave thee to the wild beasts! (*Crosses to the right and exits.*)
Helena	Run where you will. I will follow! (*Exits right, following Demetrius.*)
King Oberon	(*Crosses to center*) Ho, ho! So the young man spurns the lady! Well, I will turn things about for them! Before he leaves this wood, he shall seek the young lady's love. Puck! Have you not yet returned?
Puck	(*Enters from the right*) Yes, my King?
King Oberon	Did you bring the flower?
Puck	Aye, here it is. (*He gives the flower to the King.*)

King Oberon	With the juice I'll rub Titania's eyes. Puck, you must take some of the juice of this flower and find a sweet Athenian lady in this wood. She is with a youth who scorns her. Find the youth asleep and rub some of the juice on his eyelids and when he awakens he will fall in love with the fair lady. You will know the man by the Athenian garments he wears.
Puck	I will do as you bid (*Leaves, right*).
King Oberon	'Tis well (*Leaves, left*).

(*Music*)

Lysander	(*Enters from the left, with Hermia*) Fair Hermia, you are faint with wandering in the wood, and alas, I fear we have lost our way. Let us rest a while before we go on.
Hermia	Be it so, Lysander. I upon this bank will rest my head (*Lies down at right*).
Lysander	Good-night, sweet Hermia. Sleep give thee rest. (*Lysander lies down, left, back.*)
Puck	(*Enters from right*) Through the forest I have searched, but I cannot find the lover. Night and silence! Who is here asleep? Dress of the Athenian he is wearing. This must be the one of whom my master spoke. Here is the maiden, too. Mortal, upon thine eyes I throw all the power this charm doth know. (*Rubs the juice upon Lysander's eyelids*) When you awaken, the first you see that one will your true love be! (*Exits, left.*)
Helena	(*Enters from right*) I am out of breath with this chase. Oh, that I might be any maiden but the loveless Helena! Demetrius has escaped me, and I am weary and afraid. But who is here? Lysander! Dead or asleep? If you live, good sir, awake!
Lysander	(*Awakens, rises*) And run through fire I will for thy sweet sake. Oh, Helena, how I love thee! Where is Demetrius? I would find him and run him through with my sword!
Helena	Say not so, Lysander. Hermia loves you; be content.
Lysander	Not Hermia, but Helena, now, I love.

Helena

Oh, was I born to be mocked and scorned by everyone? Is it not enough that I can never get a sweet look or kind word from Demetrius, but you, sir, must pretend in this manner to court me. (*Crosses to left*) I thought, Lysander, that you were a man of more true gentleness. Fare you well. (*Exits, left*)

Lysander

She saw not Hermia. (*Crosses to Hermia*) Sleep on Hermia. I will follow my own true love. Helena— wait! Helena! (*Exits, left*)

Hermia

Help! Lysander, help! Ah me— 'twas but a dream! Lysander, I quake with fear! I dreamed of wild beasts. Lysander, where are you going? Wait for me, Lysander! (*Follows Lysander, left*)

Demetrius

(*Enters from the right*)
At last I have succeeded in freeing myself of Helena. But such a chase has left me weary indeed. I cannot find Hermia and Lysander, but I am too weary to search farther without rest. I shall sleep here a while (*Lies down at right of Fairy Queen's bower*).

(*Puck and King Oberon enter from the left.*)

King Oberon

Puck, did you put the love juice on this cruel lover's eyelids?

Puck

I put the love juice on one lover's eyelids, but 'twas not this one. It was another. Methinks I have made a mistake.

King Oberon

Or else have done it purposely. Here, I will place the love juice on this one's eyelids. Now, you see that you crush this second herb that I give thee over the other lover's eyelids, and he will be himself again. (*Crosses to right and turns back to Puck*) I go now to my queen to see if I can get the Indian boy. (*Exits, right*)

Puck

I go to do thy bidding. (*Exits, left*)

Helena

(*Enters from left, followed by Lysander*) Follow me not, Lysander. You make mockery of me. I know it! (*She sees Demetrius.*) Ah, Demetrius, at last I have found you!

Demetrius

(*Awakens*) Helena, my love! You are perfect! Divine!

Helena

Oh spite! Is everyone bent on making sport of me? First Lysander, and now you! You both love Hermia, not me (*Crosses to center*).

Demetrius	Lysander loves Hermia, not I.
Lysander	You are unkind, Demetrius, for you love Hermia. This I know and you know. Here she comes searching for you. I give Hermia to you, Demetrius, because Helena is my true love.
Hermia	(*Enters from the left*) Alas, Lysander, I have looked everywhere for you!
Lysander	Why look for me? I do not love you. I love fair Helena.
Helena	They are plotting against me! Oh, Hermia, how can you treat me so unfairly!
Hermia	Dear Helena, I have done you no wrong.
Helena	I will have none of you. I will run from you all! (*Exits, right*)
Demetrius	I will follow! (*Exits, right. Lysander and Hermia follow.*)

(*Music*)

(*The Fairy Queen and her fairies get placed. The Queen is asleep in her bower. The fairies are asleep on the ground. Puck and King Oberon enter quietly.*)

Puck	Up and down, up and down, I will lead them up and down. I am feared in field and town; Goblin lead them up and down. Right the wrong you've done tonight, Ere the day brings forth its light!
King Oberon	Puck, you say you finally separated the two Athenians and rubbed the juice remover on the first lover's eye-lids?
Puck	Yes, my King, and now when they awaken each will love the maiden who loves him.
King Oberon	Well done, Puck. Now, for my Queen Titania. Has she yet awakened?
Puck	Not yet, but I have arranged for her to fall in love with a mortal with a donkey's head. Now let us make ourselves invisible! (*They hide.*)
Bottom	(*Enters from the left; singing*) The woosel-cock so black of hue, With orange-tawny bill.

> The throstle with his note so true,
> The wren with little quill.

Queen Titania   What angel wakes me from my flowery bed? I pray thee, gentle mortal, sing again. Thy fair face doth move me. I swear I love thee!

Bottom   Methinks, mistress, you should have little reason for that, yet, to say the truth, reason and love keep little company nowadays.

Queen Titania   Thou art as wise as thou art beautiful!

Bottom   Not so, but if I had wit enough to get out of this wood, I had enough.

Queen Titania   Out of this wood do not desire to go. Thou shalt remain here. I will give thee fairies to attend thee. Peas-blossom! Cobweb! Moth! Mustard-seed!

Peas-Blossom   Ready!

Cobweb   And I!

Moth   And I!

Mustard-seed   And I!

Queen Titania   Wait upon this sweet gentleman. Hop in his walks; feed him grapes, green figs, and mulberries. Bring for him the honey-bags of the bees. Come, my beautiful one. Allow me to embrace you!

(She places her arms about his neck.)

Bottom   Peas-blossom!

Peas-Blossom   Ready!

Bottom   Scratch my head. Where's Cobweb?

Cobweb   Ready!

Bottom   Cobweb, bring me the honey-bag yonder on that thistle. Mustard-seed!

Mustard-seed   What is your will?

Bottom   Nothing, good Mustard-seed, but to help Peas-blossom scratch my head. Methinks I must see a barber for I feel marvelously hairy about the face.

Queen Titania   Wouldst thou hear some music, my sweet love?

Bottom   Yes, let there be music!

(Music)

Queen Titania	And say, sweet love, what you desire to eat.
Bottom	I could munch good dry oats or some sweet hay. But truly, I have a great desire to sleep. I pray you, let none of your people disturb me.
Queen Titania	Sleep then, and I will wind thee in my arms. Oh, how I love thee! (*The music dies out as Bottom and the fairies sleep.*) (*Puck and King Oberon come forward.*)
King Oberon	Now I do pity my poor queen. 'Tis folly, to be in love with such a one. Come, we will release her. With the charm remover I will take the love juice from her eyes. (*He places the charm remover on her eyelids.*) Awake, my sweet, and see as you were wont to see.
Queen Titania	(*She awakens.*) Oberon, oh Oberon! What dreams I have had. I dreamed I was in love with the strangest being!
King Oberon	There is your love.
Queen Titania	That! How came these things to pass?
King Oberon	Silence a while. Puck, take off this one's donkey head and lead him on his way. Music, my fairies. And now, my Queen, if you love not this one, but do love Oberon, your King, will you allow the little boy to be his page?
Queen Titania	Yes, yes, you may have him. Ho, that music makes me merry.
King Oberon	Come, my Queen, take hands with me. Let us dance in happy glee!
Puck	Over hill, over dale, Through bush, through brier, Over park, through gale, Through flood, through fire, We wander everywhere! Oh-ho! My King, attend and mark! I do hear the morning lark.
King Oberon	Then my Queen, let us be gone.
Queen Titania	Yes, my King, and in our flight, Tell me how it came this night, That I sleeping here was found With that mortal on the ground!

(*All leave, left.*)

(*Music*)

(Hermia, Lysander, Demetrius, and Helena in this next scene are seen sleeping on the ground. Theseus, Hyppolyta, Egeus, and a guard enter.)

Guard It was here, Your Highness, that I found them, fast asleep.

Egeus It is they, my gracious Duke. There is my daughter, Hermia, and the others!

Theseus I pray you all awake!

Hermia Father!

Lysander What ho!

Demetrius What is this confusion?

Theseus Lysander, we know that you and Demetrius are enemies, how does it happen that you are friendly here in the wood?

Lysander Truly, my gracious Duke, I cannot say. I came here with Hermia. Our intention was to go from Athens to the home of my aunt where we might be wed without the peril of the Athenian law.

Egeus Enough! Enough! The law upon their heads! See, Demetrius, how they have defeated you and me!

Demetrius Not me, good Egeus. I know not by what power, but my love for Hermia has melted as the snow. 'Tis fair Helena that I love.

Theseus Fair lovers, you have happily met. Egeus, I must overbear your will and the law. Since Demetrius loves not your daughter, you will do best to consent to her marriage with Lysander. And now, come all. We will go to the palace. There we shall have a great feast, and Hyppolyta and I will share our ceremony with you. Is it not so, fair Hyppolyta?

Hyppolyta It will give us pleasure to share our happiness with you. Let us to the palace hasten, and there amongst the celebration we shall have a triple wedding!

Section E

IMPROVEMENT THROUGH CHORAL SPEAKING*

General Suggestions

The speaking of rhythmical poems in chorus can be an effective means of encouraging careful enunciation, a more flexible voice, and a better quality of voice. Poems and rhymes which express impersonal or group emotions should be selected for use in choral speaking.

Read the selection to the class, or let the pupils read it together. Discuss the characters, the story, and the mood of the selection. If the children are too young to read, the poem or rhyme must be learned. Learning, however, should be incidental and a natural result of the group work during the practice sessions.

Encourage the group to put action into words. Make them glide, leap, move swiftly or slowly, according to the interpretation and mood of the material. Work for feeling and interpretation, rather than for effect, and of course, work indirectly for more acceptable speech. Voices should be natural. Encourage clear articulation, a pleasant tone, and freedom and sincerity.

The teacher may use definite gestures to mean "ready," "go," "stop," "increase speed," "slow," and "more power." The reading may be started in unison following the count of "1-2-3," or by a lift and nod of the head. Usually it is wise to be more informal and make the choral reading period a time to enjoy the pleasure of speaking together.

* Selected references for Choral Speaking will be found in Appendix B.

The class may be divided according to the boys and girls, or according to the "light" and "heavy" voices. Certain groups may read different parts of a selection, or individual pupils may read certain lines. The assignment of reading parts depends upon the material used and upon the ingenuity of the leader. Whenever possible, work out action with the reading. Go around the mulberry bush, wash the clothes, let the pendulums swing on *Hickory, Dickory, Dock*. Ask the children to be pirates in the reading of *The Pirate Don Durk of Dowdee*; let them "slash," and "splash," and go through the world with a wonderful "swash." Beat the drums to the rhythm of the *Chimney Drummer Boy*.

The leader should be acquainted with and have a genuine liking for old and new poetry. He should have a natural talent for reading and interpreting poetry. A sense of rhythm, a pleasing tone, and possibilities for variations in tone are necessary. The leader, however, should not be a perfectionist when using choral speaking for the purpose of speech improvement. The goal is not to perfect the performance, but to improve speech habits through the use of enjoyable experiences in group reading.

When the group speaks, no individual needs to stand out as being different and no person needs to feel that the complete responsibility of successful speaking rests upon his shoulders. Even the child with a serious stuttering problem finds that he can speak normally when speaking in unison with others. This discovery often can do much to help the child establish confidence in speaking. In choral speaking, children can find an outlet for pent-up emotions. There is security in going along with the crowd, and when everyone is trying to produce sounds accurately and to speak as well as possible there is less chance of any child feeling inferior. There is a good chance that all of the children will improve in their speaking habits if the leader of the group is capable and sufficiently prepared.

In using choral reading for speech improvement and speech correction, the teacher will, as in the use of creative play, address her suggestions and corrections *to the group.* Certain selections may be chosen to emphasize practice on certain sounds. Time may be taken before the choral reading begins to explain the formation and production of certain sounds. Everyone in the group will then be working for a good (s) sound in *Sing a Song of Sixpence,* or for a good (r) or (d) sound in *The Pirate Don Durk of Dowdee.*

Much of the success of a choral reading project depends upon the ability and enthusiasm of the leader. The teacher should be sure to select material she likes, and be sure that the chosen selections are within the interest and ability levels of the children. The selections which follow range in order from easy material for the younger children to more difficult material for those who are older.

Refer to the selected bibliography in Appendix B for further suggestions on conducting choral reading groups.

Selections for Choral Reading*

Hush-a-Bye

This is for the young children in the kindergarten or first grade. They may sing the words first if they wish. Then let them speak the words. They rock the baby in their arms as they sing and speak. Let the wind 'blow' while some of the children chant 'whee' or 'oo.'

> Hush-a-bye baby, on the tree top,
> When the wind blows, the cradle will rock;
> When the bough breaks, the cradle will fall,
> Down will come baby, cradle, and all.

Sing a Song of Sixpence

Clap hands to the rhythm of this selection. Choose characters and act it out: a servant serves the King, the King counts his money, the Queen eats bread and honey, and the maid hangs out the clothes.

---

* The selections are traditional unless sources are indicated.

Sing a song of sixpence, a pocket full of rye,
Four and twenty blackbirds baked in a pie;
When the pie was opened, the birds began to sing.
Wasn't that a dainty dish to set before a King?

The King was in the countinghouse, counting out his money;
The Queen was in the parlor, eating bread and honey;
The maid was in the garden, hanging out the clothes;
Down came a blackbird and pecked off her nose.

THE MULBERRY BUSH

Is there a teacher or a school child who does not know the traditional action that goes along with this rhyme? Relax and have fun while you try speaking the lines, instead of singing them. Go around that mulberry bush in a big circle; clap your hands to keep them warm; scrub those clothes; lift that iron; scrub the floor; roll out the pie; knead that bread, and when you go to church, go solemnly, lower the voice and chant.

Here we go round the mulberry bush, the mulberry bush, the mulberry bush;
Here we go round the mulberry bush,
All on a frosty morning.

This is the way we clap our hands, clap our hands, clap our hands;
This is the way we clap our hands,
All on a frosty morning.

This is the way we wash our clothes, wash our clothes, wash our clothes;
This is the way we wash our clothes,
So early Monday morning.

This is the way we iron our clothes, iron our clothes, iron our clothes;
This is the way we iron our clothes,
So early Tuesday morning.

This is the way we scrub the floor, scrub the floor, scrub the floor;
This is the way we scrub the floor,
So early Wednesday morning.

This is the way we bake a pie, bake a pie, bake a pie;
This is the way we bake a pie,
So early Thursday morning.

This is the way we knead the bread, knead the bread, knead the bread;
This is the way we knead the bread,
So early Friday morning.

This is the way we go to town, go to town, go to town;
This is the way we go to town,
So early Saturday morning.

This is the way we go to church, go to church, go to church;
This is the way we go to church,
So early Sunday morning.

Here we go round the mulberry bush, the mulberry bush, the mul-
   berry bush;
Here we go round the mulberry bush,
All on a frosty morning.

THREE BLIND MICE

The class may be divided for this rhyme. One group may
give the first, third, and fifth lines; another group may give
the second, fourth, and sixth lines, or the rhyme may be used
as it often is, as a round.

> Three blind mice,
> Three blind mice,
> See how they run;
> See how they run.
> They all ran after the farmer's wife.
> She cut off their tails with a carving knife.
> Did you ever hear such a tale in your life
> About three blind mice?

I SAW A SHIP A-SAILING

Divide the class into two groups; the girls speak on Part I,
and the boys speak on Part II; everyone joins in on the
"quack, quack."

I. I saw a ship a-sailing,
   A-sailing on the sea;

II. And, oh! it was all laden
    With pretty things for thee!

I. There were comfits in the cabin,
   And apples in the hold!

II. The sails were made of silk,
    And the masts were made of gold.

I. The four-and-twenty sailors
   That stood between the decks,

II. Were four-and-twenty white mice,
    With chains about their necks.

I. The captain was a duck,
   With a packet on his back;

II. And when the ship began to move,
    The captain cried,

All "Quack! Quack!"

OH WHO IS SO MERRY

Girls Oh, who is so merry, heigh ho, heigh ho!
       As the light-hearted fairy, heigh ho!

Boys   She dances and sings
       To the tune of her wings,

All   With a hey and a heigh and a ho, ho, ho!

Girls Oh, who is so merry, heigh ho, heigh ho!
       As the light-hearted fairy, heigh ho!

Boys   The nectar she sips
       From the primrose's lips,

All   With a hey and a heigh and a ho, ho, ho!

Girls Oh, who is so merry, heigh ho, heigh ho!
       As the light-hearted fairy, heigh ho!

Boys   Her night is the noon
       And her sun is the moon,

All   With a hey and a heigh and a ho, ho, ho!

Hickory Dickory Dock

Group I reading the "tick-tock" throughout the selection should carefully set and maintain the rhythm. The other speakers keep pace with this rhythm in speaking their lines.

Group I	Tick-tock, tick-tock, tick-tock (*Continue throughout the reading.*)
Groups II and III	Hickory, dickory, dock,
Girls, Group II	The mouse ran up the clock,
One Child	The clock struck one, bong!
Boys, Group III	The mouse ran down;
Groups II and III	Hickory, dickory, dock; Hickory, dickory, dock,
Girls, Group II	The mouse ran up the clock!
Three Speakers	The clock struck three: Bong! Bong! Bong!
Boys, Group III	The mouse ran free,
Groups II and III	Hickory, dickory, dock; Hickory, dickory, dock,
Girls, Group II	The mouse ran up the clock.
Boys, Group III	The clock struck ten: Bong! Bong! Bong! Bong! Bong! Bong! Bong! Bong! Bong! Bong!
Girls, Group II	The mouse ran down again.
Groups II and III	Hickory, dickory, dock; Hickory, dickory, dock!
All	Tick-tock, tick-tock, tick-tock, tick-tock (*Continue and slowly fade out*).

The Crooked Man

Group I	There was a crooked man
Group II	And he went a crooked mile;
Group I	He found a crooked sixpence
Group II	Against a crooked stile;

Group I   He bought a crooked cat,

Group II   Which caught a crooked mouse,

All   And they all lived together in a little crooked house.

WHO HAS SEEN THE WIND[*]

Group I   Who has seen the wind? [Whooo?] (*Hold 'whoo, whoo, whoo,' throughout the selection.*)

Group II   Neither I nor you;

Group III   But when the leaves hang trembling,
              The wind is passing through.

Group II   Who has seen the wind?

Group III   Neither you nor I;

Group II   But when the trees bow down their heads,
              The wind is passing by.

All   [Whoo, whoo, whoo] (*Fade out on "whoo".*)

THE WIND[†]

Group I   [Ooo, oo, oo, oo] (*Continue like the wind throughout the selection*).

Group II   I saw you toss the kites on high
              And blow the birds about the sky;
              And all around I heard you pass,
              Like ladies' skirts across the grass —

Group III   O wind, a-blowing all day long
              O wind, that sings so loud a song!

Group II   I saw the different things you did,
              But always you yourself you hid.
              I felt you push, I heard you call,
              I could not see yourself at all —

Group III   O wind, a-blowing all day long,
              O wind, that sings so loud a song!

[*] From Christina Rossetti, *Poetical Works* (London: Macmillan & Co., Ltd.).

[†] "The Wind," from *A Child's Garden of Verses* by Robert Louis Stevenson, Scribner Illustrated Classics edition, Charles Scribner's Sons. Used by permission.

Group II   O you that are so strong and cold,
                O blower, are you young or old?
                Are you a beast of field and tree,
                Or just a stronger child than me?

Group III   O wind, a-blowing all day long
                O wind, that sings so loud a song!

All   [Ooo, oo, oo, oo, oo] (*Fade out on 'oo'*).

WINDY NIGHTS *

Group I   [Gallopy, gallopy, gallopy, gallopy] (*Continue in rhythm throughout the selection.*)

Group II   Whenever the moon and stars are set,
                Whenever the wind is high,
                All night long in the dark and wet,
                A man goes riding by.

Group I   [Gallopy, gallopy, gallopy, gallopy . . .]

Group III   Late in the night when the fires are out,
                Why does he gallop and gallop about?

Group I   [Gallopy, gallopy, gallopy, gallopy . . .]

Group II   Whenever the trees are crying aloud,
                And ships are tossed at sea,
                By, on the highway, low and loud,
                By at the gallop goes he.

Group I   [Gallopy, gallopy, gallopy, gallopy . . .]

Group III   By at the gallop he goes, and then
                By he comes back at the gallop again.

All   [Gallopy, gallopy, gallopy, gallopy, gallopy] (*Fade out.*)

THE NORTH WIND

Boys   The north wind doth blow,
           And we shall have snow,
           And what will the robin do then?

All   Poor thing.

* "Windy Nights," from *A Child's Garden of Verses* by Robert Louis Stevenson, Scribners Illustrated Classics edition, Charles Scribner's Sons. Used by permission.

Girls He'll sit in the barn
And keep himself warm,
And hide his head under his wing,

All Poor thing.

Boys The north wind doth blow,
And we shall have snow,
And what shall the honey-bee do?

All Poor thing.

Girls In his hive he will stay
'Til the cold's passed away,
And then he'll come out in the spring,

All Poor thing.

Boys The north wind doth blow,
And we shall have snow,
And what will the dormouse do then?

All Poor thing.

Girls Rolled up like a ball
In his nest snug and small,
He'll sleep 'til warm weather comes back,

All Poor thing.

Boys The north wind doth blow,
And we shall have snow,
And what will the children do then?

All Poor things.

Girls When lessons are done,
They'll hop, skip, and run,
And that's how they'll keep themselves warm,

All Poor things!

A Dirge for a Righteous Kitten*

This selection may be spoken to the "ringing" of bells which continue throughout the reading. The sixth and the thirteenth lines are not spoken to the rhythm of the bells,

---

* The selection from Vachel Lindsay, "A Dirge for a Righteous Kitten," in *Collected Poems*, copyright 1925, reprint 1946, by The Macmillan Company. Used by permission.

but are given in a matter-of-fact tone by one speaker. The members of Group I, acting as the bells on "ding-dong, ding-dong," raise and lower their arms as if pulling the bell.

Group I	[Ding-dong, ding-dong, ding-dong] (*Continue throughout the reading*).
Group II	Here lies a kitten good, who kept A kitten's proper place.
Group III	He stole no pantry eatables, Nor scratched the baby's face.
One Speaker	He let the alley-cats alone.
Group II	He had no yowling vice. His shirt was always laundried well, He freed the house of mice.
Group III	Until his death he had not caused His little mistress tears, He wore his ribbons prettily,
One Speaker	He washed behind his ears.
All	[Ding-dong, ding-dong, ding-dong, ding-dong] (*Fade out.*)

The Owl and the Pussy-Cat*

All	The Owl and the Pussy-Cat went to sea In a beautiful pea-green boat. They took some honey and plenty of money, Wrapped up in a five-pound note. The Owl looked up to the stars above, And sang to a small guitar,
Boys	"Oh, lovely Pussy! Oh Pussy, my love, What a beautiful Pussy you are, You are, What a beautiful Pussy you are!"
Girls	Pussy said to the Owl, "You elegant fowl! How charmingly sweet you sing! Oh, let us be married! Too long we have tarried, But what shall we do for a ring?"

* Edward Lear, *Laughable Lyrics.*

All	They sailed away for a year and a day, To the land where the bong-tree grows, And there in the wood a Piggy-wig stood, With a ring at the end of his nose, His nose, With a ring at the end of his nose.
Boys	"Dear Pig, are you willing to sell for one shilling Your ring?"
All	Said the Piggie,
One Boy	"I will."
All	So they took it away, and were married that day By the Turkey who lives on the hill. They dined on mince and slices of quince, Which they ate with a runcible spoon; And hand in hand, on the edge of the sand, They danced by the light of the moon, The moon, They danced by the light of the moon.

The Duel *

It is possible to use this and the next selection with several different reading groups, using several individual reading parts. Experiment with different divisions, and let the children help in arranging the material for choric reading.

> The gingham dog and the calico cat
> Side by side on the table sat;
> 'Twas half past twelve, and (what do you think!)
> Nor one nor t'other had slept a wink!
> The old Dutch clock and the Chinese plate
> Appeared to know as sure as fate
> There was going to be a terrible spat.
> (*I wasn't there; I simply state*
> *What was told me by the Chinese plate!*)

* "The Duel," from *Poems of Childhood* by Eugene Field, Scribner Illustrated Classics edition, Charles Scribner's Sons. Used by permission.

The gingham dog went, "bow-wow-wow!"
And the calico cat replied, "mee-ow!"
The air was littered, an hour or so,
With bits of gingham and calico,
While the old Dutch clock in the chimney place
Up with its hands before its face,
For it always dreaded a family row!
(*Now mind; I'm only telling you*
What the old Dutch clock declares is true!)

The Chinese plate looked very blue,
And wailed, "Oh, dear! what shall we do?"
But the gingham dog and the calico cat
Wallowed this way and tumbled that,
Employing every tooth and claw
In the awfullest way you ever saw—
And, oh! how the gingham and calico flew!
(*Don't fancy I exaggerate—*
I got my news from the Chinese plate!)

Next morning, where the two had sat,
They found no trace of dog or cat;
And some folks think unto this day
That burglars stole the pair away!
But the truth about the cat and pup
Is this: they ate each other up!
Now what do you really think of that!
(*The old Dutch clock it told me so,*
And that is how I came to know.)

WYNKEN, BLYNKEN, AND NOD[*]

Wynken, Blynken, and Nod one night
Sailed off in a wooden shoe—
Sailed on a river of crystal light
Into a sea of dew.
"Where are you going, and what do you wish?"
The old moon asked the three.

[*] "Wynken, Blynken, and Nod," from *Poems of Childhood* by Eugene Field, Scribner Illustrated Classics edition, Charles Scribner's Sons. Used by permission.

"We have come to fish for the herring fish
That live in this beautiful sea;
Nets of silver and gold have we!"
     Said Wynken,
     Blynken,
     And Nod.

The old moon laughed and sang a song,
As they rocked in the wooden shoe,
And the wind that sped them all night long
Ruffled the waves of dew.
The little stars were the herring fish
That lived in that beautiful sea—
"Now cast your nets wherever you wish—
Never afeared are we!"
So cried the stars to the fishermen three,
     Wynken,
     Blynken,
     And Nod.

All night long their nets they threw
To the stars in the twinkling foam—
Then down from the skies came the wooden shoe,
Bringing the fishermen home;
'Twas all so pretty a sail it seemed
As if it could not be,
And some folks thought 'twas a dream they'd dreamed
Of sailing that beautiful sea;
But I shall name you the fishermen three:
     Wynken,
     Blynken,
     And Nod.

Wynken and Blynken are two little eyes,
And Nod is a little head,
And the wooden shoe that sailed the skies
Is a wee one's trundle-bed;
So shut your eyes while mother sings
Of wonderful sights that be,
And you shall see the beautiful things
As you rock in the misty sea,

Where the old shoe rocked the fishermen three:
Wynken,
Blynken,
And Nod.

THE CHIMNEY DRUMMER-BOY*

Let the children beat the drums throughout this selection.
Let the speaking be to the rhythm of the drums: Tum-te-
tum, te tum; tum-te-tum, te tum.

All

There's a boy I know, and he drums all day,
For his chief delight is in soldier play.

One Voice

'Tis a very little boy,
And a very big drum,
And everywhere he goes he makes things hum,
With his brum, b-rrr rum-brum, Brum! Brum!
Now Santa Claus heard him, one Christmas eve,
And he said to himself:

One Voice

" 'Tis clear, I perceive,
That this idle boy is no good here;
For to study and work are not his sphere.
So I'll take him with me,
My drummer to be.
And I'll feed him on jam and peppercorn tea.
And my elves will come
When they hear him drum—"

All

Plan, rat-a-plan, tum-e-tum-tum,
Brum, br-rrr rum-brum, brum!

That night, as he slept in his trundle-bed,
With his drum and his drumsticks under his head,
They were all whisked off up the chimney flue—
The drum stuck tight,
But the boy went through.
Then Santa Claus sneezed with the soot in his nose,
(At-chooo!)

* By William J. Long. First published by The Outlook Company, New
York. From *Christmas Selections for Readings and Recitations*, compiled by
Rosamond Livingstone McNaught. Penn Publishing Company, Philadelphia.

And the boy woke up, as you may suppose.
He lost his hold on the chimney rim;
Head over heels he tumbled in—
Bim!

One Voice   (That was his head.)

All   Bim, tumble-in, bim-bim!

One Voice   (Those were his heels.)

All   There he is in his own big drum,
For he can't get out till the kingdom-come.
So he drums all day, to his heart's delight,
And the elfins feed him every night.

(*Start low*   In the fireplace dark,
and solemn;   If you listen sharp,
build up   When the house is still, and the watchdogs bark,
speed and   When the wind's northeast, and the storm is come,
volume.)   Up the chimney glum,
You can hear him drum—
B-r-r-r-r-r-r-r-r rum, Brum!

PIRATE DON DURK OF DOWDEE*

This selection should have a free and eager spirit. The boys' voices are powerful and boastful, while the girls' voices present the pirate as a fine and handsome dandy. Bring action into the reading; swing the arms up on "Ho," jiggle the plumes, slash, and splash, and swash; jingle the gold and make the pirate's boots go "slickery-slosh."

All   Ho, for the Pirate Don Durk of Dowdee!

Boys   He was as wicked as wicked could be,

Girls   But oh, he was perfectly gorgeous to see!

All   The Pirate Don Durk of Dowdee.

Boys   His conscience, of course, was as black as a bat,

Girls   But he had a floppety plume on his hat
And when he went walking it jiggled like that!

All   The plume of the Pirate Dowdee.

* By Mildred Plew Merryman. First published in *Child Life* magazine. Used by permission.

Girls His coat it was crimson and cut with a slash,

Boys   And often as ever he twirled his mustache,

Girls Deep down in the ocean the mermaids went splash,

All   Because of Don Durk of Dowdee.

Girls Moreover Dowdee had a purple tattoo,

Boys   And stuck in his belt where he buckled it through
         Were a dagger, a dirk, and a quizzamaroo,

All   For fierce was the Pirate Dowdee.

Girls So fearful he was he would shoot at a puff,

Boys   And always at sea when the weather grew rough
         He drank from a bottle and wrote on his cuff,

All   Did the Pirate Don Durk of Dowdee.

Boys   Oh, he had a cutlass that swung at his thigh

Girls And he had a parrot called Popperskin Pye,

Boys   And a ziggzaggy scar at the end of his eye

All   Had the Pirate Don Durk of Dowdee.

Boys   He kept in a cavern this buccaneer bold
         A curious chest that was covered with mould

Girls And all of his pockets were jingly with gold!

All   Oh, jing! went the gold of Dowdee.

Boys   His conscience, of course, it was crook'd like a squash,

Girls But both of his boots made a slickery slosh,

Boys   And he went through the world with a wonderful **swash,**

All   Did Pirate Don Durk of Dowdee.

Turtle Soup*

All   Turtle Soup, so rich and green,
         Waiting in a hot tureen!
         Who for such dainties would not stoop?

* From Lewis Carroll, *Alice in Wonderland.*

Group I	Soup of the evening, beautiful soup!
Group II	Soup of the evening, beautiful soup!
Group I	Beau-oootiful Sooo-ooop!
Group II	Beau-oootiful Sooo-ooop!
All	Sooo-ooop of the ee-evening, Beautiful, Beautiful Soup!

Beautiful Soup! Who cares for fish,
Game or any other dish?
Who would not give all else for two

Group I	Pennies worth only of Beautiful Soup?
Group II	Pennies worth only of Beautiful Soup?
Group I	Beau-oootiful Sooo-ooop!
Group II	Beau-oootiful Sooo-ooop!
All	Sooo-ooop of the ee-evening, Beautiful, Beautiful SOUP!

YANKEE DOODLE

Group I	Yankee Doodle came to town, Upon a little pony, He stuck a feather in his cap, And called it macaroni.
All	Yankee Doodle, doodle-doo, Yankee Doodle dandy; All the lassies are so smart, And sweet as sugar candy.
Group II	Marching in and marching out, And marching round the town, Oh! There came a regiment so gay With Captain Thomas Brown, Oh!
All	Yankee Doodle, doodle-doo, Yankee Doodle dandy; All the lassies are so smart, And sweet as sugar candy.

Group III Yankee Doodle is a tune
That comes in mighty handy;
The enemy all runs away
At Yankee Doodle dandy.

All   Yankee Doodle, doodle-doo,
Yankee Doodle dandy;
All the lassies are so smart,
And sweet as sugar candy.

My Cock

Speaker 1 I had a cock, and a cock loved me,
And I fed my cock under a hollow tree;
My cock cried Cock-a-doodle-doo!

All   Everybody loves their cock, and I love my cock, too!

Speaker 2 I had a hen, and a hen loved me,
And I fed my hen under a hollow tree;
My hen went—Cackle, cackle, cackle,

Speaker 1 My cock cried—Cock-a-doodle-doo!

All   Everybody loves their cock, and I love my cock, too!

Speaker 3 I had a duck, and a duck loved me,
And I fed my duck under a hollow tree;
My duck went—Quack, quack, quack,

    2 My hen went—Cackle, cackle, cackle;

    1 My cock cried—Cock-a-doodle-doo!

All   Everybody loves their cock, and I love my cock, too!

    4 I had a cat, and a cat loved me,
And I fed my cat under a hollow tree;
My cat went—Me-ow, me-ow, me-ow!

    3 My duck went—Quack, quack, quack!

    2 My hen went—Cackle, cackle, cackle!

    1 My cock cried—Cock-a-doodle-doo!

All   Everybody loves their cock, and I love my cock, too!

    5 I had a dog, and a dog loved me,
And I fed my dog under a hollow tree;
My dog went—Bow-wow-wow!

Speaker 4   My cat went—Me-ow, me-ow, me-ow!

       3   My duck went—Quack, quack, quack!

       2   My hen went—Cackle, cackle, cackle!

       1   My cock cried—Cock-a-doodle-doo!

All   Everybody loves their cock, and I love my cock, too!

       6   I had a cow, and a cow loved me,
           And I fed my cow under a hollow tree;
           My cow went—Moo, moo, moo!

       5   My dog went—Bow-wow-wow!

       4   My cat went—Me-ow, me-ow, me-ow!

       3   My duck went—Quack, quack, quack!

       2   My hen went—Cackle, cackle, cackle!

       1   My cock cried—Cock-a-doodle-doo!

All   Everybody loves their cock, and I love my cock, too!

TWELVE DAYS OF CHRISTMAS

All   The first day of Christmas, my true love sent to me

  1   A partridge in a pear tree.

All   The second day of Christmas, my true love sent to me

  2   Two turtle doves and

  1   A partridge in a pear tree.

All   The third day of Christmas, my true love sent to me

  3   Three French hens,

  2   Two turtle doves, and

  1   A partridge in a pear tree.

All   The fourth day of Christmas, my true love sent to me

  4   Four colly birds,

  3   Three French hens,

  2   Two turtle doves, and

  1   A partridge in a pear tree.

All   The fifth day of Christmas, my true love sent to me

  5   Five gold rings,

4   Four colly birds,
    etc. (3, 2, 1)

All   The sixth day of Christmas, my true love sent to me

6   Six geese a-laying,

5   Five gold rings,
    etc. (4, 3, 2, 1)

All   The seventh day of Christmas, my true love sent to me

7   Seven swans a-swimming,
    etc. (6, 5, 4, 3, 2, 1)

All   The eighth day of Christmas, my true love sent to me

8   Eight maids a-milking,
    etc. (7, 6, 5, 4, 3, 2, 1)

All   The ninth day of Christmas, my true love sent to me

9   Nine drummers drumming,
    etc. (8, 7, 6, 5, 4, 3, 2, 1)

All   The tenth day of Christmas, my true love sent to me

10   Ten pipers piping,
    etc. (9, 8, 7, 6, 5, 4, 3, 2, 1)

All   The eleventh day of Christmas, my true love sent to me

11   Eleven ladies dancing,
    etc. (10, 9, 8, 7, 6, 5, 4, 3, 2, 1)

All   The twelfth day of Christmas, my true love sent to me
    Twelve lords a-leaping,
    Eleven ladies dancing,
    Ten pipers piping,
    Nine drummers drumming,
    Eight maids a-milking,
    Seven swans a-swimming,
    Six geese a-laying,
    Five gold rings,
    Four colly birds,
    Three French hens,
    Two turtle doves, and
    A partridge in a pear tree.

The Circus-Day Parade[*]

Oh! the Circus-Day parade! How the bugles played and played!
And how the glossy horses tossed their flossy manes and neighed,
As the rattle and the rhyme of the tenor-drummer's time
Filled all the hungry hearts of us with melody sublime!

How the grand band-wagon shone with a splendor all its own,
And glittered with a glory that our dreams had never known!
And how the boys behind, high and low of every kind,
Marched in unconscious capture, with a rapture undefined!

How the horsemen, two and two, with their plumes of white and blue
And crimson, gold and purple, nodding by at me and you,
Waved the banners that they bore, as the knights in days of yore,
Till our glad eyes gleamed and glistened like the spangles that they
    wore!

How the graceless-graceful stride of the elephant was eyed,
And the capers of the little horse that cantered at his side!
How the shambling camels, tame to the plaudits of their fame,
With listless eyes came silent, masticating as they came.

How the cages jolted past, with each wagon battened fast,
And the mystery within it only hinted of at last
From the little grated square in the rear, and nosing there
The snout of some strange animal that sniffed the outer air!

And, last of all, the Clown, making mirth for all the town,
With his lips curved ever upward and his eyebrows ever down,
And his chief attention paid to the little mule that played
A tattoo on the dashboard with his heels, in the parade.

Oh! the Circus-Day parade! How the bugles played and played!
And how the glossy horses tossed their flossy manes and neighed,
As the rattle and the rhyme of the tenor-drummer's time
Filled all the hungry hearts of us with melody sublime!

THE POBBLE WHO HAS NO TOES*

The Pobble who has no toes
Had once as many as we;
When they said, "Some day you may lose them all";
He replied, "Fish fiddle de-dee!"
And his Aunt Jobiska made him drink
Lavender water tinged with pink;
For she said, "The World in general knows
There's nothing so good for a Pobble's toes!"

The Pobble who has no toes
Swam across the Bristol Channel;
But before he set out he wrapped his nose
In a piece of scarlet flannel.
For his Aunt Jobiska said, "No harm
Can come to his toes if his nose is warm;
And it's perfectly known that a Pobble's toes
Are safe—provided he minds his nose."

The Pobble swam fast and well,
And when boats or ships came near him,
He tinkledy-binkledy-winkled a bell
So that all the world could hear him.
And all the Sailors and Admirals cried,
When they saw him nearing the further side,
"He has gone to fish for his Aunt Jobiska's
Runcible Cat with crimson whiskers!"

But before he touched the shore,
The shore of the Bristol Channel,
A sea-green Porpoise carried away
His wrapper of scarlet flannel.
And when he came to observe his feet,
Formerly garnished with toes so neat,
His face at once became forlorn
On perceiving that all his toes were gone!

* Edward Lear, *Laughable Lyrics*.

And nobody ever knew,
From that dark day to the present,
Who so had taken the Pobble's toes,
In a manner so far from pleasant.
Whether the shrimps or crawfish gray,
Or crafty Mermaids stole them away,
Nobody knew; and nobody knows
How the Pobble was robbed of his twice five toes!

The Pobble who has no toes
Was placed in a friendly Bark,
And they rowed him back, and carried him up
To his Aunt Jobiska's Park.
And she made him a feast, at his earnest wish,
Of eggs and buttercups fried with fish;
And she said, "It's a fact the whole world knows,
That Pobbles are happier without their toes."

THE COURTSHIP OF THE YONGHY-BONGHY-BO *

I

On the Coast of Coromandel
    Where the early pumpkins blow,
      In the middle of the woods
   Lived the Yonghy-Bonghy-Bo.
Two old chairs, and half a candle,
One old jug without a handle,
    These were all his worldly goods;
    In the middle of the woods,
    These were all the worldly goods
   Of the Yonghy-Bonghy-Bo,
   Of the Yonghy-Bonghy-Bo.

II

Once, among the Bong-trees walking
    Where the early pumpkins blow,
      To a little heap of stones
   Came the Yonghy-Bonghy-Bo.

* Edward Lear, *Laughable Lyrics*.

There he heard a Lady talking,
To some milk-white Hens of Dorking,
    " 'Tis the Lady Jingly Jones!
    On that little heap of stones
    Sits the Lady Jingly Jones!' "
Said the Yonghy-Bonghy-Bo,
Said the Yonghy-Bonghy-Bo.

III

"Lady Jingly! Lady Jingly!
Sitting where the pumpkins blow,
    Will you come and be my wife?"
Said the Yonghy-Bonghy-Bo.
"I am tired of living singly,
On this coast so wild and shingly,
    I'm a-weary of my life;
    If you'll come and be my wife,
    Quite serene would be my life!"
Said the Yonghy-Bonghy-Bo,
Said the Yonghy-Bonghy-Bo.

IV

"On this Coast of Coromandel
Shrimps and watercresses grow,
    Prawns are plentiful and cheap."
Said the Yonghy-Bonghy-Bo.
"You shall have my chairs and candle,
And my jug without a handle!
    Gaze upon the rolling deep
    (Fish is plentiful and cheap);
    As the sea, my love is deep!"
Said the Yonghy-Bonghy-Bo,
Said the Yonghy-Bonghy-Bo.

V

Lady Jingly answered sadly,
    And her tears began to flow,
        "Your proposal comes too late,
    Mr. Yonghy-Bonghy-Bo!

I would be your wife most gladly!"
(Here she twirled her fingers madly)
  "But in England I've a mate!
  Yes! you've asked me far too late,
  For in England I've a mate,
Mr. Yonghy-Bonghy-Bo!
Mr. Yonghy-Bonghy-Bo!

VI

"Mr. Jones (his name is Handel—
Handel Jones, Esquire, & Co.)
  Dorking fowls delights to send.
 Mr. Yonghy-Bonghy-Bo!
Keep, oh, keep your chairs and candle,
And your jug without a handle,
  I can merely be your friend!
  Should my Jones more Dorkings send,
  I will give you three, my friend!
Mr. Yonghy-Bonghy-Bo!
Mr. Yonghy-Bonghy-Bo!

VII

"Though you've such a tiny body,
 And your head so large doth grow,
  Though your hat may blow away,
 Mr. Yonghy-Bonghy-Bo!
Though you're such a Hoddy Doddy,
Yet I wish that I could modi-
 fy the words I needs must say!
  Will you please to go away?
  That is all I have to say,
Mr. Yonghy-Bonghy-Bo!
Mr. Yonghy-Bonghy-Bo!"

VIII

Down the slippery slopes of Myrtle,
 Where the early pumpkins blow,
  To the calm and silent sea
 Fled the Yonghy-Bonghy-Bo.

There, beyond the Bay of Gurtle,
Lay a large and lively Turtle.
"You're the Cove," he said, "for me;
On your back beyond the sea,
Turtle, you shall carry me!"
Said the Yonghy-Bonghy-Bo,
Said the Yonghy-Bonghy-Bo.

IX

Through the silent-roaring ocean
Did the Turtle swiftly go;
Holding fast upon his shell
Rode the Yonghy-Bonghy-Bo.
With a sad primaeval motion
Towards the sunset isles of Boshen
Still the Turtle bore him well.
Holding fast upon his shell,
"Lady Jingly Jones, farewell!"
Sang the Yonghy-Bonghy-Bo,
Sang the Yonghy-Bonghy-Bo.

X

From the Coast of Coromandel
Did that Lady never go;
On that heap of stones she mourns
For the Yonghy-Bonghy-Bo.
On that Coast of Coromandel,
In his jug without a handle
Still she weeps, and daily moans;
On that little heap of stones
To her Dorking Hens she moans,
For the Yonghy-Bonghy-Bo,
For the Yonghy-Bonghy-Bo.

Mr. and Mrs. Discobbolos*

I

Mr. and Mrs. Discobbolos
   Climbed to the top of a wall.
And they sat to watch the sunset sky,
   And to hear the Nupiter Piffkin cry,
   And the Biscuit Buffalo call.
They took up a roll and some Camomile tea,
And both were as happy as happy could be,
   Till Mrs. Discobbolos said,
   "Oh! W! X! Y! Z!
   It has just come into my head,
Suppose we should happen to fall!!!!!
   Darling Mr. Discobbolos!

II

"Suppose we should fall down flumpetty,
   Just like pieces of stone,
   On to the thorns, or into the moat,
   What would become of your new green coat?
   And might you not break a bone?
It never occurred to me before,
That perhaps we shall never go down any more!"
   And Mrs. Discobbolos said,
   "Oh! W! X! Y! Z!
   What put it into your head
   To climb up this wall, my own
   Darling Mr. Discobbolos?"

III

Mr. Discobbolos answered,
   "At first it gave me pain,
   And I felt my ears turn perfectly pink
   When your exclamation made me think
   We might never get down again!

* Edward Lear, *Laughable Lyrics*.

But now I believe it is wiser far
To remain for ever just where we are."
      And Mr. Discobbolos said,
      "Oh! W! X! Y! Z!
      It has just come into my head
      We shall never go down again,
           Dearest Mrs. Discobbolos!"

IV

So Mr. and Mrs. Discobbolos
    Stood up and began to sing,
  "Far away from hurry and strife
Here we will pass the rest of life,
    Ding a dong, ding dong, ding!
We want no knives nor forks nor chairs,
No tables nor carpets nor household cares;
      From worry of life we've fled;
      Oh! W! X! Y! Z!
      There is no more trouble ahead,
    Sorrow or any such thing,
        For Mr. and Mrs. Discobbolos!"

SWEET AND LOW*

Sweet and low, sweet and low,
Wind of the western sea;
Low, low, breathe and blow,
Wind of the western sea;
Over the rolling waters go.
Come from the dying moon and blow,
Blow him again to me,
While my little one, while my pretty one sleeps.

Sleep and rest, sleep and rest,
Father will come to thee soon;
Rest, rest, on mother's breast,
Father will come to thee soon;
Father will come to his babe in the nest,
Silver sails out of the west,
Under the silver moon,
Sleep, my little one, sleep my pretty one, sleep.

* Alfred Tennyson.

My True Love

All Voices	My true love lives over the sea,
Light Voices	Perrie, Merrie, Dixie, Dominie;
All Voices	Many a gift he sends to me,
Heavy Voices	Petrum, Partrum, Paridis, Tempum,
All Voices	Perrie, Merrie, Dixie, Dominie.
All Voices	He sent me a chicken without a bone,
Light Voices	Perrie, Merrie, Dixie, Dominie;
All Voices	He sent me a cherry without a stone,
Heavy Voices	Petrum, Partrum, Paradis, Tempum,
All Voices	Perrie, Merrie, Dixie, Dominie.
All Voices	He sent me a book no man could read,
Light Voices	Perrie, Merrie, Dixie, Dominie;
All Voices	He sent me an apple without a seed,
Heavy Voices	Petrum, Partrum, Paradis, Tempum,
All Voices	Perrie, Merrie, Dixie, Dominie.

All Voices
When the chicken's in the shell, there is no bone;
When the cherry's in the bud, there is no stone.
When the book's in the press, no man can read;
When the apple's in the flower, there is no seed,
Petrum, Partrum, Paradis, Tempum,
Perrie, Merrie, Dixie, Dominie.

The Witches' Scenes from Macbeth*

Before working with these scenes, it may be wise to study the background of the play. The children may wish to read the version of *Macbeth* in Charles and Mary Lamb's book, *Tales From Shakespeare* in order to get an understanding of the story. The notes from the W. J. Rolfe edition of *Macbeth* will prove helpful. These scenes should be worked out with action.

* *Macbeth*, Act I, Scenes I and III.

1   When shall we three meet again
      In thunder, lightning, or in rain?

All When the hurly-burly's done,
      When the battle's lost and won.

2   That will be ere set of sun.

1   Where the place?

2   Upon the heath.

All There to meet with Macbeth.

1   I come, Graymalkin!

2   Paddock calls.

All Anon.
      Fair is foul, and foul is fair;
      Hover through the fog and filthy air.

          ❁   ❁   ❁   ❁   ❁

1   Where hast thou been, sister?

2   Killing swine.

3   Sister, where thou?

1   A sailor's wife had chestnuts in her lap,
      And munch'd, and munch'd, and munch'd.
      "Give me," quoth I.
      "Aroint thee, witch!" the rump-fed ronyon cries.
      Her husband's to Aleppo gone, master o' the Tiger;
      But in a sieve I'll thither sail,
      And, like a rat without a tail,
      I'll do, I'll do, and I'll do.

2   I'll give thee a wind.

All And I another.

1   I myself have all the other,
      And the very ports they blow,
      All the quarters that they know
      I' the shipman's card.
      I'll drain him dry as hay;
      Sleep shall neither night nor day
      Hang upon his pent-house lid,
      He shall live a man forbid;

All Weary se'nnights nine times nine
      Shall he dwindle, peak, and pine.

2 Though his bark cannot be lost,
  Yet it shall be tempest-tost.

1 Look what I have.

All Show me, show me.

1 Here I have a pilot's thumb,
  Wrack'd as homeward he did come.

All A drum, a drum!
  Macbeth doth come.
  The weird sisters hand in hand.
  Posters of the sea and land,
  Thus do go about, about;
  Thrice to thine, and thrice to mine.
  And thrice again to make up nine.

1 Peace! The charm's wound up.

In Conclusion

Hamlet to the Players°

Speak the speech, I pray you, as I pronounced it to you, trippingly on the tongue; but if you mouth it, as many of your players do, I had as lief the town crier spoke my lines. Nor do not saw the air too much with your hand, thus; but use all gently: for in the very torrent, tempest, and, as I may say, whirlwind of your passion, you must acquire and beget a temperance that may give it smoothness . . . Be not too tame neither, but let your own discretion be your tutor: suit the action to the word, the word to the action; with this special observance, that you o'erstep not the modesty of nature: for anything so overdone is from the purpose of playing, whose end, both at the first and now, was and is, to hold, as 'twere, the mirror up to nature; to show virtue her own feature, scorn her own image, and the very age and body of the time his form and pressure.

Polonius to His Son°°

This above all: to thine own self be true,
And it must follow, as the night the day,
Thou canst not then be false to any man.
Farewell: my blessing season this in thee!

°*Hamlet,* Act III, Scene II.
°°*Hamlet,* Act I, Scene III.

APPENDIX

APPENDIX

Appendix A

EXAMINATION RECORD[*]

A. General Information

Name . . . . Sex. . . . . Age. . . . .
Address . . . .
Parent or Guardian. . . . .
Birth date. . . . . Birth place. . . . .
Grade. . . . . School. . . . . School contact. . . . .
Referred by . . . . Relation. . . . .
Reason referred . . . .
Informant . . . . Relation. . . . .
Examined by . . . . Date. . . . .

Initial Evaluation

Type of Problem. . . . . Status. . . . .
Intelligence . . . .
Additional information required. . . . .
Evaluation of problem:

Prognosis: Unfavorable 2 3 4 Favorable

Recommendations:

. . . .
Signed

[*] As used in the Speech and Hearing Laboratories, University of Nebraska.

B. Speech and Hearing Mechanism

FACE
Mandible.............. Lips.......... Malformation........

ORAL CAVITY
Size.................... Opening......................

TONGUE
Size.................... Frenum/tip ....
Protrusion................ Activity ....

ANTERIOR TEETH
Overjet...... Closebite....Edentulous spaces......Jumbling....
Undershot....Openbite....Interproximal spaces....Other.......

HARD PALATE
Height........ Width........ Length........ Other........

VELUM
Length.... Asymmetry.... Activity.... Reflex..... Uvula.....

FAUCES
Size/pillars.......... Size/isthmus......... Tonsils..........

NASAL PORT
Size...... Pharyngeal activity...... Swallow...... Blow......

NASAL CAVITY
Nasal respiration.... Anterior passage.... Posterior passage....
Adenoids....

LARYNX
Size.......... Abnormal.......... Size/vocal cords..........
Color/vocal cords.......... Glottis......... activity.........

BREATHING MECHANISM
Size/chest....... Vital capacity....... Breathing type.......
Inspiration abnormality........ Expiration abnormality.........

AUDITORY ACUITY
Satisfactory...... Audiometric test required...... Other......

AUDITORY PERCEPTION
Poor 2 3 4 Good   Speech sound discrimination..........

OTHER

C. Personal Characteristics

INTELLIGENCE: Satisfactory...... Examination required.......

Report of examination

BEHAVIOR CHARACTERISTICS (details over)

Feeding difficulties	Sex problems	Cruelty
Thumb sucking	Fears	Destructiveness
Hair twisting	Self-pity	Jealousy
Nail biting	Dissatisfaction	Temper tantrums
Enuresis	Running away	Disobedience
Sleep disturbances	Lying	Fighting
Day dreams	Stealing	Other

SOCIAL RELATIONSHIPS

Personal attachments

Attitude toward family

Gregariousness

Group behavior

Other

PERSONALITY CHARACTERISTICS

					Remarks
Quiet	2	3	4	Talkative	
Inactive	2	3	4	Active	
Calm	2	3	4	Restless	
Phlegmatic	2	3	4	Excitable	
Vague	2	3	4	Concrete	
Submissive	2	3	4	Aggressive	
Indecisive	2	3	4	Decisive	
Afraid	2	3	4	Confident	
Pessimistic	2	3	4	Optimistic	
Depressed	2	3	4	Euphoric	
Feminine	2	3	4	Masculine	
Uncooperative	2	3	4	Cooperative	

ATTITUDE TOWARD PROBLEM

Reaction to problem

Reaction to speaking situations

Occupational effects

OTHER

D. Speech History

GENERAL LANGUAGE DEVELOPMENT
    Time of: first word.............. first sentences..............
    Subsequent development: slow...... normal...... rapid......
    Comprehension of speech................................
    Vocabulary ....
    Ability at: reading............... writing.................
    Comments ....

ONSET AND COURSE OF SPEECH PROBLEM
    Age.... Sudden.... Gradual.... Stationary.... Progressive....
    Congenital ...... Acquired ...... Developmental Failure ......
    Contributing factors ....
    ....
    Fluctuations ....
    Present state ....

SPEECH ENVIRONMENT (family and associates)
    Models................ Types of problems.................
    Other influences ....
    ....

SPEECH REQUIREMENTS (family and associates)
    Low   2   3   4   High
    Penalties for speech/silence...............................
    Reactions to disorder.....................................
    Comments ....
    ....

PATHOLOGIES OF SPEECH MECHANISM
    Malformation
    Delayed development
    Diseases
    Injuries
    Operations

PREVIOUS SPEECH CORRECTION

PREVIOUS MEDICAL ATTENTION RELATED TO PROBLEM

VOLUNTEERED STATEMENTS ON HISTORY OF
    SPEECH PROBLEM

E. Physical History

GENERAL

Age............. Height............. Weight.............

General appearance ....

Posture, movements, gait ....

Health ....

DISEASES (age, severity, residuals)

Measles	Sinusitis
Mumps	Hay fever
Chickenpox	Asthma
Whooping cough	Rheumatism
Diphtheria	Chorea
Smallpox	Convulsions
Tonsilitis	Poliomyelitis
Influenza	Other diseases (specify):
Pneumonia	
Pleurisy	
Aural diseases	

Frequent colds.......... Severe.......... Mild..........

INJURIES (age, severity, residuals)

OPERATIONS (age, severity, residuals)

PHYSICIAN'S REPORT

F. Personal, Educational and Occupational History

BIRTH

Mother's age
Mother's health
No. of previous pregnancies
Term
Labor
Presentation
Delivery

   Instruments

Injury
Weight
Birth cry
Activity
Type of feeding
Feeding behavior
Weaned at
Reaction to weaning
Other

DEVELOPMENT
   (age in years and months)
Sitting alone
Standing alone
Crawling
First tooth
Walking
First words
First sentences
Bowel control
   Initiated
   Successful
Bladder control
   Initiated
   Successful
Night bladder control
Use of spoon
Buttoning
First permanent tooth
Menstruation
Voice change
Shaving

EDUCATION

Present status (or highest grade completed)...................

Entered preschool: Place............ Age...... Date........

        First grade: Place............ Age...... Date........

        J. H. S.:   Place............ Age.... . Date........

        S. H. S.:   Place............ Age...... Date........

        Higher: Place............ Age...... Date........

Number of schools attended.......... Grades repeated, skipped,
   breaks in school ....

Attitude toward school.....................................
....

Behavior in school...
....

Attendance ....

Average marks in:	Liked	Disliked
Reading	.....	....
Spelling	.....	....
Handwriting	.....	....
Arithmetic	.....	....
Science	.....	....
Literature	.....	....
Languages	.....	....
Speech	.....	....

OCCUPATIONS (chronological with dates)

G. Family History

GENERAL

    Father living . . . . Mother living . . . . Together . . . . .

    Separated . . . . Date . . . . Reason . . . .

    Divorced . . . . Date . . . . Reason . . . .

    Remarried . . . . Date . . . . Reason . . . .

    Case living with father . . . . Mother . . . . Neither . . . .

    No. in household . . . . Composition . . . .

    Stepchildren . . . .

    Foster home . . . . Placing agency . . . . Date . . . . . .

    Condition . . . . Previous foster homes . . . .

FATHER . . . . Age . . . .

    Living . . . . . . Dead . . . . . . Date . . . . . . Age . . . . . . Cause . . . .

    Education . . . . Occupation . . . .

    Employer . . . . Years . . . . Salary . . . .

    Previous employments . . . .

    Group memberships . . . .

    Evenings out and where . . . .

    Physical condition . . . . Religion . . . .

    Personality

    Attitude toward children

    Methods of discipline

    Favorite child

MOTHER . . . . Age . . . .

    Living . . . . . . Dead . . . . . . Date . . . . . . Age . . . . . . Cause . . . .

    Education . . . . Occupation . . . .

    Employer . . . . Years . . . . Salary . . . .

    Previous employments . . . .

    Interests outside home . . . .

    Physical condition . . . . Religion . . . .

    Personality

    Attitude toward children

    Methods of discipline

    Favorite child

SIBLINGS (chron. order, living and dead, notable features)

Name	Age	Location	Occupation	Remarks
1	. . . . .	. . . .	. . . .	. . . .
2	. . . . .	. . . .	. . . .	. . . .
3	. . . . .	. . . .	. . . .	. . . .
4	. . . . .	. . . .	. . . .	. . . .
5	. . . . . .	. . . .	. . . .	. . . .
6	. . . . .	. . . .	. . . .	. . . .

GRANDPARENTS (if living summarize data under Parents)

	Death Age	Cause	Remarks
PGF	....	....	....
PGM	....	....	....
MGM	....	....	....
MGF	....	....	....

H. Home and Neighborhood Environment

ECONOMIC
Annual income.................. Sources...................
No. supported........ Home owned........ Value.........
Home rented.......... Rent.......... Amt. life ins...........
Car.............. Servants............. Relief.............
Other

PHYSICAL
No. cities lived in..
Time in present home........... No. in household............
Type house.......... No. rooms........ No. bedrooms........
Bath/toilet facilities.............. Heat and light.............
Eating habits..
Sleeping circumstances....................................

CULTURAL AND SOCIAL
Recreation facilities in home...............................
Television.... Radio.... Newspapers.. Magazines.. No. books..
Use of library..... No. books read/mo...... Type books read....
Hobbies ....
Type and amt. family conversation.........................
Share of work...
Intra-fam. relat...
Inter-fam. relat...
Community activities ....

NEIGHBORHOOD
Gen. location, level.......................................
Usual play area...
No. in group............. Makeup of group................
No. theaters...... churches...... taverns..... pool rooms.....
Freq. of visits to above...................................
Organization memberships ....

OTHER

Appendix B

SELECTED REFERENCES

Speech Problems (Chapter 4)

Articulatory Problems

ABNEY, L., and MINIACE, D. *This Way to Better Speech.* Yonkers, N.Y.: World Book Co., 1940. Presents a play approach in teaching the formation of sounds to young children. Includes word lists, simple sentences, and rhymes usable in speech games and activities.

ANDERSON, V. A. *Improving the Child's Speech.* New York: Oxford University Press, 1953. In Chapter 6 articulatory disorders are discussed.

BACKUS, O. L., and BEASLEY, J. *Speech Therapy with Children.* Boston: Houghton Mifflin Co., 1951. A number of group therapy techniques may be used to stimulate adequate speech production by means of play situations.

FAIRBANKS, G. *Voice and Articulation Drillbook.* New York: Harper & Brothers, 1940. The chapters on articulation will help the teacher to understand the scientific approach to the production of speech sounds.

CURTIS, J. F. "Disorders of Articulation." Chapter 3 in Johnson, W., and others, *Speech Handicapped School Children,* rev. ed. New York: Harper & Brothers, 1956. Suggestions will help the teacher, parent, and speech therapist understand the child with an articulatory problem.

McCARTHY, D. "Language Development in Children." Chapter 9 in Carmichael, L. (ed)., *Manual of Child Psychology,* 2d ed. New York: John Wiley & Sons, Inc., 1954. An extensive report of the literature and research on language development.

RASMUSSEN, C. E. *Speech Methods in the Elementary School.* New York: The Ronald Press Co., 1949. Will help the teacher and the speech therapist integrate speech development and improvement into the school program.

SCHOOLFIELD, L. D. *Better Speech and Better Reading.* Magnolia, Mass.: Expression Co., 1937. A phonetic approach to drills in sound production, through the use of words, sentences, and rhymes.

VAN RIPER, C. *Speech Correction, Principles and Methods,* 3d ed. Englewood Cliffs, N.J.: Prentice-Hall, Inc., 1954. The nature, causes, and treatment of speech disorders.

VAN RIPER, C. (ed.). *Speech Therapy: A Book of Readings.* Englewood Cliffs, N.J.: Prentice-Hall, Inc., 1953. Selected readings from the research and literature on articulation disorders are summarized, pp. 112–154.

ZEDLER, E. Y. *Listening for Speech Sounds.* Garden City, N.Y.: Doubleday & Co., Inc., 1955. Stories for the speech therapist and the classroom teacher, with emphasis on sound production.

Voice Problems

CURTIS, J. F. "Voice Problems." Chapter 4 in Johnson, W., and others, *Speech Handicapped School Children,* rev. ed. New York: Harper & Brothers, 1956. Helpful in understanding normal voice production and the causative factors in voice disorders.

FAIRBANKS, G. *Voice and Articulation Drillbook.* New York: Harper & Brothers, 1940. Chapters 7–11 give specific suggestions and drill material which will help in understanding and correcting voice problems.

KEPPIE, E. E., WEDBERG, C. F., and KESLAR, M. *Speech Improvement Through Choral Reading.* Magnolia, Mass.: Expression Co., 1942. Offers a wealth of material for use in classroom efforts to improve children's voices.

LAASE, L. T. *Speech Project and Drill Book.* Dubuque, Iowa: Wm. C. Brown Co., 1953. The voice drills in this manual can be used in group activities for older children and adults.

VAN RIPER, C. (ed.). *Speech Therapy: A Book of Readings.* Englewood Cliffs, N.J.: Prentice-Hall, Inc., 1953. Chapter 4 gives selected readings from the research and literature on "Voice Disorders."

Stuttering

GLASNER, P. J. "Personality Characteristics and Emotional Problems in Stutterers Under the Age of Five," *Journal of Speech and Hearing Disorders,* 14, No. 2 (June, 1949), 135–138. Observation and study of 70 children reported as stutterers at the Johns Hopkins Hospital revealed that these children had definite emotional problems.

HENRIKSON, E. "Children with Hesitant Speech." Chapter 9 in JOHNSON, W. (ed.), *Speech Problems of Children.* New York: Grune and Stratton, Inc., 1950. Problems of children with hesitant speech and general principles of treatment are presented.

JOHNSON, W. *People in Quandaries.* New York: Harper & Brothers, 1946, Chapter 17 is a general semantics approach to the problem of stuttering.

JOHNSON, W., BROWN, S. F., CURTIS, J. F., EDNEY, C. W., and KEASTER, J. *Speech Handicapped School Children,* rev. ed. New York: Harper & Brothers, 1956. Chapter V and pp. 534–536 are a scientifically sound and practical discussion of stuttering. Parents, teachers, and speech therapists should be familiar with "An Open Letter to the Mother of a Stuttering Child," pp. 558–567.

LAASERS, L. *Eight Keys to Normal Speech and Child Adjustment.* San Francisco: Published by the author, 1949. A guide to help parents and teachers prevent stuttering.

SCHUELL, H. *Differences Which Matter: A Study of Boys and Girls.* Austin, Texas. The Delta Kappa Gamma Society, 1947. (Based on a Ph.D. dissertation.) Evaluated facts relating to the differences in growth and development between boys and girls will help parents and teachers to understand the growing child. The studies are of special significance in relation to the problem of stuttering.

Travis, L. E., and Baruch, D. M. *Personal Problems of Everyday Life.* New York: Appleton-Century-Crofts, Inc., 1941. A practical book on mental hygiene, adjustment, and family relationships emphasizing the importance of child acceptance. Practical suggestions are given for the management of the emotionally maladjusted child with a speech problem.

Van Riper, C. *Speech Correction Principles and Methods,* 3d ed. Englewood Cliffs, N.J.: Prentice-Hall, Inc., 1953. In Chapters X and XI the nature and treatment of stuttering are discussed in the light of present knowledge.

————. (ed.). *Speech Therapy: a Book of Readings.* Englewood Cliffs, N.J.: Prentice-Hall, Inc., 1953. Different concepts and theories of stuttering in relation to nature, pathology, cause, and current methods of therapy are discussed on pp. 43–111.

Van Riper, C., and Johnson, W. (eds.). *Stuttering.* Chicago: National Society for Crippled Children and Adults, Inc., 1954. Discussion of the nature and treatment of stuttering addressed to parents and teachers.

Wischner, G. J. "Stuttering Behavior and Learning: A Preliminary Theoretical Formulation," *Journal of Speech and Hearing Disorders,* 15, No. 4 (December, 1950), 324–335. A program of research is designed as a systematic experimental approach to the problem of stuttering as learned behavior. Attempts to explain stuttering in terms of anxiety conditioning. A highly scientific report which may be difficult for the layman to understand, it should be studied by the speech pathologist and the speech therapist.

Hearing Problems

Bender, R. E. "The Discovery and Training of Hearing in Young Deaf Children," *The Volta Review,* Reprint No. 609 (November, 1948). Suggestions for checking the hearing of young children and methods of developing speech through amplification of sound.

Cypreansen, L. *First Lessons in Lip Reading.* Lincoln: University of Nebraska Extension Division, 1955. Sixteen lessons in beginning lipreading were presented as a lipreading telecourse. Material is suitable for older children and adults.

Dahl, L. A. *Public School Audiometry: Principles and Methods.* Bloomington, Ill.: Interstate Publishers, 1949. Explains audiometric testing procedures to be followed in checking the hearing of public school children and discusses hearing conservation programs.

Davis, H. (ed.). *Hearing and Deafness.* New York: Rinehart and Co., Inc., 1947. For the deaf and the hard of hearing, for their families, parents, teachers, and friends, for physicians, educators, and social workers. It is concerned with hearing conservation, testing and training programs, and adjustment of the hard-of-hearing or deaf person.

Hudgins, C. V., and Numbers, F. C. "An Investigation of the Intelligibility of Speech of the Deaf." *Genetic Psychology Monographs,* No. 25, Provincetown, Mass.: The Journal Press (1942), pp. 289–392. This scientific study shows that rhythmical or nonrhythmical utterances affect speech intelligibility and that the "elements method" may be responsible for poor speech development in the deaf.

If You Have a Deaf Child. Springfield, Ill.: Illinois Annual School for Mothers of Deaf Children, State Division of Services for Crippled Children, 1949. A number of authorities in the field of hearing tell the mother how she can help her deaf child through proper guidance and training.

KEASTER, J. "Impaired Hearing." Chapter 8 in Johnson, W., and others, *Speech Handicapped School Children,* rev. ed. New York: Harper & Brothers, 1956. Suggestions to the speech therapist and the classroom teacher regarding a program for the child with a hearing impairment.

————. "A Quantitative Method of Testing the Hearing of Young Children." *Journal of Speech Disorders,* 12, No. 2 (June, 1947), 159–160. A method using speech and pictures for testing the hearing of young children who are unable to respond to audiometric testing.

LASSMAN, G. H. *Language for the Preschool Deaf Child.* New York: Grune & Stratton, Inc., 1950. A former instructor at the John Tracy Clinic for preschool hard-of-hearing children in Los Angeles presents practical methods and procedures for the training of the deaf child in relation to his speech and language development.

Meeting the Needs of the Acoustically Handicapped Child. Commonwealth of Pennsylvania Bulletin No. 421. Harrisburg, Pa.: Department of Public Instruction, 1939. Valuable information for the parent and teacher confronted with the problems of the deaf and hard-of-hearing child.

MYKLEBUST, H. R. *Your Deaf Child: A Guide for Parents.* Springfield, Ill.: Charles C. Thomas Co., 1950. Will also be of interest to teachers, physicians, and other professional workers.

New Aids and Materials for Teaching Lip Reading. Washington, D.C.: American Society for the Hard of Hearing, 1943. A practice booklet which includes lipreading material helpful in work with the older child and the adult.

O'CONNOR, C., and STRENG, A. "Teaching the Acoustically Handicapped." Chapter 9 in *National Society for the Study of Education Forty-ninth Yearbook,* Part II: *The Education of Exceptional Children.* Chicago: University of Chicago Press, 1950. Different types of hearing loss are discussed and programs of conservation and training suggested.

UTLEY, J. *What's Its Name? A Guide to Speech and Hearing Development.* Urbana, Ill.: University of Illinois Press, 1950. A beginning manual in auditory training which uses activities and pictures to develop speech in the young hard-of-hearing child. Recordings are available with the manual. With amplification, these are valuable in giving initial sound experiences to the child with impaired hearing.

ZEDLER, E. Y. *Listening for Speech Sounds.* Garden City, N.Y.: Doubleday & Co., Inc., 1955. Material useful in teaching sound discrimination and production to hard-of-hearing children is presented in story form.

Cerebral Palsy

BROWN, S. F. "Cleft Palate; Cerebral Palsy." Chapter 7 in *Speech Handicapped School Children,* rev. ed. New York: Harper & Brothers, 1956. Concerned with the problems of cleft palate and cerebral palsied children.

CARLSON, E. R. *Born That Way.* New York: John Day Co., Inc., 1941. The autobiography of a spastic man. Interesting and helpful on the nature of therapy and mental hygiene.

CASS, M. T. *Speech Rehabilitation in Cerebral Palsy.* New York: Columbia University Press, 1951. Etiology and the elements of therapy are discussed. Includes suggestions for speech therapy for the teaching of sounds, and a total educational program for the cerebral palsied child.

CRUICKSHANK, W. M., and RAUS, G. M. *Cerebral Palsy: Its Individual and Community Problems.* Syracuse: Syracuse University Press, 1955. Brings together medical, psychological, therapeutic, social, and rehabilitation points of view in dealing with cerebral palsy.

GRATKE, J. *Help Them Help Themselves.* Dallas: Texas Society for Crippled Children, 1947. Offers practical suggestions for the social and educational development of the cerebral palsied child.

PERLSTEIN, M. A., with MCPEAK, W. *The Problem of Cerebral Palsy Today.* New York: Association for the Aid of Crippled Children. Chicago: National Society for Crippled Children and Adults, Inc., 1947. An outstanding authority on cerebral palsy helps parents and teachers to understand its problems.

PHELPS, W., and TURNER, T. A. *The Farthest Corner.* Chicago: National Society for Crippled Children and Adults, Inc., 1947. Practical information for parents and teachers.

POHL, J. F. *Cerebral Palsy.* St. Paul: Bruce Publishing Co., 1950. Describes the types of cerebral palsy, discusses etiology and pathology, and presents principles of treatment.

Realistic Educational Planning for Children with Cerebral Palsy. United Cerebral Palsy Association, Inc., Pamphlet No. 1. New York, 1952. Prepared by the United Cerebral Palsy Educational Advisory Board. Emphasizes the need of a special educational program for children handicapped by cerebral palsy.

RUTHERFORD, B. R. *Give Them a Chance To Talk,* rev. ed. Minneapolis: Burgess Publishing Co., 1950. Written as a result of work at the Michael Dowling School for Crippled Children. Explores the speech problems of cerebral palsied children and gives retraining suggestions to parents and teachers.

STRAUSS, A. A., and LEHTINEN, L. E. *Psychopathology and Education of the Brain-injured Child.* New York: Grune & Stratton, Inc., 1947. A scientific approach. Explains the problems and needs of the cerebral palsied child.

WESTLAKE, H. *A System for Developing Speech with Cerebral Palsied Children.* Columbus, Ohio: Society for Crippled Children, 1952. Reprint, *The Crippled Child.* Chicago: National Society for Crippled Children and Adults, Inc. (June, August, and December, 1951). An adaptation of speech therapy as taught by Dr. W. M. Phelps and Dr. M. A. Perlstein and the techniques used in occupational and physical therapy.

————. "Muscle Training for Cerebral Palsied Speech Cases." *Journal of Speech and Hearing Disorders,* 16 No. 2 (June, 1951), 103–109. Points out the usefulness of motor training in speech therapy with cerebral palsied cases.

Cleft Lip and/or Cleft Palate

AMERICAN ASSOCIATION FOR CLEFT PALATE REHABILITATION. Newsletters, bulletins, and periodic publications. McKenzie W. Buck, Secretary. Speech and Hearing Clinic, University of Florida, Gainesville, Florida. Publications of this organization, formed to promote the rehabilitation of the cleft palate individual, to promote cooperation among other specialities of the healing arts group, and to stimulate lay groups, contain reports which will be of interest to parents, teachers, and speech therapists.

BACKUS, O. L., CLANCY, J. N., HENRY, L. D., and KEMPER, J. *The Child with a Cleft Palate*. Ann Arbor: The University of Michigan Press, 1953.

BAXTER, H. "A Complete Rehabilitation Program for Cleft Lip and Cleft Palate Cases," Canadian Dental Association *Journal* and Ontario Dental Society (Toronto), 20, No. 2 (February, 1954), 79–83. Experiences of the Cleft Palate and Speech Clinic of the Royal Victoria Hospital are described.

BUCK, M., and HARRINGTON, R. "Organized Speech Therapy for Cleft Palate Rehabilitation," *Journal of Speech and Hearing Disorders*, 14, No. 1 (March, 1949), 43–52. Exercises for clinic and home therapy for cleft palate cases.

CHILDREN'S BUREAU, DEPARTMENT OF HEALTH, EDUCATION AND WELFARE. *The Child With a Cleft Palate*. Washington, D.C.: Government Printing Office, 1953. Helpful for parents, teachers, and speech therapists.

ECKELMANN, D., and BALDRIDGE, P. "Speech Training for the Child with a Cleft Palate," *Journal of Speech Disorders*, 10, No. 2 (June, 1945), 137–147. Explains many of the speech problems encountered by the child with a cleft palate, and outlines steps which will help him to overcome these problems.

HARKINS, C. S., and KOEPP-BAKER, H. "Twenty-five Years of Cleft Palate Prosthesis," *Journal of Speech and Hearing Disorders*, 13, No. 1 (March, 1948), 23–30. Does not attempt to review the history of cleft palate prosthesis but examines the major problems related to "the application of the prosthetic method to the complete restitution of the cleft palate patient" and evaluates its results.

KANTNER, C. E. "Diagnosis and Prognosis in Cleft Palate Speech," *Journal of Speech and Hearing Disorders*, 13, No. 3 (September, 1948), 211–222. Discussion of some of the problems in examining and diagnosing a case with cleft palate speech and in deciding what should be done, and the prospects for progress both generally and individually.

————. "The Rationale of Blowing Exercises for Patients with Repaired Cleft Palates," *Journal of Speech Disorders*, 12, No. 3 (September, 1947), 281–286. Presents general principles thought to be basic to the proper understanding and use of "blowing exercises."

LILLYWHITE, H. "Teamwork in the Oregon Cleft Palate Program," *Journal of Speech and Hearing Disorders*, 21, No. 1 (March, 1956), 18–24. In Oregon the speech consultant is considered the logical person to coordinate and guide the program for the cleft palate child, with referral to specialists in surgery, medicine, dentistry, speech and hearing.

McDONALD, E. T. *About Children With Cleft Lips and Cleft Palate: A Guide for Parents*. Harrisburg, Pa.: Pennsylvania Society for Crippled

Children and Adults, Inc., 1956. An aid to parents in understanding the problems of the child with a cleft palate, by a speech pathologist and psychologist.

McDONALD, E. T. "Speech Considerations in Cleft Palate Prosthesis," *Journal of Prosthetic Dentistry*, 1 (1951), 629–637. Explains how the cleft palate prothodontist can assist the speech therapist by constructing an appliance.

McDONALD, E. T., and KOEPP-BAKER, H. "Cleft-Palate Speech," *Journal of Speech and Hearing Disorders*, 16, No. 1 March, (1951), 9–20. Literature dealing with cleft palate is reviewed and the problems of hypernasality, nasal emission, and misarticulation are discussed.

RICKETTS, R. M. "Oral Orthopedics for the Cleft Palate Patient," *American Journal of Orthodontics*, 42, No. 6 (1956), 401–408. Discussing the importance of a good diagnosis in children with cleft lip and/or cleft palate and explanation of the possibilities of orthodontic treatment.

WELLS, C. G., and PHAIR, G. M. *Teacher-Parent Guide to Speech Training for Cleft Palate Children*. Madison: Wisconsin State Department of Public Instruction, Bureau for Handicapped Children, 1947. Cleft palate discussed from an anatomical and biological viewpoint. The problems of the cleft palate with regard to surgical repairs, adjustment, and speech development are explained.

WESTLAKE, H. "Understanding the Child with a Cleft Palate," *Quarterly Journal of Speech*, 39, No. 2 (April, 1953), 165–173. A general article intended for the non-specialist. It explains how cleft palate occurs and discusses related problems, including the group approach to therapy, prosthetic appliance, and the speech therapist's role.

Delayed Speech and Speech Retardation

BEASLEY, J. *Slow to Talk*. New York: Bureau of Publications, Teachers College, Columbia University, 1956. A guide for teachers and parents of children with delayed language development.

————. "Techniques of Therapy for Pre-School Children," *Journal of Speech and Hearing Disorders*, 14, No. 4 (December, 1949), 307–331. A report of therapy done with preschool children in experimental sessions at the University of Michigan.

GESELL, A., and AMATRUDA, C. S. *Developmental Diagnosis of Normal and Abnormal Child Development*. New York: Harper & Brothers, 1941.

GESELL, A., and Others. *The First Five Years of Life*. New York: Harper & Brothers, 1940.

IRWIN, O. V. "Speech Development in the Young Child," *Journal of Speech and Hearing Disorders*, 13, No. 1 March, (1948), 3–31.

JERSILD, A. T. *Child Psychology*, 4th ed. Englewood Cliffs, N.J.: Prentice-Hall, Inc., 1954.

KIRK, S. A., KARNES, M. B. and KIRK, W. *You and Your Retarded Child*. New York: The Macmillan Co., 1958.

KIRK, S. A., and JOHNSON, O. G. *Educating the Retarded Child*. Boston: Houghton Mifflin Co., 1951. The purpose of this book is to present information, synthesize materials, develop programs of rehabilitation and instruction, and describe the teaching procedures used with retarded children.

McCarthy, D. "Language Development in Children." Chapter 9 in Carmichael, L. (ed.), *Manual of Child Psychology*, 2d ed. New York: John Wiley & Sons, Inc., 1954. An extensive report of the literature and research.

Peacher, W. G. "Neurological Factors in the Etiology of Delayed Speech," *Journal of Speech Disorders*, 14, No. 4 (December, 1940), 344–352.

Symonds, P. M. *The Dynamics of Parent-Child Relationships.* New York: Bureau of Publications, Teachers College, Columbia University, 1949.

Thompson, G. G. *Child Psychology: Growth Trends in Psychological Adjustment.* Boston: Houghton Mifflin Co., 1952. Chapter 9 is devoted to the language development of the child.

Wallin, J. E. *Education of Mentally Handicapped Children.* New York: Harper & Brothers, 1955. A historical orientation, an exposition of individual needs as the frame of reference for organizing education, guides for administration, and general and specific methods of instruction for retarded children.

Methods and Graded Materials (Part III)

Creative Play and Group Activities

Anderson, V. A. *Improving the Child's Speech.* New York: Oxford University Press, 1953. Primarily for the classroom teacher. Includes methods, techniques, and materials for speech improvement and correction.

Arbuthnot, M. *Children and Books*, rev. ed. Chicago: Scott Foresman & Co., 1957. A source book of children's literature which will be of value to the speech therapist and the classroom teacher.

Axline, V. M. *Play Therapy.* Boston: Houghton Mifflin Co., 1947. A psychologist tells how the emotionally disturbed child may be helped through play activities and counciling.

Backus, O. L., and Beasley, J. *Speech Therapy with Children.* Boston: Houghton Mifflin Co., 1951. Playmaking and group therapy methods are presented through the use of real-life situations.

Barrows, S. T., and Hall, M. *Games and Jingles for Speech Development.* Magnolia, Mass.: Expression Co., 1936. Material adaptable to group activity.

Barrows, S. T., and Hall, V. *Jack-in-the-Box.* Magnolia, Mass.: Expression Co., 1958. The pictures and rhymes in this little book suggest group activities which can be used in speech improvement work with young children.

Irwin, R. B. *Speech and Hearing Therapy.* Englewood Cliffs, N.J.: Prentice-Hall, Inc., 1953. Directed primarily to the speech therapist but includes suggestions which will be helpful to the classroom teacher.

Pitts, L. B., Glenn, M., and Watters, L. E. *The Kindergarten Book: Our Singing World.* Boston: Ginn & Co., 1949. Short songs which express the emotions and interests of childhood. Many action songs which will lend a pleasant variety to the speech improvement program for young children.

RASMUSSEN, C. E. *Speech Methods in the Elementary School.* New York: The Ronald Press, 1949. Shows the classroom teacher how to integrate the speech improvement activities into the school program.

SLAVSON, S. R. *An Introduction to Group Therapy.* New York: International Universities Press, Inc., 1952. Tells of a project carried out with problem children. A sociological approach to group therapy.

WARD, W. L. *Creative Dramatics.* New York: Appleton-Century-Crofts, Inc., 1930. Instructs in creative dramatic techniques and gives source materials for children's stories.

———. *Playmaking with Children,* 2d ed. New York: Appleton-Century-Crofts, Inc., 1957. Methods and materials for playmaking and creative play, and how these techniques can be used in the speech improvement program.

Choral Reading

ABNEY, L. *Choral Speaking Arrangements for the Upper Grades.* Magnolia, Mass.: Expression Co., 1937.

ABNEY, L., and ROWE, G. *Choral Speech Arranged for the Lower Grades.* Magnolia, Mass.: Expression Co., 1937.

KEPPIE, E., WEDBERG, F. W., and DESLER, M. *Speech Improvement through Choral Speaking.* Magnolia, Mass.: Expression Co., 1942.

RASMUSSEN, C. E. *Choral Speaking for Speech Improvement.* Magnolia, Mass.: Expression Co., 1938.

———. *Poems for Playtime.* Magnolia, Mass.: Expression Co., 1942.

STEVENSON, R. L. *A Child's Garden of Verses.* New York: Oxford University Press, 1947.

THOMPSON, B. *Silver Pennies.* New York: The Macmillan Co., 1931.

INDEX

Adenoidal growths, 51, 106
Adjustment: cultural influences in, 6–7, 20–21, 37, 42–46; in arithmetic and speech, 38; in articulation disorders, 21–41; environmental, 25, 40–48, 87–91, 93–94; factor relationships in, 40–41, 87–91, 93–94; in hearing problems, 27, 52–53, 106–7, 118–24; immaturity, 44–45; individual differences in, 19–22, 101–2; of institutionalized children, 44–45; intellectual differences in, 19–20, 30–32, 49, 139–40; labeling, 45–46, 55, 90; maturational differences in, 13–14, 19; in mental retardation, 49, 135–40; of mother as speech therapist, 102–3; in nonfluent speech, 45–46, 112–15; in orphan children, 44–45; of parent and child, 16–17, 45–49, 87–129, 134–41; in problem solving, 48, 96–98; psychosomatic, 53; in reading and speech, 38–40; rejection in, 29–30; in retardation, 25–29, 58, 135–41; sex differences in, 19–20; social, 20–21, 32–35; in social deprivation, 44–45; in socioeconomic differences, 20–21; in speech inadequacy, 37; space age speech demands, 37; standards of speech, 44; in spelling and speech disorders, 38; in stuttering, 111–17. *See also* Cultural factors; Parent-child relations; Hearing disorders; Intelligence; Stuttering; Social development
American Speech and Hearing Association: certification in, 81–82; code of ethics, 80; history of, 79; journal of, 79; unethical practices, 81

Anastasi, A., 20
Aphasia, 51–52, 136–37
Arithmetic and speech errors, 38
Articulation disorders: accuracy of speech sounds, 14–19; adequacy of speech sounds, 21, 37–38; arithmetic and speech errors, 38; bilingualism, 45; case history, 58–59; 92–94; cause of, 41–53; classification of, 55; consistency of sounds in, 179; and consonant sound development, 8–15; and consonant combinations, 168–69; and consonant sound formation, 180–90; and consonant sounds of infancy, 9–10; and cultural influences, 6–7, 20–21, 37, 42–46; definition of, 91; and delayed speech, 43–44, 58, 135–41; diagnostic procedures in, 91–94; diphthongs, 191, 194–95; distortions, 55; effects of, 29–41; environmental factors in, 25, 40–48, 87–91, 93–94; foreign language in, 45; imitation in, 3, 10–11, 43; immaturity in, 44–45; inaccuracies of, 25–26; incidence of, 26–29; individual differences in, 19–22, 101–2; individual therapy in 64–65, 95–96; individual therapy vs. group, 65–68; in institutionalized children, 44–45; intelligence factors in, 19–20, 30–32, 49, 139–40; labeling of, 45–46, 55, 90; lalling, 55; larynx abnormalities, 51; lisping, 55; maturational influences, 13, 14, 19; motivation, 43–44; motor ability, 14; nerve injury, 51–52; normal misarticulations, 91; omissions, 55; order of sounds corrected, 98–101; organic origin of, 51–53, 57; orphan chil-